Exploring
IRISH
MAMMALS

Exploring
IRISH
MAMMALS

Tom Hayden & Rory Harrington
Illustrations by Billy Clarke

TOWN
HOUSE
DUBLIN

First published in 2000 by

Town House and Country House Ltd
Trinity House, Charleston Road
Ranelagh, Dublin 6

ISBN: 1-186059-093-4

A CIP catalogue record for this book is available from the British Library.

Designed and typeset by Creative Inputs, Dublin, Ireland

Printed in Italy by Istituto Grafico Silvio Basile

Dedicated to our supportive families

Aila, Caolan, Fiacha, Fiona, Helena, Joseph, Louisa,
Päivi, Pauline, Sarah, Sarah, Thomas and Tuula.

Contents

Acknowledgements

We are extremely grateful to Dúchas The Heritage Service of the Department of Arts, Heritage, Gaeltacht and The Islands, who commissioned this work and gave us the opportunity to work together. Dúchas is the statutory body charged with *inter alia* the conservation and management of Ireland's wildlife.

We are grateful for the encouragement and support received from Mr Michael Canny, Dr Alan Craig and Mr Michael Neff. We appreciate the assistance and patience of Mr Seamus Lynam, Mr Patrick McCusker, and Dr James B. Larner during the many metamorphoses of the text from its original concept.

We thank the rangers and conservation officers of Dúchas, the managers of the Coillte forests and members of the Irish Deer Society for providing information on mammal distribution.

We thank Professor J. Bracken, Professor E.J. Duke, Professor W.I. Montgomery, Dr G. Donovan, Dr Nigel Monahan, Dr Alan McElligott, Dr Emer Rogan, Dr Seán Rooney, Mr Brian Keeley, Ms Eanna Ní Lamhna, Mr John Meehan, Mr David O'Brien, Mr William Clarke, Mr John Casey, Ms Elaine Hurley, Ms Noinín Reynolds, Ms Fiona Saunders and Mr David Wall who discussed, read, commented upon and suggested improvements to various chapters. We owe a great debt of gratitude to our colleagues and students in Dúchas The Heritage Service of the Department of Arts, Heritage, Gaeltacht and The Islands and in the Department of Zoology, particularly the members of the Mammal Research Group at the National University of Ireland, Dublin, for providing the stimulating environments in which we work.

We are pleased that Billy Clark produced the illustrations that are a major feature of the text. We appreciate the efforts of Dr Siobhán Parkinson, Ms Helen Litton and Ms Mireia Sagarra of Town House and Country House Publishers who oversaw the final text. This publication would not have been possible without the financial assistance and steady encouragement of Dúchas The Heritage Service of the Department of Arts, Heritage, Gaeltacht and The Islands.

If you have records of any Irish mammals, the following two organisations would be delighted to hear from you:

For the Republic of Ireland:
Irish Biological Records Centre, Dúchas The Heritage Service, 7 Ely Place, Dublin 2.

For Northern Ireland:
Centre for Environmental Data and Recording, Ulster Museum, Botanic Gardens, Belfast, BT9 5AB.

Authors' Foreword

This volume arose as an initiative to update a booklet on Irish mammals originally prepared by Mr John Flynn of the then Forest and Wildlife Service in 1986. But like Alice through the looking glass, it just 'growed and growed'. This was in no small way due to the increasing general interest in and scientific research on our mammalian fauna. As a result it was decided to provide a more comprehensive treatment of Irish mammals involving a collaboration between conservation and management interests represented by Dúchas and the research interests represented by the universities. This brought the authors together, although not for the first time, to apply their various perspectives to producing an up-to-date overview on Ireland's mammals. This book is intended to be a general introduction to our mammals. Each species is treated separately and is considered in the broader historical context and in relation to its habitat and the other species with which it interacts. The increase in understanding which has emerged since the original booklet is highlighted, but also the major gaps in our knowledge are emphasised.

Our philosophical approach to Ireland's mammals is holistic, scientific and firmly grounded in evolutionary biology. Between us we are involved in research on deer, feral goats, cattle, foxes, badgers, mink, seals, otters, hares, rabbits, bank voles, and bats. We are mainly involved in fundamental research into the biology and conservation of mammals. The conservation of Ireland's mammals requires an integrated approach taking full cognisance of their biological requirements and their need for sympathetic but realistic accommodation within a largely man-made environment.

Mammals feature largely in Ireland's myths and legends and Ireland has a long tradition of natural history writing. Nevertheless most people are unaware of how many species are found here and what an unusual assemblage they represent. Ireland has acquired more species of mammals during the last millennium than in the previous 9000 years. This book seeks to explore the diversity, richness and heritage value of our wild mammals.

Introduction

This book describes the wild mammals that are to be found on the land mass of Ireland or in the waters round our coasts.

Apart from the opening chapters, which describe the history and evolution of mammals, each chapter covers an order of mammals – insectivores, bats, rodents and so on – beginning with a general description of the characteristics of the order, telling you where they evolved, where they are to be found worldwide and how many species are currently in Ireland. After that, chapters are divided into sections on the various species in the order that are to be found in Ireland, and these sections have the following general structure:

- Names
- Identification
- Distribution
- Habits and habitats
- Reproduction
- Watching mammals
- Conservation and management

These headings may vary slightly from chapter to chapter, depending on the type of information that is relevant to the particular mammal.

There should be enough information in the text and illustration to make it possible to identify each species, though in the case of some mammals – some bats and whales, for example – where differences are not obvious, specialist advice would probably be needed for an accurate identification.

Measurements given refer to adults. Juveniles that have become independent of their mothers will of course be smaller than adults but some species mature faster than others and the differences may be slight.

The world distribution of each species is given and the current status of the species in Ireland is summarised in distribution maps. Available data on the distribution and abundance of mammals in Ireland differ in detail. Surveys tell us whether or not a species is present in a particular location, whereas a census gives information on population size in particular locations and so helps us to estimate how abundant the species is. In each case we have at least enough information to be able to report presence for 20km squares. We have indicated relevant 20km squares with dark circles to denote that the species has been recently recorded there and can be expected to occur throughout those squares in suitable habitat.

In the case of marine mammals, the sea areas are shaded where they are found and locations where whales or dolphins were stranded or washed ashore in Ireland are indicated by dark circles.

CHAPTER 1

The Story of Mammals

Tá an eilit 's an fiadh 's gach uile sórt 'gaém' ann
An madadh ruadh 'leimnigh, an broc 's an míol buidhe.

Fauna of all types are to be found there, hinds and deer,
Pouncing foxes, the badger and hare.
A. Raftery (1784-1835)

In the very beginning

Once there were no mammals. Before the time of the dinosaurs, there were small insectivorous reptiles that foraged among the branches of trees. These creatures were the predecessors of our modern mammals. Over a period of about 50 million years, these reptiles began to acquire the characteristics of mammals and eventually, about 200 million years ago, the first mammals appeared on earth. Remains of these first mammals – little shrew-like creatures – are fairly widespread and have been found as close as south Wales. They seem to have been nocturnal, insect-eating creatures. The Jurassic period (144–208 million years ago) was totally dominated by the dinosaurs, but during this time, mammals went on evolving, though they were never very abundant. Dinosaurs still ruled during the Cretaceous period (144–65 million years ago). Mammals were still relatively inconspicuous, but already the earliest marsupial and placental mammals had evolved.

Exit the dinosaurs

About 65 million years ago a mass extinction of dinosaurs and some other animal types occurred. Exactly why and how this took place is not certain. It may have been due to climate change that occurred when an asteroid struck the earth. What is certain is that the way was now clear for the rise of the mammals. Their twilight time was over. They emerged into the vacant habitats and niches to be tried and tested by natural selection. The descendants of the small nocturnal creatures of about 200 million years ago began to diversify into the many different sorts of mammals that we know today.

Mammals take the stage

Exactly why some mammals avoided the fate of the dinosaurs is not clear. Survival may have been due as much to chance as any feature of the animals themselves. In any event it appears that, of the surviving animal types, mammals were the best able to exploit the opportunities that were presenting themselves. There was a rapid evolution (over a period of about 10 million years) of a wide range of mammals of all shapes and sizes. All the types of mammal that still survive appeared during this period. So, although the first mammals appeared about 200 million years ago, modern mammals diversified only as recently as 25 to 35 million years ago.

What makes mammals different?

The earliest mammals evolved from reptiles, but this does not mean that modern mammals are superior to modern reptiles: they are different life forms descended from the same ancestor and which address the problems of staying alive in different ways. Their different lifestyles depend on particular features of their anatomy and physiology.

Mammals are built like sports cars; they are high-performance organisms but are expensive to run and maintain. In other words, they have a high metabolic rate and require much more food and much more oxygen than a reptile. They use metabolic heat to maintain a high and stable body temperature. For some mammals, however, this is too costly and so they lower their body temperature, by night or during the winter. Mammals reduce heat loss and thus fuel consumption by having hair for insulation. Skin glands maintain the hair and, by sweating, prevent overheating. Some of these glands have become specialised as mammary glands that secrete milk, allowing rapid growth of the young and more complex social interactions. Other skin glands, known as scent glands, produce odours used in communication.

Mammals' jaws and teeth have been modified. They have a single bone in each side of the lower jaw (reptiles may have as many as six) and teeth of different types (incisors, molars and so on). This is because they must be more efficient in acquiring and processing the large quantities of food they require. Reorganisation of the jaw was accompanied by changes in the skull. This facilitated improvements in the muscles used in chewing. The new jaw design required changes in the middle ear. Some of the bones which were originally in the jaw migrated into the middle ear, and mammals now have three ear bones, whereas reptiles have only one. While nobody could mistake a living mammal for any other life form, it is not so easy to identify a fossil as a mammal if only the bones survive. In fact, for a palaeontologist, the key diagnostic features are the nature of the bones that form the lower jaw, the types of teeth or the structure of the ear.

A most important feature of mammals is their relatively large brains. Increased brain power evolved because of their active lifestyle, which requires that mammals must exert more precise control over their bodies and process more information.

How evolution works

We know that once there were no mammals, and that gradually some reptile species appeared to 'turn into' mammals. But how could this happen? All the animals in any population – all the mountain hares in Ireland, for example – are generally similar but they are not identical. Some of the differences between them may have been acquired by the particular life experiences of the individual animals; others are due to genetic differences between them. All individuals must cope sufficiently well with environmental conditions if they are to survive and reproduce. Since all individuals are not the same, then some may not survive to breeding age. The ones who do breed have offspring, some of whom may themselves survive to breed, some not.

There are many factors that can have an influence on whether any one animal survives and succeeds in breeding, and some of those factors are genetic. If a particular genetic trait tends to make an animal successful – i.e. helps the animal to survive in the particular conditions the animal finds itself in, and to breed – then, obviously, animals with that particular trait are more likely to breed and have offspring. Their offspring are in turn likely to have that same trait, because of course we are talking about a genetic trait here. And so it will happen that individuals carrying this particular genetic trait, which tends to help the animal to survive and be successful, will be more common in the next generation. This is how *natural selection* works: certain types of individuals leave more offspring than others do and their success is determined by the environment acting on those individuals. If environmental conditions remain the same, then the population comes to be dominated by animals who are best suited to cope with those conditions.

If, however, environmental conditions change – if, for example, the climate were to become warmer or cooler – then an animal type that had been successful in the past might now be unable to cope with the new conditions. These animals would tend to die off and not leave any offspring, making way for other individuals who have traits that help them and their offspring to cope better with the new conditions. And so, over time, if the offspring of those individuals who were better able for the new conditions continued to be successful and to produce offspring that were genetically better adapted to the conditions, the population would gradually come to be dominated by the newly successful animal type, instead of by the type that had been dominant in the past. In retrospect, it will look as if one animal type has changed into another. In fact what has happened is that one type has *replaced* another. All this can only happen, of course, if the population contains a genetic type that by chance can cope well with the new conditions. If not, the population becomes extinct.

Genetic variation (or why all Irish hares are not identical)

The raw material of evolution is genetic variation. Genetic variation affects characteristics which themselves may affect reproductive success. All genetic variation results from changes in the chemical structure of DNA in cells. These random changes may be caused by chemicals or radiation in the environment. Or they may arise from copying errors when cells reproduce copies of themselves as they divide. Before printing was invented a writer would produce a text in manuscript, and then somebody would copy the manuscript. It is likely that the copyist might make an error or two in copying the manuscript, and then another copyist might come along and copy the copy, along with the errors, and maybe introduce a new error of his own. You can imagine that over time a copy of the manuscript might come to be quite different from the original. The same thing can happen with the copying of DNA in cells, but it takes a long time and many generations for a substantial number of changes to accumulate.

However, an individual hare, for example, can produce an offspring that is substantially different in shape, size or colour from itself, and so we see what looks like a genetic change, that should take several generations, happening in one generation. This can happen because of the random way that genetic traits are handed on from one generation to the next.

Genes are carried on chromosomes, and chromosomes occur in pairs. Only one chromosome from each pair goes into the creation of an individual ovum (egg) or sperm. During the production of an egg, for example, the chromosome chosen from the first pair might be a copy of that inherited by the female from her mother, or it might be the one inherited from her father. The same applies for all other chromosomes in that egg and the same applies also to every chromosome that makes up the sperm that will eventually fertilise that egg. At the point of fertilisation, new pairs of chromosomes are created, from the sperm and the egg, to create the genetic makeup of the offspring. Thus a fertilised egg and all the cells descended from it contain an equal contribution from each parent.

Obviously, the number of different combinations of chromosomes, or different eggs or sperm, that might be produced is enormous. Added to this is the lottery of which egg gets finally released and which of all the sperm wins the race to fertilise it. Thus sexual reproduction acts to shuffle the existing variations (originally produced by mutation or copying errors) into new combinations, which produce the variety of individuals on which natural selection can act. So if a female Irish hare which is normally dark-coloured produces an offspring that turns white in winter, it is almost certainly not due to a mutation which occurred *recently*, but rather to the recombination of variations that already exist in the population.

Why are there so many types of mammals?

The earliest known mammals, as far as we can determine, were generalised insectivores, and some modern mammals, such as shrews and hedgehogs, still pursue the selfsame lifestyle 200 million years later. If living like a hedgehog is so successful, why do not all mammals live like this? The answer seems to be that in a universe of generalists, a specialist may prosper when local conditions allow. This is the zoological equivalent of the contrast between marathon running and the decathlon. Mammals that specialise may enjoy certain advantages. A resource may be monopolised or used better than by any competing type.

Specialisation is a good strategy as long as conditions remain stable. The downside is that if conditions change markedly populations of specialists may not have retained the variations that might allow them to adapt to the new conditions. In times of major environmental crises, the specialists are usually the first to go extinct. The generalists usually inherit the earth. Of course the process then begins anew and another wave of specialisation spreads. Conditions for specialising usually present themselves when major extinction events occur or when new resources become available. For example, there was a phase of specialisation when the dinosaurs became extinct and a wide range of mammal types rapidly appeared to replace them. Similarly, when grasslands began to spread across the globe about 20–30 million years ago, several different groups of mammals produced specialised grazers: horses, deer and antelopes.

The diversification observed when an animal type suddenly produces a range of different descendants to exploit different habitats is termed adaptive radiation. For mammals, the major radiation had taken place by about 40 million years ago. Of course none of this would be possible unless the appropriate variation to be tried out in different circumstances existed in the ancestral stock in the first place. However, when the variation was present, the same general forces of natural selection often produced a very similar animal. For example, deer and antelope are the result of selection for large-bodied grazers applied independently to two different stocks. When animals of different ancestry come to evolve similar characteristics this is termed convergent evolution. It is because the same selective pressures often favour a particular design of animal that we can often infer a great deal about the lifestyle of extinct animals.

Mammals, although built on the same basic plan, display an amazing diversity. These represent different solutions to the three great imperatives with which all animals are preoccupied; to eat, to avoid being eaten and to reproduce. Mammals have some interesting and exotic variations on the main themes. Some specialise in a narrow range of food types; others will eat almost anything. Some are active by day, others by night. Some are protected by large size, others by being small and inconspicuous. Some can produce a litter about 13 days after mating; others take over 12 months. Some get pregnant within a day of mating, others not for months afterwards. This extraordinary variety comes about under pressure to adopt a lifestyle that gives a competitive edge in the race for reproduction.

What is a mammalian species? (Or why Irish hares are similar)

We have seen how natural selection applied to a population either drives it to extinction or alters the characteristics of the population, because only certain types of animals thrive and reproduce. We have also seen that applying the same pressure to two different animal types often produces quite similar results. What happens if a population of mammals becomes separated into two parts with little or no contact between them? Each, of course, becomes subject to the selective forces acting in the area where it is found. Unless these are identical, it is certain that over sufficient time, the populations will become less like one another. This is because each population is becoming adapted to local conditions.

This has happened to the populations of mountain hares in this country and in Scotland. Mountain hares in Scotland turn white in winter, where this camouflage is clearly beneficial, because dark-coloured hares would otherwise be dangerously conspicuous in an area where snow in winter is the general rule. In Ireland, mountain hares do not grow a white winter coat. In fact they are the only population of mountain hares in the world not to do so. This is presumably because, in a country where winter snow is unusual, darker coloured hares are better camouflaged all year round, and in fact the genes controlling development of a white winter coat are very rare in the Irish population. This is a good example of the processes that occur when two populations become separated.

If the separation persists for a sufficiently long time, then individuals may become so unlike that if a male from one population and a female from the other were to be introduced, they might be incapable of producing fertile offspring. (This has not yet occurred between the mountain hare of Ireland and Scotland.) When such a failure to reproduce occurs, the populations would be considered to belong to different *species*. This is the phenomenon that preoccupied Charles Darwin for most of his life. A male and a female are said to belong to different species when transfer of genetic information from both to the same offspring is impossible under natural conditions. (By contrast specimens of extinct animals belong to different species when palaeontologists say so!)

The reproductive isolation that may develop between separate populations has an evolutionary function: it ensures that individuals are more likely to mate with individuals from within the same population who are, after all, likely to possess the characteristics suited to that environment. If a particular animal type works well in an environment that is stable, that environment will continue to discriminate against individuals which differ markedly from the average. This includes processes and mechanisms to avoid introduction of alien DNA by mating with an extremely different organism. Mammals therefore exhibit a range of mechanisms that prevent exchange between one species and another.

Put simply, a male and female belong to different species if it is impossible for them to produce offspring. This seems simple, but is a troublesome subject for those who like their biology cut and dried. Are sika deer and red deer different species? It certainly appears so. But sika deer, originally from Japan, have interbred with red deer in Ireland, and elsewhere, when they were confined in the same area. So it seems that in the case of closely related species separated only by great geographical distances, reproductive barriers may be slight or non-existent.

Names of animals: putting mammals in pigeonholes

Somewhere in the vast scientific literature there is a formal description of each species. This includes an account of the animal, together with the location of the particular specimen on which the account is based and an official name to match the specimen described.

The scientific names of animals may appear a little intimidating if one is not used to Latinised names of species, but there are good reasons for using them, mainly in order to avoid the confusion that can sometimes arise when common names are used. For example Americans use the word 'elk' to refer to the red deer (*Cervus elaphus*), Europeans use 'elk' to refer to the moose (*Alces alces*) and in Ireland 'elk' is often used to refer to the extinct giant deer (*Megaloceros giganteus*) which was neither red deer nor moose! (The common names are nevertheless used mostly throughout this book, as these are the names by which most readers will know them.)

All species are correctly referred to by a double Latinised name or a 'binomial identifier'. For example, the hedgehog is known as *Erinaceus europaeus*. The first part of the name identifies the genus to which the animal belongs. It corresponds, in a sense, to the surname of a human. For example the mink and the stoat are sufficiently similar to be classified into the same genus and thus share the same generic name *Mustela*. The second part of the scientific name is called the specific name – the specific names of the mink and the stoat are *vison* and *erminea* respectively. Thus the combination of generic and specific names uniquely identifies which animal is being referred to. *Mustela vison* is the mink; *Mustela erminea* the stoat. Note that the generic name always begins with a capital letter and the specific name begins with a small letter; the whole name is always shown in italic (*sloping like this*) type. While it is useful to have an unambiguous label attached to each species, there is more to scientific names than that. The second role of scientific names is to form part of the framework for a filing system for animals. This helps to cope with the overwhelming diversity of life.

Organisms may be arranged into a hierarchy of increasingly general categories. Into each category are placed animals that are most like one another. Now the characteristics used to decide similarity could be chosen arbitrarily. For example, we could choose to group all the striped animals and all the spotted animals together. This would place the tiger and some snakes in the one group, while the leopard and other snakes would be classified in another – not a very sensible arrangement really, for scientific purposes. The ideal hierarchical classification of living things is based on the evolutionary relationships between organisms. For example, the species stoat (*Mustela erminea*) and mink (*Mustela vison*) are included in the same genus, *Mustela*, because they are genetically related to one another. This genus (*Mustela*) is in turn contained within the family Mustelidae, which also contains the closely related *genera* (plural of 'genus') *Martes* (eg the pine marten), *Meles* (the badger) and *Lutra* (the otter). Families are grouped together to form orders. Thus the family *Mustelidae* is combined with the *Felidae* (cats) and *Canidae* (dogs) to form the order Carnivora. Orders are further merged to form classes. So the *Carnivora* is included with twenty other orders to form the class *Mammalia*. We have members of eight of these orders living wild in Ireland. These are *Insectivora* (shrew and hedgehog), *Chiroptera* (bats), *Lagomorpha* (hares and rabbits), *Rodentia* (rodents), *Cetacea* (whales and dolphins), *Carnivora* (foxes, badgers etc), *Pinnipedia* (seals) and *Artiodactyla* (deer and goats).

Classes of related animals are grouped together to form a phylum (plural 'phyla'). For example *Mammalia* are combined with *Aves* (birds), *Amphibia*, *Reptilia* and a number of classes of fish to form the phylum *Chordata*. These are animals that have a backbone (although it is not always bony!). And finally, phyla are further grouped into kingdoms. For example *Chordata*, together with a number of other phyla such as *Mollusca* (snails) and *Annelida* (worms) together form the kingdom *Animalia*, or what we generally think of as the animal kingdom. There are four other kingdoms: *Monera* (bacteria), *Protists* (mostly single-celled creatures), *Plantae* (plants) and *Fungi* (moulds and mushrooms). All organisms can be logically filed into this seven-level classification system.

Humans and other mammals

It is not surprising that we humans have empathy with mammals. We are after all mammals ourselves. But more than that we have drawn and continue to draw important goods and services from mammals. The evolution of humans went hand in hand with the exploitation of other mammals for food. In fact it may be that this foraging strategy helped to drive the evolution of humans. Without it, the low-density populations of protohumans might not have left any descendants. In fact it was not until the development of agriculture that settled communities and higher densities of humans became sustainable.

A major element in the agricultural revolution that transformed human history was the domestication of a small group of species on which we still depend. These mammals provide sustenance in the form of food and raw materials for clothing. They provide power for transport. They act as logistical support in herding flocks, as guide dogs and in pest control.

Early man was dependent on hunting for survival, and this exploitative relationship gave rise to some of the most inspired animal art ever produced – the cave paintings of palaeolithic (Old Stone Age) and mesolithic (Middle Stone Age) Europe. This cave art went beyond the mere utilitarian and assumed a quasi-religious significance. It seems improbable that the detailed observations that went into the production of these masterpieces were driven entirely by the desire to kill. Such art required empathy. This empathy is given expression today by the increasing interest in wildlife observation and study in the field as exemplified by the increase in eco-tourism or in an ersatz form in the proliferation of wildlife television programmes. The rehabilitation of the killer whale in the popular perspective and the development of the whale-watching industry are the proof of this. Indeed as this is being written the main news bulletins have reports from Mayo of attempts to entice a group of dolphins in danger of being stranded back to the open sea.

How other mammals see the world

We humans tend to see the world in our own terms, and we find it hard to realise the effect of scale on other mammals. Most mammals, at least most wild mammals in this part of the world, are smaller than humans are, and small animals interact with the environment in a fine-grained way. A motorway, for example, may prove an insurmountable barrier for a mouse. Small mammals usually have short lifespans too.

Humans are primates, descended from ancestors that lived in trees, and thus we are highly reliant on visual and acoustic information from our environment. Most other mammals, however, rely more on information passing up their noses. The world for most mammals is a place throbbing with vibrant smells, as you can see if you watch a dog's behaviour. When a cat cuddles up to its owner it is anointing him or her with scents which are more to its liking. And while you and I are probably not very interested in human faeces, foxes are extremely interested in the signals conveyed by the 'scats' deposited by other foxes.

CHAPTER 2

The Story of Mammals in Ireland

*Quis enim, verbi gratia, lupos cervos, et sylvaticos porcos, et vulpes,
taxones, et lepusculos, et sesquivolos in Hiberniam deveheret?*

*Who then really brought wolves, deer, forest pigs, foxes,
badgers little hares and squirrels to Ireland?*
Augustine (7th Century)

Where have Ireland's mammals come from?

There are about 4400 species of mammals in the world. Ireland's land and seas now contain about 50. This may seem a poor mammalian fauna but that is not necessarily so, given Ireland's area, range of latitudes and isolation.

During the Pleistocene period (1.6 million to 10,000 years ago) Ireland probably suffered as many as six ice ages. The cold icy periods are known as stadials, while the warmer periods, like the one we are living in, are termed interstadials. Unfortunately, as a result of the series of ice ages, there is little trace of the flora and fauna of Ireland that existed during the periods in between. Each successive advance of the ice sheets obliterated most traces of what had existed before. So profound was the effect of the ice on the fauna of Ireland that little trace of any mammal from earlier than about 45,000 years ago has ever been found.

Ireland probably finally became isolated from continental Europe about 12,000 years ago. The melting of the last great ice sheets, which began about 14,000 years ago, poured huge volumes of water into the oceans, so at the end of the Woodgrange interstadial (about 11,000 years ago) the sea level between Ireland and Britain on the one hand and Britain and continental Europe on the other rose by about 120 metres. This ended the last opportunity for natural exchange of land mammals between Ireland and lands to the east (Britain and continental Europe). Ireland at that time had a diverse mammalian fauna but it was not to survive intact. The ice was not yet finished and a final cold snap finally led to the extinction of a number of warmer-climate species, including the giant Irish deer and red deer. This lasted from about 11,000 to 10,000 years ago and was at its coldest about 10,500 years ago. This period is known as the Nahanagan stadial. Then, when the ice finally (for the moment) retreated, about 10,000 years ago, the more cold-adapted species such as reindeer, lemmings and arctic fox also disappeared and the process of assembly of Ireland's modern fauna began. It is not entirely clear in the case of all species how they got here.

Human intervention

Ireland's mammalian fauna is unusual due to the particular combination of natural circumstances and human intervention that have led to their introduction or extinction. For example, Ireland has half the species of carnivores that Britain has, but only one-quarter of the species of rodents.

The current fauna is a mixture of species which probably arrived by different routes. A few might possibly have survived the last cold spell (e.g. stoat, mountain hare). Some might have colonised Ireland naturally by sea or air (e.g. bats, seals, otter). Many were introduced/released deliberately by man (e.g. red deer, fallow deer, grey squirrel, sika deer, brown hare). Yet others were introduced or released accidentally by man (e.g. wood mouse, house mouse, the rats, mink, bank vole).

It is clear that humans were the most important single factor in the establishment of Ireland's mammals. There is convincing evidence that of the twenty-two species of land mammals (excluding bats and seals), at least thirteen were introduced by humans, one was reintroduced and another may well have been so. In this, mammals are not unusual among Ireland's vertebrates. Over 50% of all our mammals, reptiles, amphibians and freshwater fish were introduced by humans. Furthermore Ireland has acquired more species of the above animal types during the millennium just ended than in the previous nine. Although Ireland has been acquiring mammals relatively recently, some have also been lost. Two species, the wolf and the wild pig, are now extinct here, while another pair, the muskrat and the roe deer, briefly established themselves in the wild but were exterminated. Thus there has been an ebb and flow in the composition of Ireland's mammals in historical time.

The current status of the landscape and habitats of Ireland and the vertebrate fauna which inhabit them are almost entirely due to the actions of ice and of mammals – man, cattle and sheep. Other domestic animals such as horse, pig, goat, dog and cat have had a lesser influence.

After man, cattle and sheep are the single most important mammalian influence on the Irish landscape. For example, the total weight of all the cattle in Ireland far exceeds the combined weights of all other mammals (including humans, the other domestic mammals and all the wild species). Cattle have always been important to the ecology and economy of Ireland. They were central to the earliest agricultural systems practised in Ireland. In the face of the overwhelming numbers of domestic mammals, wild mammals have relatively little impact. The rabbit, however, is an important agent in maintaining short-grass/herb communities in some coastal areas that in turn provide important foraging areas for Ireland's rarest member of the crow family, the chough (*Pyrrhocorax pyrrhocorax*). In other areas an abundance of rabbits or deer prevents natural regeneration of woodland plant species.

Mammals as pests

Although humans had a major influence on assembling Ireland's mammalian fauna, conflicts of interest arise and a wild mammal may be considered as a nuisance or as a pest. This is sometimes an extremely controversial and emotive issue. The degree of public concern depends on whether humans or domestic animals are the injured party and whether the effect is primarily a health risk to humans or an economic loss.

Wild mammals may compete directly or indirectly with humans or their domestic animals for resources. It would be extremely surprising if predators did not attempt to exploit potential prey. Foxes and mink are not averse to raiding hen-houses. The diet of both humans and seals includes salmon, although the impact of seals is difficult to quantify. The actions of a wild predator might be severe locally. This could be due either to local scarcity of the usual prey, to overpopulation or to the activities of a rogue individual. Rabbits may reduce the amount of fodder available to sheep and cattle. The activities of rodents may severely reduce the palatability of stored foodstuffs.

A wild mammal may act as a reservoir for a disease organism that affects humans or domestic animals. Rats transmit Weil's disease (leptospirosis) and, in the past, bubonic plague. Foxes may suffer from and transmit rabies. Ireland has been rabies-free since the beginning of the twentieth century, and there is no evidence that Irish wild foxes ever contracted rabies. In certain localities of Ireland, badgers and deer are infected with bovine tuberculosis. Small mammals may act as intermediate host for tick-borne diseases such as Lyme's disease.

Devising management strategies to minimise the impact of wild mammals may not be simple. A suitable strategy must take into account the biology of the mammal, information on the importance of the mammal relative to other factors and welfare considerations. For example, trapping regimes to control mink are unlikely to succeed because of the animal's territorial behaviour. Although mammals may be infected with organisms which cause disease in humans and domestic animals, their role in the maintenance of the disease may be minor. It is not always easy to distinguish between a mammal acting as a host (in which the disease organism is maintained) or a vector (an important link in transmitting the disease to humans or domestic mammals). It is also difficult to measure how much disease in humans or domestic animals is due to transmission from wild species given the much more numerous and widespread domestic mammals.

Conservation

Our mammalian fauna exists due to a combination of geological and historical factors. The fact that sika deer, for example, were introduced in the nineteenth century in no way alters the fact that it is now an established member of our fauna. Whether attempts should be made to exterminate it – as has often been advocated – is a matter of politics, practicality and judgement. Red deer were also probably introduced by man, albeit some 4500 years ago – does the same argument apply to them? Probably not.

The concept of conservation without a narrow utilitarian perspective is a relatively modern one. We now have legislation and an infrastructure in place to protect and conserve our fauna from further changes and to reverse recent trends where it is necessary to restore former states. But how retrospective should such restorative efforts be? Although Ireland has in one sense an artificial assemblage of mammals, there are now constraints to the introduction of species, even those that are threatened elsewhere but which might thrive here. Whatever its origins, the mammalian fauna acquired by Ireland contributes to the unique biodiversity on the island and should therefore be sustained through appropriate management and conservation.

CHAPTER 3

Order Insectivora – Insect-Eaters

The little lives that lie
Deep hid in grass join in a long-drawn sigh
More softly still.
AE (George Russell; 1867-1935)

The earliest mammals were small, insignificant-looking, insect-eating animals. These early mammals were extraordinarily like some members of the modern Insectivora, particularly the shrews. The Insectivora themselves first appeared in the fossil record about 100 million years ago. The most primitive of the families, the hedgehogs, were abundant 30 million years ago and all the families had evolved by at least 20 million years ago. The modern Insectivora order includes some of the most primitive of the living mammals. This is not to imply that they are in any sense inferior. Rather, the ancestors of these mammals evolved a form which worked well, and still works well, under particular conditions and thus there was no selection pressure for a different design. Many of the modern Insectivora, therefore, follow lifestyles that must presumably be similar to those of their distant ancestors.

Diversity
The Insectivora are the third most diverse order of living mammals. Of the 4400 species of modern mammals, 354 are Insectivora. The families within the order Insectivora fall into two groups. The first includes the hedgehogs, the moles, the golden moles, the solenodons, the tenrecs and the shrews. The elephant shrews and the tree shrews form the other group. There is, however, a suspicion that this order contains a number of families which are not really closely related. They are grouped together because of similar characteristics that they have retained from their distant ancestors.

Characteristics
Members of the order Insectivora are in general small. The largest species is the otter shrew, which weighs about 1kg, and the smallest, the pygmy white-toothed shrew, which is also the smallest mammal, weighs only 2g.

It is difficult to produce a short and simple definition of the Insectivora. Many features of the Insectivora are relatively primitive or ancestral. The tooth rows are continuous and the general design of the sharply pointed teeth evolved relatively early in the history of the order. The limbs are relatively unspecialised and have five fingers or toes. They walk on the soles of their feet (unlike deer or horses, for example, which walk on hooves that are modified finger and toenails).

As the name suggests, they feed on insects and other invertebrates and the digestive system, as in meat-eaters, is relatively simple. However, some of the larger species can digest fruits, vegetables and some seeds.

The brain is, in general, moderately developed and in many species the part which processes information from the nose is almost as large as the remainder of the brain. Nevertheless, modern members of the Insectivora exhibit many advanced and unusual features. Some species have developed protective spines or the ability to produce venom from their salivary glands. Others use echolocation to navigate and hunt in the dark among undergrowth much as bats use when foraging on the wing.

Distribution

The Insectivora are widely distributed across the globe, but are absent from most of the Australasian region, most of South America, the polar regions and most oceanic islands. A number of species have been introduced into areas outside their natural range, the most notable of which is the hedgehog, which is now thriving in New Zealand. Of the 354 living species, 22 are found in Europe. Ireland has only two members of the Insectivora, the pygmy shrew and the hedgehog.

Hedgehog – *Grainneóg*
Erinaceus europaeus, Linnaeus 1758

It is almost impossible to confuse the hedgehog with any other mammal.

The names

The scientific description was written by the great Swedish biologist Linnaeus, based on specimens from Sweden in 1758. The generic name (*Erinaceus*) used is Latin for hedgehog and means 'spiky wall'. The specific name (*europaeus*) is Latin and refers to the hedgehog's geographical distribution, in Europe. The Irish name, *grainneóg*, is rather uncomplimentary; it means the horrible one. Probably for this reason and also because of its relatively late arrival in Ireland, it does not occur very often in placenames. Three of these are Inchagreenoge, which means hedgehog meadow (*inch*), in Co Limerick, Garrynagranoge, the hedgehog's garden (*garraí*), in Co Cork, and Meenagranoge, the hedgehog's field (*mín*) in Co Donegal.

Identification and characteristics

The hedgehog is unmistakable. It has a short, dumpy body covered by a coat of up to six or seven thousand protective spines. Each spine has, attached to the base, a muscle that allows it to be raised in defence. The hedgehog moves with a characteristic trundling gait. Its legs, however, are quite long and a hedgehog can travel remarkably quickly when necessary, holding its body well clear of the ground.

The overall colour is greyish brown. The spines are dark brown with a pale tip. The spines are gradually and continuously being replaced. Each spine lasts from 12 to 18 months before it is renewed. The head and belly are covered by coarse grey hairs. Hedgehogs can harbour impressive populations of fleas. These, however, are host-specific and do not pose any threat to humans or other animals.

When hedgehogs sense danger they tend to crouch close to the ground, hiss threateningly and erect their spines. If the danger is more serious they may roll into a ball. Hedgehogs have special muscles that allow them to do this. One muscle pulls the spiny skin over its head and another pulls it over the rump. A band of muscle that runs around the edge of the spiny skin acts like a drawstring. When it contracts, it pulls the edges of the skin together and encloses the body within the protective spiny area.

The hedgehog has small eyes and ears. The snout is pointed and relatively mobile. Hedgehogs' teeth, like those of insectivorous mammals generally, are sharp, for piercing and crushing hard-bodied prey. There are 18 teeth in both the upper and lower jaws. The length of the head and body may be 26cm or more. Hedgehogs have a short tail measuring about 2cm. There are five digits on the fore- and hind-legs. The hind-foot length is between 4 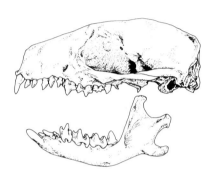 and 4.5cm. Adult males usually weigh 800–1100g; females are smaller, at 500–700g. The weight varies seasonally and often decreases by 40% during winter.

Hedgehogs are quite noisy and emit a snorting or snuffling sound as they search for food. They may emit a hoarse hiss or snort if alarmed and a loud scream if distressed. They are otherwise not very vocal, and their main system of communication is by scents and odours. Hedgehogs occasionally produce large amounts of frothy saliva which they use to anoint themselves. This behaviour is usually triggered by contact with one of a variety of substances with a strong smell or taste. If this happens, a hedgehog may spend up to an hour, almost oblivious to its surroundings, flicking frothy saliva over its spines. The purpose of this behaviour has not been satisfactorily explained.

Distribution

The European hedgehog first appeared in the fossil record about 15 million years ago. It is now found throughout western Europe, southern Scandinavia and northern Russia. In eastern Europe it is replaced by a similar and closely related species.

It is not clear when and how the hedgehog reached Ireland. It was presumably absent during the prolonged cold period between about 15,000 and 30,000 years ago. It was present in England, but not apparently in Ireland, from about 10,000 years ago, as the ice retreated at the end of the last ice age. There may have been a short-lived land connection between Britain and Ireland, but whether the hedgehog would have colonised the country by that route is unclear. It does not seem very likely. There are no remains of the hedgehog

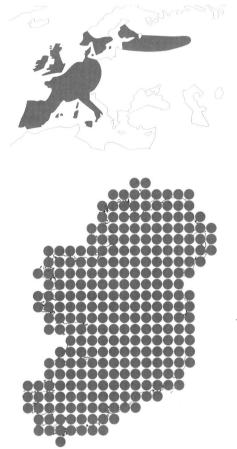

from Ireland during the early post–glacial period nor has it been recorded from prehistoric sites.

It was declared to be absent at the end of the 12th century and it is currently believed that it was probably introduced to Ireland by humans, either accidentally or deliberately as food. This may have been a relatively recent event, as late as the 13th century, after the arrival of the Normans. The earliest record of the hedgehog is from a mid–13th-century site in Waterford city. The map shows 20km squares in which hedgehogs may be found in suitable habitats. The hedgehog is widespread in Ireland today. Population densities range from one hedgehog per 0.5ha to one per 3ha.

Habitats, habits and diet

The hedgehog is essentially an animal of deciduous woodland and wherever grassland meets woodland or scrub. It is quite common in suburban areas, particularly in gardens that are not totally enclosed by walls. It is usually scarce in coniferous woods, marshy areas and moorland or above the treeline in mountainous areas. The availability of food and hibernation sites and the presence of predators are the main factors that limit its distribution.

Hedgehogs are primarily nocturnal, but they often begin foraging at dusk and may still be active at dawn. Although their eyesight is rather poor, their hearing and sense of smell are very well developed. They find their food by searching rather than hunting and they can often be detected on foraging trips by their noisy progress through vegetation in search of food. Hedgehogs may forage over an area ranging from 0.5 to 25 hectares during their nightly wanderings. Since they do not appear to be territorial, they may range over an area from 10 to 50 hectares in the course of a year. A hedgehog may travel up to 3km each night in search of food. Hedgehogs on pastures tend to wander more widely than those in woodland. A hedgehog usually has several sleeping nests, which are used intermittently, located throughout its home range.

They will eat almost any invertebrate animal found at ground level such as beetles, earthworms, caterpillars, slugs, earwigs and millipedes. They will also eat eggs, small mammals and carrion. Berries and fruit are also taken when available. They eat about 50–70g of food a night, depending on the nature of the prey. There is no detailed information on the composition of the diet of hedgehogs in Ireland, but a study in Britain indicated that about half of the diet consists of beetles and caterpillars.

Social organisation and reproduction

Hedgehogs are essentially solitary. They do not seem to defend an exclusive territory. Many hedgehogs may share the same area but use it independently of the others. Occasionally more than one may be seen close together, particularly if food is put out for them. In these circumstances access to the food seems to be based on a dominance hierarchy or a pecking order. However, the social relationships between hedgehogs inhabiting the same area are not well understood.

Hedgehogs breed for the first time at one year of age. The breeding season extends from about May to October. In the breeding season, hedgehogs are quite vocal. Courtship is a noisy business, with much circling of the female by the male until she decides to co-operate. It is not clear if the males mate with more than one female or vice versa but probably both events occur.

Most litters are born in June, after a gestation period of about 33 days. The average litter size is about four or five, although as many as seven may be born. The young are born in a large maternity nest. Mothers are extremely sensitive to disturbance over the first few days after birth and may eat the young or abandon them if disturbed.

The young are born with the developing spines covered by a layer of loose skin that protects the mother during delivery. The young are quite immature and are blind and hairless. The baby spines are white and begin to appear soon after birth. By two weeks of age the eyes are open and the young are able to roll into a protective ball. Young hedgehogs may be found outside the nest after about three weeks and they are weaned after about five weeks. They disperse from the nest at that stage and lead solitary lives thereafter. Females who breed early in the year may breed again in September.

The average lifespan of a hedgehog in the wild is about three years, but individual animals may survive for up to ten. Hedgehog populations vary from year to year, depending mainly on the abundance of food and the severity of the weather. The main cause of mortality is probably death during hibernation due to insufficient stored reserves, but many hedgehogs are also killed by traffic.

Hibernation

Hedgehogs accumulate large quantities of fat in summer and autumn. Two kinds of fat, white and brown, are laid down. White fat is a fuel store accumulated around the internal organs and under the skin. Brown fat is found in a special depot, sometimes called the hibernating gland, under the skin, particularly over the shoulder region. Its main function is to generate heat and it is used to warm the body when the hedgehog is emerging from hibernation or if it is in danger of freezing. Their first winter is a difficult time for young hedgehogs. They need to weigh over 450g before hibernation; otherwise they would probably have insufficient reserves to last until spring. For this reason, late-born litters are unlikely to survive the winter.

In general, hedgehogs enter hibernation about October or November, depending on the weather. They build special hibernation nests of leaves and grass in sheltered areas such as in undergrowth or under sheds. During hibernation hedgehogs allow their body temperature to cool from its normal value, about 34°C, to the temperature of the surroundings. The heart rate slows from about 150–190 to about 20 beats a minute. However, to avoid freezing to death hedgehogs will increase their metabolic rate to generate heat if their body temperature drops close to 4°C.

Hedgehogs do not remain in hibernation continuously throughout winter. They awake from time to time to urinate. In some instances they may even move to a new nest, particularly during a mild spell. Hedgehogs generally resume normal activity in March or April, depending on the weather. In general, hedgehogs in the south of the country emerge from hibernation a few weeks before those in the north.

Watching hedgehogs

The presence of hedgehogs is indicated by their droppings and tracks and by their foraging activity at night. The droppings are often found on lawns or in vegetable patches. Hedgehog droppings are usually black and shiny and are dropped indiscriminately as the animal forages for food. They are cylindrical, about 4cm long and 1cm in diameter. They usually have a somewhat granular texture but, depending on the composition of the diet, may be quite loose and liquid. It is possible to discover some of the food items by examining the droppings. Wing cases of beetles, mouth parts of slugs and the tiny spines of earthworms can be identified.

Wandering trails may also be seen in the grass in the early morning, particularly after dewy nights. Clear footprints of the fore- or hind-legs show five toes but are quite different in size. The fore-print is about 3.5–4cm long, while the hind-print is 4–4.5cm. They could be confused with those of larger rodents such as the brown rat or the squirrels, but prints of squirrels are slightly smaller and those of the brown rat clearly smaller. (Furthermore, the rodents have only four digits on the front feet.)

Hedgehogs are quite noisy and can often be heard as they move about or eat certain items. The crunching of snail shells or the lip smacking which occurs when eating snails may often be heard. The best way to view hedgehogs is to encourage them by putting out suitable food for them in the garden. They will soon learn to check the area for free food and then they can be readily observed.

Conservation

Many hedgehogs are killed on the roads. When confronted by danger, the hedgehog's instinct is to roll into a defensive ball which is no protection against a car, if the hedgehog is directly in the path of an approaching wheel. It is difficult to assess the threat posed by traffic to hedgehogs. It may be a significant element in the annual mortality among certain populations, but it seems that deaths on roads increase when hedgehogs are most abundant, and death on the road is probably not a major factor controlling hedgehog numbers. Accidental deaths are more likely soon after hedgehogs emerge from hibernation and breeding activity begins. Males are twice as likely as females to be killed on the roads, probably because males travel further in search of females at mating time. There is some evidence that particular areas on roads are accident black spots for hedgehogs. It may be that hedgehogs do not wander about entirely at random and have particular routes that are used regularly particularly when crossing roads. Some hedgehogs are killed by badgers and foxes. Badgers are particularly skilled at preying on hedgehogs and where badgers are abundant hedgehogs are usually scarce. Hedgehogs are particularly vulnerable to pesticides used in gardens and hedgehogs are usually uncommon in areas where pesticides are heavily used. Many are poisoned by eating slugs which have consumed toxic bait. They are rather accident-prone and, although they are good swimmers, they may fall victim to garden ponds with steep sides or overhanging edges. They also get trapped in cattle grids, but fitting a ramp allows a trapped hedgehog to scramble free.

Hedgehogs which build nests in garden refuse are sometimes accidentally killed in garden bonfires. Hedgehogs were traditionally considered to be vermin and were trapped because of their predation on the eggs of game birds, a reputation they scarcely deserved. They have also been captured by people for food.

Hedgehogs readily accept supplementary food and are often fed in gardens. Milk is not suitable as a sole food for hedgehogs older than about a month, as they cannot easily digest the milk sugars and they may get diarrhoea. If you would like to offer supplementary food to wild hedgehogs or if it is necessary to rescue an underweight hedgehog late in the autumn, then tinned pet food is an appropriate diet. If they are to be nursed indoors to avoid entry to hibernation then treatment with a proprietary flea powder formulated for cats is advisable. They are engaging although rather single-minded little beasts and will readily readjust to life outdoors in the spring. They do not appear to have a shorter life expectancy after release than their wild counterparts, provided they are released into suitable habitats.

The hedgehog is strictly protected in the Republic of Ireland but not in Northern Ireland. It is listed in Appendix III of the Bern Convention as a species requiring protection.

Pygmy shrew – *Luch féir/Dallóg fhraoigh*
Sorex minutus, Linnaeus 1766

The pygmy shrew holds a number of Irish records. It is our smallest mammal and it has the shortest lifespan.

The names
The scientific description was written by the Swedish biologist Linnaeus in 1766, based on specimens from western Siberia. The generic name used (*sorex*) is the Latin for shrew. The specific name (*minutus*) is Latin for tiny. In Irish it is sometimes known as the grass (*féir*) mouse (*luch*). Its tiny eyes inspired its alternative Irish name, the blind animal (*dallóg*) of the heather (*fraoch*).

Identification and characteristics
The pygmy shrew has a narrow, pointed, flexible snout that is almost constantly twitching as it searches through surface leaf litter for food. It has long whiskers, small eyes, short ears, which are almost completely hidden in the hair, and a medium-length slender tail which is rather sparsely covered by hair. The body is covered by short, dense, brownish fur that is paler on the belly. Pygmy shrews grow their winter coat in autumn and moult this to their shorter summer coat in April or May. The teeth have red tips because of the deposition of iron. There are 20 teeth in the upper jaw and only 12 in the lower. They have only one pair of incisor teeth in the lower jaw. These project forwards and are moveable so they can act as pincers. Shrews have poor eyesight and rely on their acute senses of hearing, smell and touch.

They are quite vocal but many of their sounds are high-pitched and just on the borderline of audibility for adult humans. Children can hear them more easily. They produce a short hiss when alarmed or threatened and a series of whistle-like twitterings as they move about their territories. When involved in disputes with their neighbours they are much more noisy.

If seen in the open they scuttle rapidly along the surface. They are agile climbers and can also swim. Their skin is well-equipped with scent glands and there is a particularly large pair extending along the flanks. It is believed that these glands play a role in marking territorial boundaries.

The head and body length ranges from 40 to 60mm. The tail is 32–46mm long and the hind-foot 10–12mm. There are five digits on both fore- and hind-legs. Immature adults weigh about 4g in autumn and then get smaller during winter so that by spring they weigh about 3g. They not only become thinner but their skeleton shrinks and they also become shorter. In spring they rapidly increase in weight in preparation for breeding. Adult pygmy shrews in breeding condition weigh 5–6g.

Distribution

The pygmy shrew has existed for at least two million years in Europe. It is now widespread throughout northern Europe, extending to the arctic coast of Russia and into eastern Siberia. Although it is generally considered to be native, bones of pygmy shrew have never

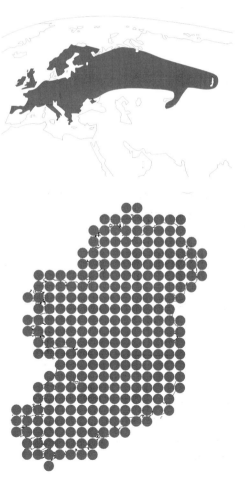

been recorded from archaeological sites in Ireland, possibly because they are so small and fragile, so it is not clear if the pygmy shrew – or indeed any other shrew – was present in Ireland during the period before the last glaciation. If so, it was presumably absent during the prolonged cold period between about 15,000 and 30,000 years ago. There may have been a short-lived land connection between Britain and Ireland, but whether the pygmy shrew would have colonised the country at that time by that route is unclear. The pygmy shrew is not deterred by damp conditions and this has been used to explain why only this shrew and not its close relative, the common shrew, colonised Ireland from Britain after the last ice age. All that can safely be said is that either it colonised or recolonised the country about 10,000 years ago or it may have been introduced to Ireland fairly recently. Only genetic comparisons of pygmy shrews from Ireland with those of adjacent countries will resolve the matter.

The pygmy shrew is now common and widespread in Ireland in all areas of suitable habitat. Population densities may range from five to 40 shrews per hectare, depending on the habitat, and also vary greatly at different times of the year. Population density is greatest in summer and lowest in winter when most of the adults in the population have died. There has never been a detailed systematic survey of the country for pygmy shrews. The distribution map shows the overall distribution of the pygmy shrew per 20km square, based on small-scale local surveys and occasional records and reports.

Diet

Food requirements of animals are related to body size. Larger animals, although they need more food than smaller ones, need proportionately less food. For example, ten animals weighing 10g each need much more food than one animal weighing 100g. The metabolic rate and thus the fuel consumption of the pygmy shrew is so high relative to its size that it will starve to death if deprived of food for about three hours. Shrews have voracious appetites and must eat at least their body weight in food every day. As a result of their constant need for food, shrews are active by night and day, with hunting expeditions every two or three hours. Since they do not hibernate, this high level of feeding activity continues throughout the year. They also appear to practise refection, that is, they eat some of their droppings and thus pass food through the gut twice. This is also performed by rabbits and hares, and is believed to extract nutrients more completely from the food and thus avoid waste.

With such a high fuel consumption, pygmy shrews cannot afford to be too choosy. They are opportunistic predators and eat a wide variety of invertebrates, mainly beetles, woodlice, flies, insect larvae, spiders and bugs. In Ireland beetles are the main component of the diet and, together with woodlice and flies, constitute about half of the food items taken. (The tissues of the bodies of their prey are highly nutritious, although they contain a high proportion of water and the skeletons are relatively indigestible.) Earthworms seem to be generally too big for a pygmy shrew to tackle.

Habitats and habits

In Ireland the pygmy shrew is found in most habitats where there is heavy ground cover, particularly in grassland and hedgerows. It is also abundant in deciduous and coniferous woodland and on peatlands. It has been found on the tops of our mountains and is present on many offshore islands. (Although it can climb quite well, the shrew spends most of its time on the ground surface. In other parts of the world the pygmy shrew may share its habitats with other species of shrews.) Shrews build spherical nests, usually of dried grass, concealed in long grasses, in dense vegetation or under rocks or logs. They tend to forage above ground and rarely burrow, although they may use tunnels excavated by other small mammals. They use regular pathways to search for prey which are detected by smell or movement. In grassland these pathways appear as tunnels through the vegetation.

Social organisation, reproduction and life-cycle

Pygmy shrews are usually extremely aggressive toward each other. If a pair of shrews meet, there is usually a bout of threats involving short explosive hisses and tail lashing. Sometimes these encounters escalate to physical violence. Thus they are essentially solitary animals and adults occupy exclusive territories ranging from as small as 200m² to as large as 1500m². Shrews appear to be quite familiar with their territories and regularly patrol the boundaries. Shrews without territories have a low life expectancy and this probably explains their intolerance of other shrews. If a resident shrew dies, the vacant territory is soon occupied by a vagrant. Territoriality is relaxed in the breeding season when males travel about in search of females. If a group of shrews is seen, this is usually a mother and her litter. These parties break up when the young are between 20 and 25 days old as they become independent and disperse to find territories of their own.

Pygmy shrews may breed from April to October but do so mainly in June and July. Females are receptive for only about a day in each reproductive cycle. Courtship is a whirlwind affair, carried out during a brief lull in hostilities. Males and females then resume solitary lives. Pregnancy lasts for 22–25 days and the young are born in a nest. Newborn shrews are born naked and quite helpless and cannot control their body temperature as readily as adults. The litter size ranges from four to seven but five is most usual for the first litter of the year. The young weigh only 0.25g at birth, but within 14 days may be ten times heavier, particularly if the litter is a small one. On average young shrews are weaned at about 21 days of age and usually weigh at least 2.5g at that point. Females may breed two or three times during the summer and then die before winter. Juveniles who overwinter to breed the following spring maintain the population. The lifestyle of the pygmy shrew is fast and furious. About 50% of shrews die as juveniles and only about 25% of shrews survive long enough to breed. The maximum lifespan is about 16 months, although it is unusual for either male or female shrews to survive beyond about 13 months in the wild.

Pygmy shrews have potent scent glands, but these do not deter predators since foxes and cats regularly kill shrews, although they apparently usually find them distasteful. Foxes will, however, eat them in certain areas such as on peatlands in the west of Ireland where other food is scarce. Owls regularly kill and eat shrews. In places pygmy shrews form up to one quarter of the diet of barn owls particularly in spring. They are also occasionally taken by long-eared owls.

Studying pygmy shrews

The field signs of pygmy shrews are rather inconspicuous. They are so light that it is unusual to find a clearly identifiable example of their tiny footprints. The droppings of pygmy shrews are extremely small (2–3mm long) and slightly tapered at one end. They may range in colour from black through brown to grey and usually have a granular or rough appearance due to the fragments of insect remains. They do not appear to have a marked territorial function since they are not deposited at specific latrine sites but are scattered throughout the territory.

Pygmy shrews are best detected by listening for rustling sounds as they forage in long grass, undergrowth or fallen leaves. They are frequently vocal and emit a high-pitched chi-chi-chi-chi as they move about. Careful parting of the vegetation will, with patience, reveal a shrew or perhaps a family party as it scurries along.

Domestic cats often catch and kill shrews and many people who have never seen a live pygmy shrew may have had one delivered to their door by their cat. The most practical way to see a pygmy shrew is to use a live-trap to catch one. It should, however, be promptly released at the capture site. Otherwise it may have lost its territory and be unable to gain one elsewhere and become a vagrant with a low life expectancy. See page 121, under the bank vole, for advice on how to use a live-trap. A licence is required from Dúchas The Heritage Service of the Department of Arts, Heritage, Gaeltacht and The Islands (RoI) or the Environment Service of the Department of the Environment (NI) to trap pygmy shrews.

Conservation

The pygmy shrew is common in Ireland wherever suitable prey, mainly insects, is found. It may be locally rare where there is heavy use of pesticides. It consumes enormous numbers of potential pest insects. It is totally protected in the Republic of Ireland and Northern Ireland in accordance with its listing in Appendix III of the Bern Convention as a species requiring protection.

CHAPTER 4

Order Chiroptera – Bats

We are little airy creatures
All of different voice and features.
Jonathan Swift (1667-1745)

Bats are the only order of mammals that are capable of true powered flight. The name Chiroptera comes from the Greek words for hand (*chiros*) and wing (*pteron*). This aptly describes the most distinctive feature of bats. The wing surface that generates lift is formed from an extensive thin web of skin supported mainly by extremely long fingers.

There are two types of bat in the Chiroptera: the Microchiroptera (little bats) most of which are insectivorous and the Megachiroptera (big bats) which feed mainly on fruit or nectar. All our Irish bats are Microchiroptera.

Evolution

Apart from specialisation relating to flight, the body plan of bats is remarkably similar to that of ancestral mammals or modern Insectivora such as shrews. Unfortunately, bats are relatively scarce in the fossil record and the earliest known fossils of bats known give little help in deciding their ancestry. The earliest fossil microchiropteran, which dates from about 55 million years ago, and the earliest megachiropteran, from about 35 million years ago, are very similar to their modern counterparts. This indicates that bats are a relatively ancient mammalian order. They had evolved their present structure relatively early in their history, much earlier than modern mice or rats, for example, which evolved only about 10 million years ago.

Some experts suspect that the Microchiroptera may be descended from insectivore-like ancestors and therefore are related to shrews and their relatives, while the Megachiroptera may be more closely related to the primates, particularly the lemurs or monkeys. However, recent genetic analysis suggests that some of what we call Microchiroptera are more closely related to the Megachiroptera than they are to other Microchiroptera. This strongly suggests that flight evolved at least twice independently in bats.

Diversity

Bats are the second most diverse order of mammals and about 970 living species are known. Only the order Rodentia (rodents) contains more species. The Microchiroptera, which is the more widespread family, includes 800 species and contains most of the smaller bats. These are mainly insectivorous and use echolocation to find their prey. At higher latitudes they hibernate in winter and may save energy by becoming torpid by day during the rest of the year. Some microchiropterans, however, feed on nectar and pollen, a few catch fish, others hunt small vertebrates and three feed solely on blood. The Megachiroptera, a group containing about 170 species, are confined to tropical and sub-tropical areas and feed on fruit or nectar and pollen.

Characteristics

Bats are in general small. However, the largest of the Megachiroptera, the kalong from the East Indies, has a wingspan of up to 1.7m and weighs about 900g. Weight is a major consideration for flying animals. The heaviest megachiropteran bats rarely exceed 1kg and most are much lighter, less than 20g. The bat skeleton is somewhat simpler and lighter than that of non-flying mammals in the same size range.

The main characteristics of bats relate to the requirements of flight. In flight the body is almost completely encircled by the wing membrane, which is supported by the fingers, arms, flanks, hind-legs and tail. There is often, on the ankle, an inwardly directed spur, the calcar, that also supports the wing. The shape of the wings determines bats' aerodynamic properties. Broad, relatively short wings are characteristic of slow, highly manoeuvrable flight. In fact some broad-winged bats can hover or even fly backwards. By contrast, bats with longer, pointed wings are usually fast fliers and fly over longer distances.

The hind-legs are generally thin and, although essential to support the wing in flight, are not ideal for supporting the bat when at rest, although they can crawl. This is probably why bats roost by hanging upside-down. The legs, which could not well withstand the sustained compression while standing, can readily cope with the tension generated while suspended. Bats may hang from their front legs when urinating or defecating and some do so when giving birth. A further feature of the hind legs is the rotation of the knees so that they point either outwards or backwards. This gives bats their characteristic crab-like gait when on the ground.

The teeth of Microchiroptera are typical of insectivores. The tooth rows are continuous. In other words the teeth are relatively close together with no gaps, and in general the teeth, even the molars, are narrow and sharply pointed. They are more square and flatter in the fruit-eating bats. The digestive system of the insectivorous, carnivorous, pollen-eating and nectar-eating bats is relatively simple. That of fruit eaters is more complex. The hind brain, which controls movement and analyses information from the ears, is much better developed in insectivorous bats than in fruit-eating bats.

Microchiropteran bats forage at night. This habit probably evolved to exploit the high abundance of flying insects that occurs just after sunset. They therefore avoid competition with birds that hunt almost exclusively by day. The Microchiroptera mainly use echolocation to detect insects although sight may also be used. They emit short pulses (five to thirty per second) of high-frequency sounds produced by the larynx (voice box) in the throat. These sounds are emitted either through the open mouth and nostrils or, in the case of the horseshoe bats, through the nostrils only. The sounds are reflected back by objects in the path of the bat and so it develops an acoustic image of its environment. The frequency range of sounds emitted by bats (30–140 kHz) is generally above the threshold of our hearing, although children can usually hear some of them. Although adult humans usually cannot hear them, the sounds emitted are extremely loud, and the bat has special modifications to its ear so that it is not confused by its own sounds. It temporarily shuts off its ear while the sound is travelling outward.

Bats probably use high-frequency sounds for two reasons. Firstly, high-frequency sounds operate over short distances only and therefore inform the bat of what is in the immediate vicinity. Secondly, high-frequency sounds have a short wavelength and thus detect small objects such as flying insects. Drops of water in the atmosphere such as in fog, light mist or rain absorb some of the frequencies emitted by bats and interfere with echolocation. Therefore bats avoid hunting on foggy or misty nights. Bats usually use one of two sorts of sound in each pulse, a frequency-modulated (FM) sweep across a range of frequencies or a constant frequency (CF) single note. Most species found in Ireland use an FM sweep only. The lesser horseshoe bat, however, uses a CF sound, and the pipistrelle species use a combination of the two, a descending FM sweep which merges into a CF note. Its audible equivalent might be a 'wolf-whistle'. In general, there is a close relationship between the wavelength of the sound and the size of prey detected and eaten. From the returning echoes a bat can determine the size of an object (if it reflects a particular wavelength from the FM sweep). In addition the frequency of the echo of the constant frequency component depends on whether the object in its path is moving towards or away from the bat (the well-known Doppler effect experienced on railway platforms) and so the bat can detect the direction of movement of its prey by the change in frequency of the echo. Bats emit pulses at an increasing rate as they approach a target; from about ten per second when searching, to 25–50 per second when they are locked in on the target, rising to as high as 200 per second as they strike.

Each species emits a particular type of ultrasound that allows them to specialise in particular types and sizes of insects and thus several species can coexist in the same general area. Some prey, particularly moths, have evolved defensive tactics. They can hear the approaching bat and can take evasive action, while others emit sounds of their own to jam the bat's echolocation system. Bats catch their prey in a number of ways, either directly in the mouth, in the mouth after juggling them in the wings or by scooping them up in the tail membrane.

It is possible to hear the sounds of hunting bats using a device that electronically lowers the frequencies to within the audible range. These devices are sold as 'bat detectors'. These devices can be tuned to detect the frequencies being emitted by a bat and can be used to help identify the species of a particular bat in flight.

World distribution

Bats are one of the most diverse orders of mammals and are widely distributed throughout the world. They are absent only from the polar regions and some extremely remote oceanic islands. Bats are quite abundant in temperate climates but are extremely common in the tropics and, in certain areas, they outnumber all other mammalian species. Of the 970 living species (in 18 families), 32 (in three families) are found in Europe. All the European bats are insectivorous Microchiroptera.

Distribution in Ireland

Nine species of Microchiroptera (from two families) have been identified as breeding in Ireland. Until recently, it was thought that we only had seven species in this country, but a new breeding species has been discovered here, and also, we have recently realised that one long-established species is in fact two (very similar) species. There is circumstantial evidence for the presence of two further species here, but it is still unclear if the records relate to vagrant individuals rather than members of a breeding colony.

It appears that suitable wooded habitats for bats would have developed in Ireland by about 9000 years ago, but bats have never been reported from palaeontological or archaeological sites in Ireland, since bats do not fossilise well and this subject has been little studied here. For these reasons, it is not clear when the various bat species arrived here. It is known, however, that most of our bat species were well established in Britain by about 6000 years ago, and may have been there much earlier. The distribution of bats in Ireland is known mainly from the locations of summer roosts reported by householders.

Metabolism and hibernation

Bats in flight have a high metabolic rate and thus must consume large amounts of food. When insects are abundant this poses no problem. However, maintaining a high body temperature is extremely costly and needs abundant food; so when food is scarce bats save energy by lowering their body temperature. They even do this when in their day-time roosts during their active season in summer. When they return from hunting, their temperature remains relatively high until they have completed digestion of their food, and then it may drop from almost 35°C to about 15°C. In this state the bats are described as torpid, feel slightly cool and do not move about. They increase their body temperature to almost 40°C just prior to leaving the roost at dusk to hunt.

Bats hibernate during winter, usually, depending on the weather, from mid-November to the end of March. In autumn they may increase their weight by about 30% in preparation for winter hibernation. During hibernation they remain torpid by day and for most of the night and their body temperature may fall as low as about 5°C. Bats must wake up at intervals during winter to excrete metabolic wastes by urination or to avoid freezing if the temperature of the roost falls close to zero. Since hibernating bats require substantial amounts of energy to assume a normal body temperature, they are vulnerable to disturbance in their winter roosts. If they are disturbed to such an extent that they have to wake up unnecessarily, their fat reserves will be seriously depleted and they may not have sufficient reserves to survive until spring. For example, causing a bat to wake up inappropriately from hibernation may use up as much energy as it would otherwise use in a month.

Reproduction

Mating appears to occur among Irish bats in the autumn and early winter, but female bats do not become pregnant immediately. They store the sperm from the males in their reproductive tract through the hibernation period and only use it to become pregnant in the spring, when they emerge from hibernation. This is known as delayed fertilisation. When they emerge from hibernation and become pregnant, the female bats move to summer nursery roosts or maternity colonies, where the young are born, usually in June or July. A single offspring is usual, and is reared exclusively by its mother.

Watching and learning about bats

If you know of a bat roost in your area, you may be able to watch the bats as they emerge at dusk to feed. (See also the sections on the various bats for information on their feeding times and habits.) Sit somewhere out of their direct line of hearing so that your silhouette is not so conspicuous to the bats' ultrasonic sonar. Roosts usually have droppings near them. These are usually between 8 and 10mm long and are shiny when fresh. Bat droppings somewhat resemble mouse droppings except that mouse droppings become hard and shiny when dry whereas the droppings of bats tend to crumble to a fine powder. The diet can be established by identification of the fragments of the prey which pass undigested through the gut.

Because of the legal protection accorded to bats and their susceptibility to disturbance it is difficult to develop skills in identification of bats. Mounted specimens of all the species of bats found in Ireland may be seen in the Natural History Museum, Dublin. Interested persons should contact their local bat group which will have events organised for those who wish to learn more about bats. Further information may be obtained from Merryfalls Cottage, Harristown Lane, St Margarets, Co Dublin (Tel. 01-8347134; http://www.clubi.ie/dbg/irish.htm) or The Northern Ireland Bat Group, Ulster Museum, Belfast BT9 5AB. The bat groups in the Republic of Ireland are affiliated to the Irish Wildlife Trust, which is dedicated to the conservation, welfare and study of mammals and their habitats. Various activities are organised and a newsletter is produced regularly. The Irish Wildlife Trust can be contacted at 39 Upper Fitzwilliam St. Dublin 2; tel. 01-6614926. The Ulster Wildlife Trust is based at 3 New Line, Crossgar, Co Down BT30 9EP.

Conservation

Most bat species in Ireland are listed as internationally important in the Irish Red Data Book, although Natterer's bat and the whiskered bat are both listed as indeterminate, which means that their status is unclear. All Irish bats are listed under Annex IV of the Habitats Directive and Appendix II of the Bern Convention as species requiring strict protection, and they are strictly protected in both the Republic of Ireland and Northern Ireland. Any action which is likely to impact on roost sites of bats must be notified in advance to Dúchas The Heritage Service of the Department of Arts, Heritage, Gaeltacht and the Islands (RoI) or the Environment Service of the Department of the Environment (NI). They will advise, after a site inspection, if, how or when the intended action is appropriate. The local ranger will be glad to hear of the location of roost sites.

Lesser horseshoe bat –
Ialtóg crúshrónach/Crú-ialtóg beag
Rhinolophus hipposideros, Bechstein 1800

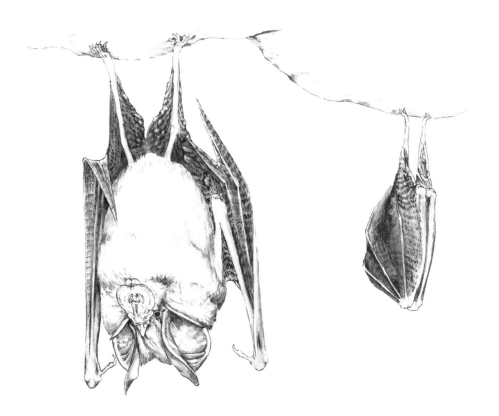

The lesser horseshoe bat is found in western coastal counties.

The names

The scientific description written by Bechstein in 1800 was based on a specimen collected in France. The scientific name is based on Greek words that describe the facial features. The generic part is formed from *rhinos* (of the nose) and *lophos* (a crest). The specific part is formed from *hippos* (horse) and *sideros* (iron) and refers to the nose leaves, which are shaped like a horseshoe.

The Irish name means horseshoe-nosed (*crúshrónach*) bat (*ialtóg*). It is also known as the small (*beag*) horseshoe-bat (*crú-ialtóg*). There is now some evidence that the horseshoe bats are more closely related to fruit bats than they are to other Microchiroptera.

Identification and characteristics

When roosting, the lesser horseshoe bat hangs freely from horizontal surfaces by its feet, and, unlike other bats found in Ireland, wraps its wings around its body almost completely covering it. At rest it appears about as large as a plum and is one of our smaller species.

The snout has a complex series of nose leaves. These form a lower horseshoe-shaped structure around the nostrils and a central triangular lobe pointing upwards. The ears are set wide apart and lack a central tragus (earlobe). The ears may be moved independently of one another. The eyes are relatively small. The fur is greyish in young bats and becomes buff-coloured in adults. Its wings, typical of highly manoeuvrable fliers, are relatively broad. Wing span ranges from 22 to 25cm.

Its body length ranges from 35 to 39mm. The forearm is about 37mm and the tail ranges from 23 to 33mm. Its legs are rather long and slender and its hind-foot measures about 8–10mm. Adults may weigh up to 8 or 9g in autumn just before they enter hibernation, but during this period their weight may decline to about 6g. After the birth of her young, the adult female weighs about 5.5g.

The female, in addition to two nipples on the chest from which the young are fed, also develops two false nipples in the groin area to which the young attaches when the mother is in the roost. Thus while the mother hangs upside down her offspring hangs head upwards.

Lesser horseshoe bats fly at medium speeds with rapid wing beats and are extremely manoeuvrable. The wings are broad and the flight path has frequent changes in height and direction. The horseshoe bat locates its prey using a relatively constant frequency call – a narrow range of ultrasound between 105 and 115 kHz. The complex nose leaves are used as a reflector to alter the shape of the sound beam, either as a concentrated narrow beam or a diffuse sonic glow. These frequencies are much higher than those used by any other bat in Ireland. On a bat detector these calls sound like a continuous warble.

Distribution

The lesser horseshoe bat was once widespread in Europe and western Asia. Its range has been contracting and it is now found across southern Europe and southern Russia as far east as the Caspian sea and in parts of northern Africa. In Britain it is confined to Wales and southwest England and its numbers are declining there also. It is not known how long the lesser horseshoe bat has been in Ireland, as no fossils have been found. It was present in Britain about 6000 years ago, but may have been there substantially earlier. The first specimen to be positively identified in Ireland was found in Clare in 1859.

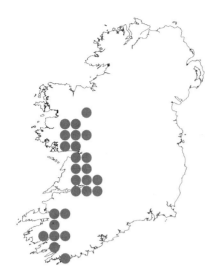

Although Ireland is at the extreme northwestern edge of its range, over 157 lesser horseshoe bat roosts were reported by a national bat survey in 1994 and the national population is about 12,000. In Ireland the lesser horseshoe bat appears to prefer sheltered valleys in partially wooded countryside in limestone areas, and it is generally confined to the counties of the western seaboard south of Sligo. In north Clare there are at least four lesser horseshoe bats per square kilometre. The distribution map shows the 20km squares that contain at least one known roost used by lesser horseshoe bats.

Roosts

Lesser horseshoe bats prefer sheltered valleys with deciduous woodland. They often roost in large colonies and prefer to occupy relatively open spaces with open access. In Ireland most of its summer roosts are found in the spacious attics of big houses or castles or under the roofs of stables and barns, particularly if access is easy. The bats enter their summer roosts from April onwards. Summer roosts are usually maternity colonies, containing breeding females and their dependent young. These roosts may be quite large, with about fifty bats, although numbers may vary markedly over a short period. Distribution throughout the roost depends on temperature; on cold days bats will roost closely together in the warmest part of the roost. Males and non-breeding females roost alone or in small groups.

Throughout their world range, lesser horseshoe bats, which prefer humid hibernation sites, choose caves, mines, souterrains or similar sites for their winter roosts and hibernation sites. In Ireland, buildings are the most important winter roost sites. In some big houses in Ireland colonies often transfer from the summer roost in the attic to the cellar or adjacent icehouse in winter and thus move little over the year. In the west of Ireland, winter roosts are also regularly found in many archaeological sites such as souterrains.

Food and foraging

Lesser horseshoe bats start to emerge from their roosts about 30 to 50 minutes after sunset. They are usually active all night and finally begin to return about 60 minutes before dawn. Lesser horseshoe bats are extremely manoeuvrable. They can easily take off from the ground in confined spaces. When hunting they fly low, circling frequently, and are capable of hunting in dense vegetation. They hunt close to riverside vegetation or close to walls in farmyards. Ultrasounds are emitted through the nostrils and thus they can continue to hunt even when their mouth is full of food. A study in County Clare revealed that their main foods are craneflies (daddy-longlegs) and other flies, as well as moths, caddis flies and lacewings.

Reproduction and life-cycle

The mating season probably extends from late September through November, but fertilisation is delayed until spring, when female bats emerge from hibernation and move to nursery roosts. The length of pregnancy depends on the weather because during cold periods the bats become torpid and development of the foetus slows down. The young are born in the maternity colonies from mid-June through July. A single offspring, weighing about 1.7–2g, is usual. The young are left in the roost while the mothers are foraging. The young are capable of flight by late July or early August, at about five or six weeks of age. They are finally weaned later that month. They become mature at one year of age. The average lifespan of the lesser horseshoe bat in Ireland is not known for certain but is probably about five years. The maximum lifespan recorded for this species is 18 years.

Watching lesser horseshoe bats

The lesser horseshoe bat is largely confined to the west of Ireland. It is often found foraging along waterside vegetation or close to old buildings and walls. The lesser horseshoe bat often has favoured rest sites in its home range where it perches to eat prey. Wings and legs of its food items may often be found under such perches. A pile of wings of daddy-longlegs is usually indicative of such a perch. The droppings are small and cylindrical, about 6–8mm long and about 1.5–2mm in diameter.

Because of the extreme sensitivity of this bat to disturbance it is not recommended that roosts be entered. However, lesser horseshoe bats may be seen in flight, foraging in the vicinity of the protected and secure roosts at Edenvale Cave, Co Clare and an ice-house near Kilgarvan, Co Kerry, for example. If a roost site is known it will be possible to obtain good views of the bats as they leave on their hunting trips. You should be in position about sunset because these bats tend to emerge within the hour after sunset. There will usually be an increase in activity within the roost before the bats emerge. Lesser horseshoe bats tend not to emerge in groups but singly at varying intervals. They may also return to the roost after varying periods spent hunting.

This species can be easily positively identified using a bat detector. If using a detector it is important to remember that the frequency of the ultrasound used by lesser horseshoe bats is much higher than that used by any of our other bats and might be missed if the detector is not tuned to about 110 kHz.

Conservation

The lesser horseshoe bat is decreasing in numbers throughout most of its range in Europe. It is not clear why this is so, but changes in agricultural and forestry practices and the use of organochlorine pesticides may be responsible. Although it is confined to parts of the west of the country, Ireland holds the largest European population of this bat. It is of international importance and deserves particular care and protection.

In Ireland, the major threats appear to be disturbance and loss of roost sites. This bat is very sensitive to disturbance or interference. Even in summer, when at rest by day, the lesser horseshoe bat lowers its metabolic rate and body temperature. If disturbed it begins to restore normal metabolic activity. This is extremely costly if it cannot immediately begin to feed. Since this bat requires spacious roost sites, often in disused buildings, its summer breeding roosts are particularly vulnerable to deterioration by neglect. Such sites may need particular attention to stabilise their structure. Colonies are extremely sensitive to changes in the use of buildings or to timber treatment. If forced to abandon roosts, lesser horseshoe bats usually do not travel long distances in search of alternatives. Local populations therefore need careful management and protection. This bat is also extremely vulnerable when hibernating, since it tends to hang in the open in its winter roosts. Dúchas The Heritage Service of the Department of Arts, Heritage, Gaeltacht and The Islands have protected some roosts by fitting lockable metal grills across entrances to exclude intruders.

The lesser horseshoe bat is listed in the Irish Red Data book as internationally important. It is in Annex IV of the Habitats Directive and Appendix II of the Bern Convention as a species requiring strict protection, and in Annex II of the Habitats Directive as a species requiring the designation of Special Areas of Conservation.

Whiskered bat – *Ialtóg ghiobach*
Myotis mystacinus, Kuhl 1819

The small whiskered bat is one of Ireland's rarest mammals.

The names

The scientific description, based on a specimen collected in Germany, was made by the German naturalist Kuhl in 1819. The scientific name is derived from Greek. The generic part is formed from *mys* (mouse) and *otos* (of the ear). The specific part is based on the Greek *mystakos* (of the moustache). The scientific name thus means the mouse-eared moustached one. The Irish name refers to its coat, the shaggy (*giobach*) bat (*ialtóg*).

Identification and characteristics

The whiskered bat is one of Ireland's smaller and rarer bats. It is quite difficult to identify. Its ears are moderately long and pointed, while the tragus (earlobe) is about half as long as the ear. Its fur is shaggy, brown or black on the upper parts and greyish below. It has a darker face with long fine sensory vibrissae (whiskers) on the lips and at the corners of the mouth. The wings, typical of moderately fast fliers, are somewhat broad but pointed and wing span ranges from 21 to 24cm.

Its total (head and body) length ranges from 35 to 48mm, its forearm from 30 to 37mm, its tail from 30 to 40mm and its hind-foot from 7 to 8mm. Adults weigh between 5 and 6g in summer but increase in weight to about 8g in autumn just before they enter hibernation. During this period their weight may decline again to 5g.

They have a fluttering flight and fly straight and at medium speed above treetops or hedges and occasionally glide or make rapid smooth turns when chasing prey. They are easily confused with pipistrelles, which have somewhat similar habits. This species is probably most easily identified using a bat detector. It detects prey using ultrasonic calls in the frequency range 40–65 kHz, but mainly at about 50 kHz. Over the range 30–40 kHz its echolocation call sounds like a click on a bat detector. By contrast, at the lower end of this range, the calls of a pipistrelle change from a click to a more metallic clink.

Distribution

The whiskered bat is widespread from Ireland through Europe and central Asia as far to the east as Japan. The whiskered bat was present in Britain at least about 6000 years ago and

probably earlier. It is not known when whiskered bats colonised Ireland. The first specimen recorded from Ireland was captured by a cat in 1852.

Although Ireland is at the extreme northwestern edge of its range, it is widely distributed here. However, it is not abundant, and is in fact one of our rarest bats. Fewer than forty roosts were recorded in a national bat survey in 1994, and most of these contained fewer than five bats. It is difficult to obtain a precise estimate of the total population, however, since the whiskered bat is regularly found roosting with other species, such as pipistrelles, brown long-eared, lesser horseshoe and Natterer's bats. The distribution map shows the 20km squares that contain at least one known roost used by whiskered bats.

Food and foraging

Whiskered bats emerge early in the evening, about 20-30 minutes after sunset. They hunt mainly over open deciduous and coniferous woodland and in scrub areas and along hedgerows. They may also be seen flying or hunting near water. They seem to have regular beats along which they hunt. They catch small insects, such as moths, on the wing. These they locate by emitting ultrasound calls, mainly at 50 kHz. They also pick small insects and spiders directly from foliage. They may be active all night and return to their roosts at dawn.

Roosts

The whiskered bat is generally considered to be a creature of open forest or woodland. In Ireland most of its known summer roosts are found in houses. They are usually found between the rafters in roofs or other narrow recesses and are difficult to detect. The summer roosts are usually maternity colonies containing small numbers of breeding females and their dependent young together with immature females. In summer males are solitary. In winter whiskered bats hibernate in hollow trees or cavities or recesses in buildings.

Reproduction and life-cycle

Very little is known about the reproductive cycle of whiskered bats (but see page 43 for a general account of bats' reproductive behaviour). Mating apparently takes place in the hibernation roosts during winter and the young are born in the maternity colonies in June or July. The young are finally weaned in autumn before the females enter hibernation. The average lifespan of the whiskered bat in Ireland is not known for certain but is probably at least four years, although individuals of this species have lived to over 20 years of age.

Watching whiskered bats

Although the whiskered bat is widespread in Ireland, the total population is small. Thus to see a whiskered bat and positively identify it in the wild in Ireland is a relatively rare event. The droppings are small and cylindrical, about 6–9mm long and 2–2.5mm in diameter. It is almost impossible to use droppings to identify the roost site of whiskered bats since they often share roosts with other species.

Conservation

There may be fewer than a thousand whiskered bats in this country, and the population is vulnerable. The main threats in Ireland are the treatment of timber in attics with preservatives such as chlorinated hydrocarbons and the decline in insect populations due to habitat change and use of pesticides. In other countries the whiskered bat is associated with woodland, so it seems likely that an increase in afforestation will increase the area of suitable habitats. Whiskered bats will occasionally use artificial roosts (bat boxes) in woodland. Like all bats, whiskered bats in their winter roosts are vulnerable to disturbance.

The whiskered bat is listed in the Irish Red Data book as of indeterminate status and in Annex IV of the Habitats Directive and Appendix II of the Bern Convention as a species requiring strict protection.

Natterer's bat – *Ialtóg Nattereir*
Myotis nattereri, Kuhl 1818

Natterer's bat is widespread but not abundant in Ireland.

The names

This species was first described from a specimen collected in Germany by the German naturalist Kuhl in 1819. The scientific name is derived from Greek. The generic part is formed from *mys* (mouse) and *otos* (of the ear). The specific part commemorates the Austrian naturalist Natterer who first discovered the species. The Irish name is a direct translation of the English.

Identification and characteristics

Natterer's bat is one of Ireland's smaller bats. Adults may weigh up to 12g in autumn just before they enter hibernation. During this period their weight may decline to 7g. A Natterer's bat's wings are relatively broad. The wing span ranges from 21 to 24cm. Its flight is moderately fast and manoeuvrable.

The fur is light brown on the upper part and changes on the flanks to quite pale below. It has a relatively long and pink face. The wings are also pinkish-brown. The ears are moderately long and narrow. The tragus (earlobe) is thin and pointed and is about two-thirds as long as the ear. The tail membrane has a fringe of short stiff hairs or bristles along the edge. Its total (head and body) length ranges from 40 to 50mm, its forearm from 36 to 43mm, its tail from 38 to 47mm and its hind-foot from 7 to 9mm.

Natterer's bats are moderately vocal and communicate by a series of hums, chirps and squeaks. They hunt using a series of weak-pulsed FM signals that sweep over the range 40–60 kHz with a peak at 50 kHz. On a bat detector these sound like a series of soft irregular crackles. They also sometimes emit audible high-pitched calls in flight.

Distribution

Natterer's bat is widespread in Ireland, Britain and continental Europe and occurs in small isolated populations as far east as SE Russia and Korea. Natterer's bat was present in Britain about 6000 years ago and may have been well established by then. It was first recognised in Ireland in 1845 about 26 years after the publication of its scientific description.

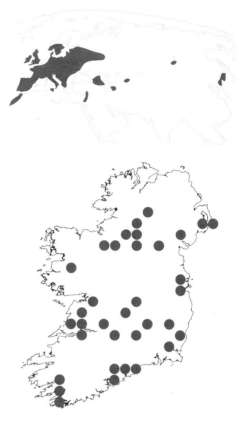

Although it is widely distributed in Ireland, it is not abundant and is one of our rarest and least known bats. Fewer than fifty roosts were recorded in the national bat survey in 1994, and most of these contained fewer than five bats. It is therefore difficult to obtain a precise estimate of the total population. The distribution map shows the 20km squares which contain at least one roost known to be used by Natterer's bat.

Roosts

Natterer's bat is generally considered to be a forest or woodland animal and roosts in tree-holes. In Ireland, however, most of its summer roosts are found in old houses and churches. They are usually found in cracks and crevices in stone archways or between the rafters or in narrow recesses in roofs. Because of this they are difficult to detect. The summer roosts are usually maternity colonies containing small numbers of breeding females and their dependent young, together with immature females. In summer, males are solitary. In winter, Natterer's bats hibernate in cavities or recesses in caves or buildings.

Food and foraging

Natterer's bats usually emerge about 45-60 minutes after sunset. They may be seen flying moderately fast around trees or in the woodland canopy. They can catch prey, such as caddis flies and moths, on the wing. They will pick resting insects and spiders directly off foliage (gleaning). These they locate by flying low and slowly, often along favoured beats. When prey is located they may hover briefly while it is being identified before dipping down and catching it with the feet or scooping it up using their tail. The bat then flies up briefly and transfers the prey to its mouth and eats it. The fringe of hairs on the tail may act like whiskers to feel the prey just before it is captured or they may simply act as a basket. Although gleaning is usually carried out on the wing, these bats are quite manoeuvrable on the ground and often land to catch earwigs or centipedes. They usually return to their roosts a few hours before dawn.

Reproduction and life-cycle

Very little is known about the reproductive cycle of Natterer's bats (but see page 43 for a general account of the reproductive behaviour of bats). They may be found in mixed-sex groups during August to October, and these are presumably mating groups. Natterer's bats enter hibernation roosts in November and December. Fertilisation is delayed and the young are born in the maternity colonies in June or July. The young are finally weaned in autumn before the females enter hibernation. The average lifespan of Natterer's bat in Ireland is not known for certain but is probably at least seven years. The maximum lifespan recorded elsewhere is 20 years.

Watching Natterer's bats

Although Natterer's bat is widespread in Ireland, most roosts contain fewer than five individuals, and so positive identification of Natterer's bat in the wild is unlikely. A bat detector may help in identifying this bat although its ultrasound calls are relatively weak. The droppings are small and cylindrical, about 8–11mm long and 2.3–3.3mm in diameter and shiny when fresh, but it is almost impossible to use droppings to identify a roost site of Natterer's bats since they often share roosts with other species.

Conservation

The Irish population of Natterer's bat is vulnerable. The main threats are the loss of suitable hollow trees, the treatment of timber in attics with preservatives such as chlorinated hydrocarbons and the decline in insect populations due to habitat change and use of pesticides. Natterer's bat is not well known and its habitat and roost requirements are not well understood.

Natterer's bat is listed in the Irish Red Data book as of indeterminate status and in Annex IV of the Habitats Directive and Appendix II of the Bern Convention as a species requiring strict protection.

Daubenton's bat – *Ialtóg uisce*
Myotis daubentoni, Kuhl 1819

Daubenton's bat has a characteristic flight pattern close to the surface of slow-flowing or still water.

The names
The scientific account published in 1819 is based on a specimen collected in Germany by the German naturalist Kuhl. The scientific name is derived from Greek. The generic part is formed from *mys* (mouse) and *otos* (of the ear). The specific part commemorates the 18th-century French doctor and biologist Jean Daubenton. The Irish name means the water (*uisce*) bat (*ialtóg*).

Identification and characteristics
Daubenton's bat is typically seen flying steadily and fairly rapidly at about 25 km per hour, with a flickering wing-beat, close to the surface of slow-flowing or still water. Daubenton's bat is one of our medium-sized bats. Adults weigh about 9g in summer but may increase to 14g by autumn just before they enter hibernation. During this period the weight of a Daubenton's bat may decline again from about 14g to about 9g. Its body length ranges from 45 to 50mm, its forearm from 35 to 40mm, its tail from 31 to 44mm.

It has a pinkish face, hairy except around the eyes. The ears are short, rounded and dark brown. There are four or five transverse folds or ridges on the inner surface of the ear. There is also a slight notch at the mid-point of the outer edge. The tragus (earlobe) is about half as long as the ear and has a straight front and curved rear edge tapering to a rounded tip. The short fur is dull brown on the back and is usually greyish on the underside. The change in colour is quite abrupt. Young bats have a dark patch or spot on the chin. This disappears after about a year. The spur (calcar) on the inner side of the hind leg extends about two-thirds of the distance from the leg to the tail. There is a fringe of fine long hairs along the edges of the tail membrane.

The wings are dark brown and fairly broad. The wing span ranges from 25 to 30cm. Its feet are relatively large and its hind-foot ranges from 8 to 11mm. They fly fairly fast, but their wing beats seem rather slow and fluttering and they often zigzag between river or canal banks as they hunt, mainly over water. Daubenton's bats hunt using pulses of an FM signal that sweeps from about 30 to 80 kHz but is mainly at about 48 kHz. On a bat detector these sound like a series of short, sharp, evenly spaced clicks.

Distribution

Daubenton's bat is widespread in Ireland and Britain. In continental Europe it extends from the Mediterranean coast to southern Scandinavia and in a band across central Asia to China and Japan. Daubenton's bat was certainly present in Britain by about 6000 years ago. It was first recorded here in 1838 relatively soon after it was first scientifically described. Although Daubenton's bat is widely distributed here, the colonies are small. In 1994 over two hundred roosts were identified in a national bat survey, but about 85% of these contained ten bats or fewer.

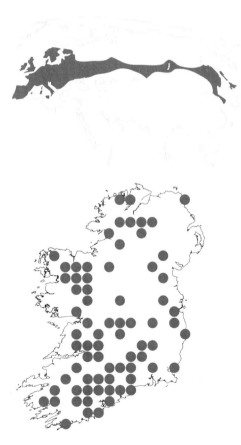

Most of the known roosts are found close to water bodies, but roosts are difficult to find. The bats are usually well hidden and difficult to count in roosts, and attempts to estimate the total population in the country are subject to fairly large uncertainty. The figures we have are almost certainly an underestimate. The distribution map shows the 20km squares in which at least one roost used by Daubenton's bat was found.

Food and foraging

Daubenton's bats usually emerge from roosts between 30 minutes and an hour after sunset, probably to avoid the attentions of birds of prey. They may also often be seen by day, because their preferred food items are on the wing in greatest numbers before dusk. Daubenton's bats may be active all night and return to their roosts at dawn. They usually hunt within about 6km of the roost. They hunt mainly over water, less than one metre and usually between 5 and 10cm from the surface. They generally hunt by aerial hawking, that is catching insects on the wing. In Ireland caddis flies and midges are the major components of the diet. They also take mayflies, bugs and other flies. These are located by emitting a buzz of ultrasound calls, although under some circumstances they seem to be able to catch prey without emitting any echolocation calls. These bats prefer to hunt over still water because echoes from ripples in the water make it more difficult to locate insects. For this reason they tend to emit their calls nearly parallel to the water surface and this is probably why they fly so close to the surface. The insects are captured with the feet. A Daubenton's bat also takes insects from the water surface by gaffing them with its feet or scooping them up with its tail. Sometimes it ends up in the water itself but seems able to take off again without much difficulty.

Roosts

Daubenton's bat is generally considered to be an animal of low-lying, flat, open, wooded country with water bodies. In Ireland most of its roosts are found under bridges but it also uses buildings, caves and trees. In summer they may be found sharing attics or lofts with brown long-eared bats. Large summer roosts are usually maternity colonies containing breeding females and their dependent young together with immature females. In winter Daubenton's bats hibernate in cavities or crevices under bridges or in caves or tunnels. They are usually solitary but numbers in certain winter roosts may increase during the winter.

Reproduction and life-cycle

The mating season probably extends from October to February when the bats are in their winter hibernation roosts, but fertilisation is delayed until spring. The young are born in the maternity colonies in late June and early July. A single offspring weighing between 2 and 2.5g is usual. The duration of gestation depends on the prevailing temperature and may last from five to seven weeks. The mother exclusively cares for the young. They are weaned after five or six weeks and may be capable of solo flight after about four weeks, but certainly by about six or seven weeks of age. They usually become mature in their second year. Females may not breed every year. The average lifespan of the Daubenton's bat in Ireland is not known for certain but is probably about seven years. Elsewhere individuals have lived for over 15 years and the maximum recorded is 40 years, which is exceptionally long for such a small mammal.

Watching Daubenton's bat

Although Daubenton's bat is widespread in Ireland most roosts contain fewer than ten individuals, and so it is not easily identified in the wild. A bat detector may help. It is typically found along rivers, lakes and ponds, but feeding over water is not absolutely diagnostic of Daubenton's bat, since other species of bats may also forage low down close to the water's surface. The droppings are small and cylindrical, about 8–9mm long and about 2mm in diameter. They are shiny and relatively moist when fresh and may have a muddy smell.

Conservation

Daubenton's bat requires bodies of clean, relatively unpolluted water within its home range. These provide breeding sites for aquatic insects on which the bats depend. Daubenton's bat is therefore susceptible to serious deterioration in water quality and pollution is a serious threat to this bat. The increasing numbers of artificial water bodies such as reconstructed wetlands will increase the number of suitable foraging sites, but some of its preferred roost sites, in crevices under bridges, are under constant threat from maintenance work. The use of liquid concrete, which is sprayed or pumped into cavities under arches to repair the substructure, is a particularly lethal operation. If it is carried out in summer it destroys roost sites. Carried out in winter, it may seal hibernating bats into the crevices and kill them. Reconstructed or new stone walls should incorporate some crevices and cavities which would act as refuges for this bat.

Daubenton's bat is listed in the Irish Red Data book as internationally important and in Annex IV of the Habitats Directive and Appendix II of the Bern Convention as a species requiring strict protection.

Leisler's bat – *Ialtóg Leisler*
Nyctalus leisleri, Kuhl 1818

Ireland has Europe's largest population of Leisler's bat.

The names
Leisler's bat was first described from a specimen found in Hessen in Germany by the German naturalist Kuhl in 1818 and he named it after another German scientist, Leisler. The generic name is a combination of Greek, *nyx* (night), and Latin, *ala* (wing); its name may be translated as the night-winged bat of Leisler. It is sometimes known as the hairy-armed bat. The Irish name is a translation of the English.

Identification and characteristics
Leisler's bat is Ireland's largest bat. Adults may weigh up to 20g in autumn just before they enter hibernation. During winter the weight of a Leisler's bat may decline to 15g. Its total (head and body) length ranges from 54 to 64mm, its forearm from 35 to 45mm, its tail from 39 to 44mm and its hind-foot from 7 to 10mm. Its wings, typical of fast-fliers, are narrow and pointed and wing span ranges from 29 to 32cm. Its ears are relatively short and the tragus (earlobe) is short and mushroom-shaped. Its fur is reddish-brown and slightly shaggy around the shoulders and back. The long fur extends down to the forearm. The wing membrane is covered with fur along the sides of the body and on the underside of the wing. The face is dark brown.

There is a small narrow flap or lobe of wing membrane, called the post-calcaral lobe, running along the hind margin of the bony spur (calcar) on the inner side of the ankle. (The common and soprano pipistrelles and Nathusius' pipistrelle are the only other bats in Ireland with this feature.)

Its fast, relatively high flight is quite characteristic, and it is conspicuous in flight since it is also the largest of our bats. It can probably fly at 40 km per hour. It flies straight and fairly fast in the open at the level of the treetops and occasionally swoops or makes rapid smooth turns when chasing prey. Leisler's bat emits ultrasonic hunting calls in the range 20–50 kHz. The calls are mainly emitted at around 25 kHz, lower than any other bat in Ireland. At these lower frequencies the calls may be audible as a short metallic hiss. On a bat detector the ultrasounds are converted to a series of loud plip-plops which crackle somewhat like frying eggs.

Distribution

Although Leisler's bat is widespread in Europe, particularly in the southeast of the continent, it is quite rare. In Ireland, however, it is both abundant – it is our third commonest bat – and widely distributed, and Ireland's population of Leisler's bat is the largest in Europe and is thus internationally important. Ireland also holds some of the largest colonies. The abundance of Leisler's bat here may be due in part to the absence of a related larger species, the noctule bat *Nyctalus noctula* from Ireland.

It is still impossible to say with any reliability when Leisler's bat joined the Irish fauna, but it was first identified here in 1848. A national bat survey in 1994 reported over seventy roosts. One of these, a breeding colony in west Cork, was formerly reported to contain between 800 and 1000 individuals and was the largest known roost of this species in the world. However, the colony contains about a hundred bats at present.

In Europe Leisler's bat is migratory. This does not appear to be the case, except perhaps on a small scale, in Ireland, and this may account for the larger colony sizes reported here. The distribution map shows the 20km squares that contain at least one roost site used by Leisler's bat.

Food and foraging

Leisler's bats emerge from roosts early in the evening at or just before sunset. They tend to emerge earlier on overcast nights but delay their emergence when light intensity is high. They may sometimes be seen hunting, at twilight, in the presence of swallows and swifts. Leisler's bats may be active all night, not returning to their roosts until dawn, but there are usually two periods of intense activity, the first and most intense about dusk and the other just before dawn particularly on warm nights. They appear not to like flying during heavy rain.

They locate their prey by emitting ultrasound calls in the range 15–45 kHz, mainly at 25 kHz. The calls may just be audible as a metallic-sounding zitt. Children are particularly likely to be able to detect these calls, and some adults may retain this ability. The relatively low frequency of their echolocation calls suggests that their preferred targets are medium-sized insects such as moths, caddis flies, crane flies and beetles, which they take on the wing. In Ireland up to 50% of their diet consists of yellow dung flies, beetles and the mites that live on them. Their flight is fast, but they are not particularly manoeuvrable and cannot usually pick insects directly off foliage.

Leisler's bats hunt mainly over open deciduous and coniferous woodland and scrub areas. They may also forage in parkland and suburbs where they may often be seen around street lamps. They may occasionally be seen flying or hunting near water. Their preferred foraging areas may be more than 10km from their roost. In a study in Wexford they foraged over all habitat types and quite frequently in areas with street lights. In Ireland, they also take considerable numbers of smaller insects such as midges and dung flies that are detectable when a swarm is dense enough. These and other swarming insects are captured by flying straight and fast through the swarm in the manner of a whale catching krill.

Roosts

Leisler's bat, across its European range, is generally considered to be a forest or woodland animal and usually roosts in tree-holes. In Ireland, however, most of its known summer roosts are found in buildings, in attics, in lofts around the gable end, between slates and under felt, under loft insulation and so on. Depending on the location, these bats may use a number of summer roosts in turn. Large summer roosts are usually maternity colonies containing breeding females and their dependent young, together with immature females. In summer, males are solitary or live in small groups and use hollow trees or other recesses. In winter Leisler's bats probably hibernate in hollow trees or cavities and recesses in buildings, but we know relatively little about winter roosts in Ireland. There is often a characteristic sweet pungent smell associated with winter roosts of male Leisler's bats. It has been suggested that there may be a migration to cooler parts of the country in winter where more suitable roost temperatures may be found.

Reproduction and life-cycle

Males become extremely territorial and establish mating roosts in autumn. These are visited by females which can form a harem of up to about ten individuals. The mating season probably extends from September to mid-November, but fertilisation is delayed until the spring, after hibernation (mid-November to the end of March, depending on the weather). The young are born in the maternity colonies mainly in June but also in early July after a gestation of about 70–75 days. A single offspring is usual. Twins are extremely rare, but are more common in eastern Europe. The mother, as is usual for bats, exclusively cares for the young. They remain in the roost when she is foraging. If she changes roost then she will carry them with her. The young are capable of solo flight after about 3 or 4 weeks and are finally weaned in autumn before the females enter hibernation. The average lifespan of Leisler's bat in Ireland is not known for certain but is probably about seven years, although it is likely that some individuals may live for 15–20 years.

Watching Leisler's bats

This widespread bat is one of the easiest bats to observe in Ireland. If a roost site is known it should be possible to obtain good views of the bats as they leave on their hunting trips. You will need to be in position about an hour before sunset because this bat tends to emerge rather early. There will usually be an increase in activity and noise within the roost before the bats emerge. Emergence may be fast and furious when the colony finally decides to begin hunting. Leisler's bats often forage on the insects that gather around mercury-vapour lamps. Installing such a lamp in a garden will often be rewarded by excellent views of Leisler's bats at the hunt. The presence of Leisler's bat will often be revealed by its droppings near the entrances to the roosts or occasionally inside roosts. The droppings are small and cylindrical, about 6–9mm long and 2.5–3mm in diameter and shiny when fresh.

Conservation

The Irish population of Leisler's bat is of international significance. The main threats are the loss of suitable roost sites in hollow trees, the treatment of timber in attics with certain organochlorine preservatives and the decline in insect populations due to habitat change and use of pesticides. The general intolerance of householders to bats also poses a major threat to the conservation of Leisler's bat. It seems likely, however, that the increase in afforestation will eventually increase the area of habitats suitable for Leisler's bats particularly when hollow trees become available. They will also use artificial roosts (bat boxes) and these can be very effective in woodland where they may even be used for breeding. Like all bats, Leisler's bats are vulnerable to disturbance in their winter roosts, particularly as they tend to roost in large groups.

Leisler's bat is listed in the Irish Red Data book as internationally important and in Annex IV of the Habitats Directive and Appendix II of the Bern Convention as a species requiring strict protection.

Common pipistrelle – *Ialtóg fheascrach*
Pipistrellus pipistrellus, Schreber 1774

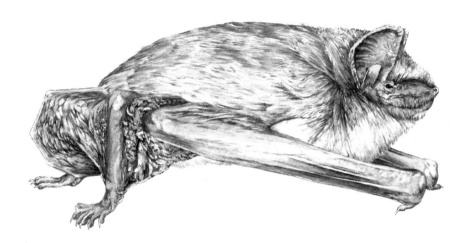

This is probably our most widespread and abundant bat.

The names

The common pipistrelle was first scientifically named by Schreber in 1774, based on a specimen originating in France. The generic and specific names are probably derived from the Latin verb *pipio*, 'I squeak', combined with the Latin ending *-ellus*, meaning small. Thus the scientific name means little squeaker. The Irish name means the bat (*ialtóg*) of the evening (*feascar*). Recent research indicates that what we formerly recognised as the common pipistrelle in fact includes members of more than one species. Two genetically distinct types of pipistrelle have been identified so far, each of which has a distinct ultrasound waveband – 45 kHz and 55 kHz respectively – which is used when hunting. Since two species cannot have the same name, the name common pipistrelle must be used for whichever of the two types was described by Schreber. We obviously cannot establish how Schreber's type specimens echolocated, but on the basis of fine details of anatomy and DNA the name *Pipistrellus pipistrellus* now refers to the 45 kHz species. The 55 kHz species is known as the soprano pipistrelle.

Identification and characteristics

Although the common pipistrelle is distinct from the recently identified soprano pipistrelle, the species are almost impossible to tell apart, except with careful examination or by means of their different ultrasound frequencies. Much of what we know of the biology of the bat formerly known as the common pipistrelle probably consists of a mixture of information from the two species.

The common pipistrelle is Ireland's second smallest bat. The wings of the common pipistrelle, typical of fast fliers, are narrow and pointed. The wing span is about 22cm but ranges from 20 to 25cm. The colour of the fur is variable and ranges from reddish brown to dark brown on the back and grey–brown on the belly. The exposed skin also varies between colonies from pinkish-brown to black. The snout is short and the ears are short and broad and the tragus, a fleshy lobe on the lower margin of the ear, is blunt and is about half as long as the ear. There is a small flap or lobe of wing membrane, called the post-calcaral lobe, running along the trailing edge of the bony spur (calcar) on the inner side of the ankle. This is an important diagnostic character, as the soprano pipistrelle, Nathusius' pipistrelle and Leisler's bat are the only other species in Ireland with this lobe.

Common pipistrelles have a relatively complete set of teeth, 16 in the upper and 18 in the lower jaw. The teeth are longer than those of the soprano pipistrelle and are extremely sharp and ideal for piercing the relatively tough outer skeleton of insects.

Adults may weigh about 5g in summer and up to 8g in autumn just before they enter hibernation. The body length ranges from 33 to 52mm, its forearm from 28 to 33mm, its tail from 26 to 33mm and its hind-foot from 4 to 7mm. They locate flying insects by emitting FM ultrasonic calls in the range 40-90 kHz but mainly at 45 kHz. On a bat detector these sound like a series of clicks, grading into a series of slaps at the lower end of the range.

Distribution

Current information on the distribution of each type of pipistrelle is incomplete. The pipistrelle (common, soprano or both) is widespread in Europe from southern Scandinavia to the Mediterranean region east of the Caucasus mountains. It is now becoming clear that the common pipistrelle is relatively scarce in northern Europe, while both it and the soprano pipistrelle are found further south. Both species are found in Ireland.

Although Ireland is at the extreme northwestern edge of its range the common pipistrelle is abundant and widely distributed here. The pipistrelle (common, soprano or both) has been our most common bat since records began to be collected in the mid-19th century. It is regularly found in urban areas. Although the whole country has not yet been adequately

surveyed, it appears that the common pipistrelle is less common than the soprano pipistrelle. The 1994 bat survey recorded almost 600 roosts. About 10% of these contained over 200 bats each. The map shows the 20km squares containing at least one roost. It is not yet known whether the records refer to the common pipistrelle or the soprano pipistrelle.

Food and foraging

Although their favoured food is most abundant before dusk, common pipistrelles normally emerge from roosts within a half-hour after sunset. This is probably to avoid being eaten by birds of prey, particularly kestrels, which hunt in daylight. Bats tend to emerge slightly earlier from roosts situated near woods or hedgerows, because in shaded areas the poorer light conditions make them more difficult to be seen and the vegetation may also provide some physical protection from predators. (Common pipistrelles are preyed on by kestrels, barn owls and long-eared owls.) Foraging is most intense just after dusk during summer, but the length

of time spent foraging depends on temperature and weather conditions. They begin feeding at a time of night when their favoured insects are becoming less active and may hunt for up to four hours a night.

Common pipistrelles usually forage within 2km of, and rarely more than 5km from, the roost. They feed in many habitats, flying along particular routes in favoured hunting areas. They feed along hedgerows, woodland edges, in suburban gardens and even in urban areas near streetlamps. They also hunt over water. The mouth of the common pipistrelle opens wider than that of the soprano pipistrelle and it catches larger prey. This probably explains why two such similar creatures can coexist in the same locality. The common pipistrelle catches small insects such as flies, midges, mosquitoes, caddis flies and moths, on the wing. While the diet is broadly similar to that of the soprano pipistrelle, the prey items tend to be slightly larger with tougher bodies. When feeding intensely, common pipistrelles may catch 15 insects a minute and may eat up to 3500 insects in one night. They usually catch them directly in their mouths. They may also capture prey using the tail membrane or the wings before transferring them to the mouth.

Roosts

Common pipistrelles like to roost in confined spaces. In Ireland most of their summer roosts are found in buildings, old and new. They do not seem to be particularly choosy about the structure or design of the buildings they occupy. It seems more important that the roost site is close to trees, woodland or hedgerows. They tend to roost behind window-sashes, under weather boards, behind fascia boards, within the roof space of flat roofs and in cavity walls. Entrances are often revealed by urine stains or by droppings nearby.

Each colony may have several roost sites in its home range and may transfer between them during the summer. Some of these colonies may contain up to 600 individuals.

Common pipistrelles are extremely faithful to their colony and rarely transfer to another. Large summer roosts are usually maternity colonies containing breeding females and their dependent young, together with immature females and these are often found in modern buildings, particularly at the south-facing side. In winter, common pipistrelles of both sexes hibernate together in small groups in cavities or recesses in buildings or in hollow trees. Entry to hibernation by common pipistrelles depends somewhat on weather and may occur any time from November to the end of March, but common pipistrelles do not enter deep continuous hibernation and may even become active in winter when conditions allow. This allows excretion of metabolic wastes.

Common pipistrelles are quite vocal. Colonies are very noisy, particularly as the bats prepare to emerge. A range of chattering and chuckling sounds may be heard. When alarmed or disturbed, pipistrelles emit a series of shrill, high-pitched calls.

Reproduction and life-cycle

During the breeding season males become aggressive and territorial. They set up mating roosts and embark on courtship flights in an attempt to collect a harem of usually up to ten females. Mating may occur at any season but mainly takes place from September to mid-November, though fertilisation is delayed until after hibernation, in April or May. During spring and autumn when bats are roosting by day they may lower their body temperature and become torpid. The gestation period depends on temperature and in warm weather is about 44 days but may be as long as 80 days in colder summers. The young are born in the maternity colonies in June or July. A single offspring, weighing between 1 and 1.5g, is usual, but twins are occasionally produced. Most females breed in alternate years. The young remain in the nursery colony when the mother is hunting. The mothers recognise their own young by a combination of their smell and voice. Occasionally if the mother is moving to another roost after disturbance or where the temperature is more suitable, she will carry her young on her back.

The young grow fairly rapidly and are capable of solo flight after three weeks by which time they are almost half their adult weight. They can hunt independently by about six weeks of age and are finally weaned in August. Female pipistrelles may become mature during their first autumn, at about two to three months of age and produce their first offspring around their first birthday. Males usually mature in their second winter. The lifespan of common pipistrelles in Ireland is not known for certain but is probably at least seven and may be as long as 15 years. Bats are relatively long-lived for such small animals. The pygmy shrew, for example, has about the same body size as a pipistrelle but survives for less than 15 months.

Watching common pipistrelles

The common pipistrelle is abundant throughout the country and is one of the bats most likely to be seen in Ireland. If a roost site is known it will be possible to obtain good views of the bats as they leave on their hunting trips. It is a good idea to be in position about an hour before sunset because this bat tends to emerge relatively early. There will usually be an increase in activity and they become particularly noisy within the roost as they prepare to emerge; emergence may be fast and furious when the colony finally decides to begin hunting. Their flight is fast and the flightpath is irregular. The presence of common pipistrelles in houses will often be revealed by their vocalisations, particularly in the summer maternity colonies.

Bat droppings may often be detected near the entrances to the roosts or inside the roosts particularly in roof spaces or attics. Pipistrelle droppings are small and cylindrical, about 7–9mm long and 1.5–2mm in diameter. They are shiny when fresh and become duller and paler as they age. Undigested fragments of prey can be detected in the droppings, and this is how it was discovered that the diets of the common and the soprano pipistrelles differ in significant ways. Sometimes large fragments of prey with characteristic puncture marks may be found near roosts.

Conservation

The common pipistrelle is probably the most abundant bat in Europe. Pipistrelle populations, however, have declined by over 50% in Britain over the last 15 years. It seems likely that a similar change may have occurred here, but reliable data have only become available since the 1980s. The major threats to pipistrelles are some of the chemicals used to treat timbers in buildings, agricultural pesticides and destruction of trees suitable for roost sites. It seems likely, however, that the increase in afforestation and set-aside land will increase the area of habitats suitable for common pipistrelles. These could provide trees suitable as roost sites and improved foraging areas. Like all bats, common pipistrelles in their winter roosts are particularly vulnerable to disturbance. Common pipistrelles will use special artificial roosts (bat boxes) if provided but such schemes are only recommended where other aspects of the habitat, such as foraging areas, are suitable.

The common pipistrelle is listed in the Irish Red Data book as internationally important and in Annex IV of the Habitats Directive and Appendix II of the Bern Convention as a species requiring strict protection.

Soprano pipistrelle – *Ialtóg fheascrach sopránach*
Pipistrellus pygmaeus, Schreber 1774

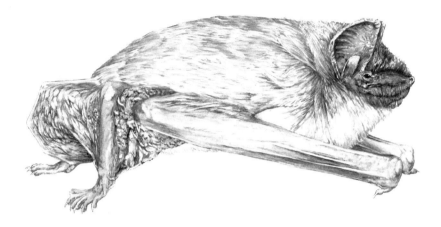

For centuries nobody realised that this was not the same species as the common pipistrelle.

The names

The soprano pipistrelle has only recently been distinguished from the common pipistrelle, the main difference between the two species being the frequency of their hunting calls (55 and 45 kHz respectively). The two species cannot have the same name, and the name 'common pipistrelle' is now correctly applied only to the 45 kHz type. The soprano has only recently acquired its common name in recognition of the higher frequency of its hunting call. But in some circles it has acquired the nickname 'bandit pipistrelle' referring to its dark, mask-like face. An appropriate Irish name would be *ialtóg fheascrach* (pipistrelle) *sopránach* (soprano).

The generic name is probably derived from the Latin verb *pipio*, 'I squeak', combined with the Latin ending *-ellus*, meaning small, and the specific name means 'pygmy', to distinguish it from the slightly larger common pipistrelle.

Identification and characteristics

It is almost impossible to tell the common and the soprano pipistrelles apart, though there are small differences. The soprano pipistrelle is probably Ireland's smallest bat. Adults may weigh up to 8g in autumn just before they enter hibernation. The body length ranges from 33 to 50mm, its forearm from 27 to 32mm, its tail from 26 to 33mm and its hind-foot from 4 to 7mm. The wings of the soprano pipistrelle, as of other fast fliers, are narrow and pointed. The wing span ranges from 20 to 25cm, and the wings are slightly shorter and broader than the common pipistrelle. Females are slightly larger than males. The colour of the fur is variable and ranges from reddish brown to dark brown on the back and grey–brown on the belly. The exposed skin also varies between colonies from pinkish-brown to black. The face is noticeably darker than that of the common pipistrelle. The snout is short and slightly swollen. The ears are short and broad and the tragus, a fleshy lobe on the lower margin of the ear, is slender. There is a small flap or lobe of wing membrane, called the post-calcaral lobe, running along the trailing edge of the bony spur (calcar) on the inner side of the ankle. This is an important diagnostic character, as the common pipistrelle, Nathusius' pipistrelle and Leisler's bat are the only other species in Ireland with this lobe.

Soprano pipistrelles have a relatively complete set of teeth, 16 in the upper and 18 in the lower jaw. The teeth are shorter than those of the common pipistrelle but are extremely sharp and ideal for piercing the relatively tough outer skeleton of insects. They locate flying insects by emitting FM ultrasonic calls in the range 50-80 kHz but mainly at about 55 kHz. On a bat detector these sound like a series of clicks, grading into a series of slaps at the lower end of the range. Their peak sound emission is at about 55 kHz.

Distribution

Information on the distribution of the soprano pipistrelle is much the same as for the common pipistrelle (see page 64). However, it is now becoming clear that the soprano pipistrelle is more common in northern Europe, while both types are found further south. This is probably one of our most widespread and may be our most abundant bat. It appears that the soprano pipistrelle is the more common of the two in Ireland, although both types are found here. The distribution map shows the 20km squares which contain at least one roost used by pipistrelles. It is not yet clear which species is found in each square. It seems likely that both species occur in the same locations although they roost separately. Squares where soprano pipistrelles have been positively identified are shown by paler symbols.

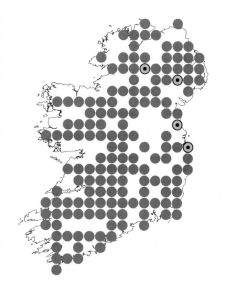

Food and foraging

Soprano pipistrelles' favoured insects are usually more abundant just before dusk. The pipistrelles, however, emerge after dusk and they may hunt for up to four hours a night. They normally emerge from roosts within a half hour after sunset. The individuals emerging earlier, when the light is still good, usually do so in large groups, presumably as a defence against birds of prey which hunt by sight. Foraging is most intense just after dusk during summer but the length of time spent foraging depends on temperature and weather conditions. They usually forage within 2km of the roost. They feed almost always in habitats associated with water. They particularly favour woodland or hedges along the edge of water bodies. They fly along particular routes in favoured hunting areas. They may also catch insects attracted to streetlights emitting white light.

The mouth of the soprano pipistrelle is smaller than that of the common pipistrelle and it catches smaller prey. This probably explains why two such similar creatures can coexist in the same locality. The soprano pipistrelle catches small insects such as chironomid midges, mosquitoes, small caddis flies and other aquatic insects, on the wing. These are smaller and somewhat softer than the prey taken by the common pipistrelle. When feeding intensely soprano pipistrelles may catch 15 insects per minute and may eat up to 3500 insects in one night. They usually catch them directly in their mouths. They may also capture prey using the tail membrane or the wings before transferring them to the mouth.

Roosts and reproduction

Soprano pipistrelles have similar roosting and breeding habits to common pipistrelles (see page 65-66), except that soprano pipistrelles appear to prefer roost sites that have suitable foraging habitats close by. These are hedgerows with some emerging trees and water bodies with hedge or woodland along at least one bank. They appear to be more dependent on water than the common pipistrelle. Female soprano pipistrelles respond only to the mating songs of males of the same species – soprano pipistrelles. Soprano pipistrelles can probably live for 7 to 15 years.

Watching soprano pipistrelles

Advice on watching common pipistrelles (page 66-67) also applies to soprano pipistrelles.

Conservation

The soprano pipistrelle is probably one of the most abundant bats in Europe. Pipistrelle populations, however, have declined by over 50% in Britain over the last 15 years. It seems likely that a similar change may have occurred here but reliable data have only become available since the 1980s. However, our data do not allow us to distinguish between the soprano and the common pipistrelle. The major threats to soprano pipistrelles are some of the chemicals used to treat timbers in buildings, agricultural pesticides and destruction of trees suitable for roost sites. There are usually many other apparently suitable roost sites in the vicinity of maternity roosts and therefore the suitability of foraging areas may be a main factor determining the status of the soprano pipistrelle.

Since it was originally confused with the common pipistrelle, the soprano pipistrelle must be classified in the Irish Red Data book as internationally important and in Annex IV of the Habitats Directive and Appendix II of the Bern Convention as a species requiring strict protection.

Nathusius' pipistrelle – *Ialtóg Nathusius*
Pipistrellus nathusii, Keyserling and Blasius 1839

Nathusius' pipistrelle is Ireland's most recently discovered mammal.

The names

In 1839 Keyserling and Blasius based the first scientific description of this pipistrelle on a specimen found in Germany. The generic name is probably derived from the Latin verb *pipio*, 'I squeak', combined with the Latin ending *-ellus*, meaning small. Thus the scientific name means Nathusius's little squeaker. Nathusius was a German naturalist, born in 1809 at Magdeburg. The Irish name means Nathusius's bat (*ialtóg*).

Identification and characteristics

Nathusius' pipistrelle is slightly larger than the common pipistrelle. The body length ranges from 33 to 52mm, its forearm from 32 to 37mm, its tail from 30 to 40mm and its hind-foot from 6.5 to 8mm. Adults may weigh from about 8.5 to 9.5g in autumn just before they enter hibernation. By the end of hibernation this may have decreased to about 5g. Its wings, typical of fast fliers, are narrow and pointed but are slightly broader than those of the common and soprano pipistrelles. The wing span ranges from 22 to 25cm. The fur on the back is long and shaggy and the hairs have a pale tip. This gives the animal a somewhat frosted appearance. The colour of the fur is variable and ranges from reddish-brown in spring and summer to darker brown after the autumn moult. The fur on the underside is paler than on the back. The tail, ears and wing membranes are usually dark brown or black.

The head and face are very similar to those of the common pipistrelle. The snout is short and the ears are short and broad and the tragus, a fleshy lobe on the lower margin of the ear, is short and curved with a blunt end. There is a small flap or lobe of wing membrane, called the post-calcaral lobe, running along the trailing edge of the bony spur (calcar) on the inner side of the ankle. This is an important diagnostic character; Leisler's bat, the common pipistrelle and the soprano pipistrelle are the only other species in Ireland with this lobe.

Nathusius' pipistrelles have a relatively complete set of teeth, 16 in the upper and 18 in the lower jaw. The incisors of Nathusius' pipistrelles are taller and narrower than those of the common pipistrelle. There is also an obvious gap between the second and third incisors in the lower jaw. The most marked but not most obvious difference between Nathusius' pipistrelle and the other pipistrelles is in the relative positions of the canine teeth and the first premolar in the upper jaw. In Nathusius' pipistrelle the premolar is in line with the canine and the other teeth. In the other pipistrelles the premolar is quite small and lies inside the canine and is almost hidden behind it. The teeth are extremely sharp and ideal for piercing the tough outer skeletons of insects.

Their flight is fast, faster than other pipistrelles, and the flightpath is irregular but when flying in a straight line they use deep wing beats. Nathusius' pipistrelles locate flying insects by emitting FM ultrasonic calls in the range 38–50 kHz. On a bat detector these sound like a series of clicks grading into a series of slaps at the lower end of the range. Their peak sound emission is at about 40 kHz.

Distribution

Nathusius' pipistrelle is widespread in lowland Europe south of the Baltic Sea from eastern France to the Ural mountains. It is most abundant at the southeastern segment of its range. There are a few scattered populations in western Europe. It is one of the most migratory of bats. Whole populations in Europe migrate southwestward in autumn and  return in spring. The maximum recorded journey is 1600km, covered by an individual in Russia, but several instances of over 100km are known. Single individuals, presumably migrants, have occasionally been recorded in Britain although they are not yet considered to breed there.

It is not known how long Nathusius' pipistrelle has been in Ireland. It is quite similar to the common pipistrelle with which it may have been confused. It seems likely, though, that it is a recent colonist and it is probably resident throughout the year, because the winters in Ireland are mild and there is no winter range situated to the southwest of Ireland.

Ireland is at the extreme northwestern edge of the range in which birth occurs, but it is neither abundant nor, as far as is known, widely distributed here. At present it seems to be one of our rarest bats. It was first recorded here in 1996 and was confirmed as a breeding species

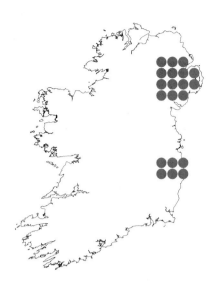

in May 1997, when several roosts were identified, the largest containing 150 bats. Most records in Ireland so far are from Ulster. It has been found near Lough Neagh and in County Down. There are also reports that it has been detected in the Republic. The map shows the 20km squares in which roosts or specimens have been recorded so far.

Food and foraging

Nathusius' pipistrelles normally emerge from roosts soon after dusk within 15-30 minutes after sunset. Foraging is most intense at this time during summer but the length of time spent foraging depends on temperature and weather conditions. They feed in many habitats flying along particular routes in favoured hunting areas. They hunt along woodland paths and rides or woodland edges. They seem to avoid hunting close to human settlements. They also hunt over water. They usually fly between 4 and 15m from the ground. They catch small to medium-sized flying insects such as flies, midges, mosquitoes, caddis flies and moths, on the wing. They usually catch them directly in their mouths, but they may also capture prey using the tail membrane or the wings before transferring them to the mouth.

Roosts

In Europe Nathusius' pipistrelle is considered to be a woodland bat. It prefers hollow trees or crevices and walls of isolated and abandoned buildings for its summer roosts. Large summer roosts are usually maternity colonies containing breeding females and their dependent young together with immature females. At least one such colony has been located in County Antrim, but few roosts of Nathusius' pipistrelle are known in this country. In winter Nathusius' pipistrelle roosts in rock crevices, caves, cracks in walls and hollow trees. Nathusius' pipistrelles are quite vocal. Colonies are very noisy, particularly as the bats prepare to emerge. A range of chattering and chuckling sounds may be heard. When alarmed or disturbed, Nathusius' pipistrelles emit a series of shrill, high-pitched calls.

Reproduction and life-cycle

Little is yet known of Nathusius' pipistrelles' breeding habits in Ireland but studies in Europe have revealed that mating mainly takes place during the period from September to mid-November. Their breeding habits seem to be similar to those of the common pipistrelle (see page 66).

Conservation

Nathusius' pipistrelle is one of the most migratory species throughout its range in Europe and is thus in double jeopardy. The major threat to Nathusius' pipistrelles is the destruction of roost sites. It seems likely, however, that the increase in afforestation and set-aside land, if ponds are incorporated, will increase the area of habitats suitable for Nathusius' pipistrelles, particularly if trees suitable as roost sites are preserved. It seems likely that Nathusius' pipistrelle is a recent arrival to Ireland. It is particularly important that if it hibernates in Ireland such roosts be absolutely protected. Like all bats, Nathusius' pipistrelles in their winter roosts are particularly vulnerable to disturbance.

Nathusius' pipistrelle is not specifically mentioned in the Irish Red Data book but is internationally important and is listed in Annex IV of the Habitats Directive and Appendix II of the Bern Convention as a species requiring strict protection.

Watching Nathusius' pipistrelles

Nathusius' pipistrelle is not common throughout the country and is one of the bats least likely to be seen in Ireland, but if a roost site is known it will be possible to obtain good views of the bats as they leave on their hunting trips. The detection of Nathusius' pipistrelles in an area will most likely depend on either the identification of injured or dead specimens or identification of their characteristic echolocation calls using a bat detector. Bat groups are currently on the alert for further records. When roosts are found it will be interesting to analyse the droppings that may be found nearby. There is a particular need for more information on this species in Ireland. The authors, Dúchas (RoI) or the Department of the Environment (NI) would appreciate further information on the distribution or occurrence of this bat.

Brown long-eared bat – *Ialtóg fhad-chluasach*
Plecotus auritus, Linnaeus 1758

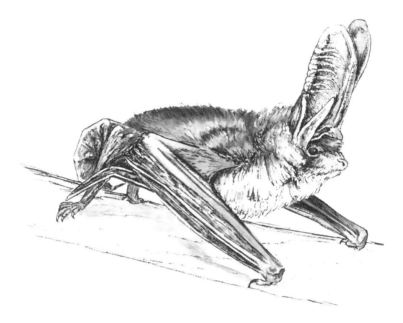

The enormous ears of one of our most common bats makes the brown long-eared bat quite easy to identify.

The names

The brown long-eared bat, a Swedish specimen, was first scientifically described by Linnaeus in 1758. The scientific name relates to the most obvious characteristic of this bat, its ears. The generic name is derived from the Greek *pleko* (twist or fold) and *otos* (of the ear). The specific name is Latin and means having ears. The Irish name means long-eared (*fad-chluasach*) bat (*ialtóg*).

Identification and characteristics

The ears are the most characteristic features of this bat. At more than 25mm long, they are about three-quarters the length of the head and body combined. The inner surface of the ear has 20–24 small ridges or folds running across its long axis. The ears may be less obvious when the bat is at rest, because then they are tucked under the wings so that each tragus (earlobe) projects downwards like a little horn.

The eyes are large and bright. The face is pinkish brown. The snout is slightly bulging. The fur is fluffy and is buff to mid-brown in adults; juveniles are grey. The wing membranes are pale grey and semi-transparent. The brown long-eared bat has a relatively complete set of sharp teeth with 16 in the upper jaws and 20 in the lower. Adults may weigh up to 12g in autumn just before they enter hibernation. The body length ranges from 37 to 48mm, the forearm from 34 to 42mm, the tail from 34 to 55mm and the hind-foot from 7 to 10mm. They weigh about 12g, but during hibernation their weight may decline to about 7g.

The brown long-eared bat usually hunts near trees and bushes. It has a slow, fluttering flight and the wings are broad, typical of agile fliers. The wing span ranges from 23 to 29cm. This bat emits weak ultrasound pulses over the range 25–80 kHz when hunting and although the sound is loudest between 35 and 40 kHz they are quite difficult to register on a bat detector unless the bat is within 5m. When they are detected they sound like soft, sharp clicks. The bats may also emit audible chirps when in flight.

Distribution

The brown long-eared bat is widespread in Britain and Europe and in parts of eastern USSR, China and Japan. It is not known when this bat colonised Ireland, but it has been our second most common bat since records began to be collected in the mid-19th century. It is widely distributed throughout the country and also occurs on many offshore islands. A national bat survey in 1994 listed almost 300 roosts. Most of these generally contained fewer than 50 bats each. The distribution map shows the 20km squares that contain at least one roost site used by long-eared bats.

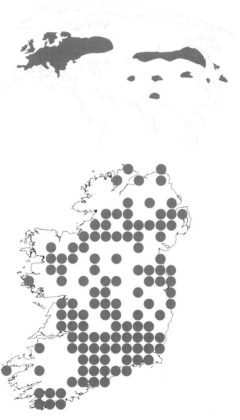

Food and foraging

Brown long-eared bats tend to become active in the roost about sunset. They may make short flights inside the roost and emerge about an hour later when it is quite dark. They may be active all night and return to their roosts at dawn. They forage, usually within 2km of the roost, in woodland, near trees and shrubs and often near old stone walls. They may be seen hovering generally close to thick vegetation. Brown long-eared bats can feed equally well whether their prey are in flight or at rest. Their hunting method is referred to as foliage gleaning. This means that they usually pick their prey, spiders and insects such as moths, beetles and earwigs, directly from the leaves of shrubs and trees. They occasionally swoop down to capture insects on the ground. They locate prey items primarily by sound and sight. The bat uses its large ears and well-developed hearing to amplify and detect the low frequency sounds made by the wing beats of its prey. They may also catch flying insects detected by echolocation, but their calls, emitted through the nose with the mouth kept closed, are weak and difficult to detect with a bat detector. Larger prey items are taken to a favoured feeding perch where they are eaten. These perches are often revealed by the pile of insect remains such as wings and legs that accumulate beneath them.

Roosts

Although the brown long-eared bat is generally considered to be a forest or woodland animal and roosts in trees, it has adapted well to roosting in buildings. It seems to have a preference or requirement for certain types of buildings close to woodland and water. In Ireland, most of its roosts are found in the open roof spaces of older buildings such as churches or in large attics. In the west of Ireland lesser horseshoe bats are sometimes found sharing the same roosts. The brown long-eared bat roosts in small clusters high under the roof ridge with the wings partly folded around the body with the ears tucked under the wings. The body is held at about a 70 degree angle from the roof (whereas lesser horseshoe bats hang vertically).

They select relatively warm summer roosts but they may disperse, with partly open wings, within the roost on warm days if the temperature rises too high. Some of these bats are believed to occupy the same roost throughout the year. In summer, maternity colonies, containing breeding females and their single dependent young together with immature females, gather in attics. In winter brown long-eared bats may disperse and hibernate singly or in small groups in cavities or recesses in buildings or in hollow trees. They are quite tolerant of cold and can survive temperatures as low as 4°C. Hibernation occurs, depending somewhat on the weather, from about mid-November to early March.

Reproduction and life-cycle

Males come into breeding condition in late summer and they may lose weight during this period because, if their reproductive organs are to develop, they must maintain a high body temperature. Therefore they cannot take advantage of becoming torpid during cold spells. Mixed-sex groups are found from late summer onwards. The mating season begins in September and may extend throughout the winter. Males attempt to defend harems from the attentions of other males. Many female bats do not mate until they enter the hibernation site, and in any case fertilisation is delayed until after hibernation, in the spring.

The young are born in the maternity colonies in July. A single offspring is usual. The eyes open within the first week and the ears are erect by the end of the second. The young are fed exclusively on milk for the first three weeks. For about the first ten days the young are permanently attached to their mother's nipples. Thereafter they are left in the roost when the mother leaves to hunt. The mothers recognise their own offspring by a combination of vocal signals and their individual smell. Lactating females produce, from glands on the face, an oily secretion that is thought to assist the young bat to recognise its mother. The young practise flying in the roost and are capable of solo flight after about a month. They are weaned at the end of August, when they are about six weeks of age.

A few males become mature in their first year but most are not capable of breeding until they are one year old but usually do not do so until they are two. By contrast most females do not breed before two years of age and some do not do so until they are three. The average lifespan of the brown long-eared bat in Ireland is not known for certain. It is probably about five years but some individuals may live for as long as 20 years.

Watching brown long-eared bats

Brown long-eared bats occur almost everywhere in Ireland and are found on many offshore islands. They are sometimes difficult to see because they tend to hunt within the tree canopy. The flight is quite characteristic, slow and fluttery, and this bat often hovers within thick vegetation or swoops gently to the ground. If a roost site is known they can often be best observed as they leave. A lamp giving a diffuse light can sometimes allow observation of their hunting technique as they search among vegetation. They are relatively quiet bats and difficult to locate with a bat detector. On the other hand, they are quite conspicuous in roosts and unlikely to be confused with any other.

The presence of long-eared bats will often be revealed by droppings near the entrances to the roosts or inside the roosts particularly in roof spaces or attics. The droppings are small and cylindrical, about 8–10mm long and 2.5–3mm in diameter and are shiny when fresh. The droppings usually include many scales from moth wings.

Conservation

Brown long-eared bats are vulnerable to water pollution and habitat loss, particularly destruction of hollow trees. They are extremely sensitive to chlorinated hydrocarbons such as HCH and pentachlorophenol (PCP) used for timber treatment in attics. These chemicals have killed many long-eared bats. Brown long-eared bats are vulnerable to domestic cats, particularly when they are foraging on the ground. Owls also occasionally kill long-eared bats. It seems likely that the increase in afforestation will increase the area of habitats suitable for long-eared bats. They will use artificial roosts such as bat boxes or even bird boxes and these can be very effective in woodland where long-eared bats may use them as breeding sites. Like all bats, long-eared bats in their winter roosts are vulnerable to disturbance, particularly as they tend to roost in the open spaces of large attics.

The brown long-eared bat is listed in the Irish Red Data book as internationally important and in Annex IV of the Habitats Directive and Appendix II of the Bern Convention as a species requiring strict protection.

Key to distinguish between bats known to occur in Ireland

By a process of elimination it should be possible, using the following key, to identify any bat likely to be found in Ireland. The features used to distinguish between the species of bats that currently occur in Ireland are shown in the composite diagram on the following page. Each feature is labelled with the code of the corresponding line of text in the key.

1.	a.	Ears more than 25mm long	Brown long-eared bat
	b.	Ears less than 20 mm long	go to 2
2.	a	Nose with leaves	Lesser horseshoe-bat
	b.	Nose without leaves	go to 3
3.	a.	Post-calcaral lobe on tail-membrane	go to 4
	b.	No post-calcaral lobe on tail-membrane	go to 6
4.	a.	(i) Tragus slender and thumb-shaped and (ii) Forearm less than 40 mm	go to 5
	b.	(i) Tragus short and mushroom–shaped (ii) Fur shaggy	Leisler's bat
5.	a.	(i) First upper premolar small and almost hidden inside canine tooth and (ii) Forearm less than 30 mm	Pipistrelle (common/soprano)
	b.	(i) First upper premolar is in line with other teeth and (ii) Forearm between 32 and 40mm	Nathusius' pipistrelle

6. a. (i) Edge of tail membrane with stiff bristles and
        (ii) Tragus thin and sharply pointed   Natterer's bat

    b. Tail without stiff bristles   go to 7

7. a. (i) Calcar extends half length from foot to tail and
        (ii) Foot about 1/3 the length of shin and
        (iii) Tragus tapering and pointed   Whiskered bat

    b. (i) Calcar extends 3/4 of length from foot to tail and
        (ii) Foot more than half the length of shin and
        (iii) Tragus tapering with a rounded tip   Daubenton's bat

This key applies to adult specimens in the hand. These are most likely to be dead specimens found in the vicinity of roosts. This scheme has been simplified to allow identification of only the species known to occur in Ireland.

If a specimen does not fit easily into this scheme then it should be reported to Dúchas The Heritage Service of the Department of Arts, Heritage, Gaeltacht and the Islands (RoI) or the Environment Service of the Department of the Environment (NI). It might be a new species for Ireland.

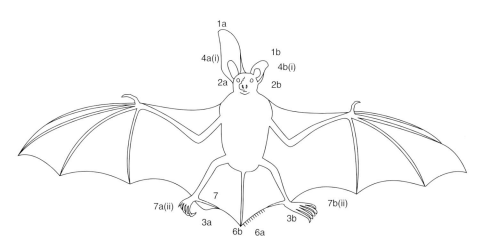

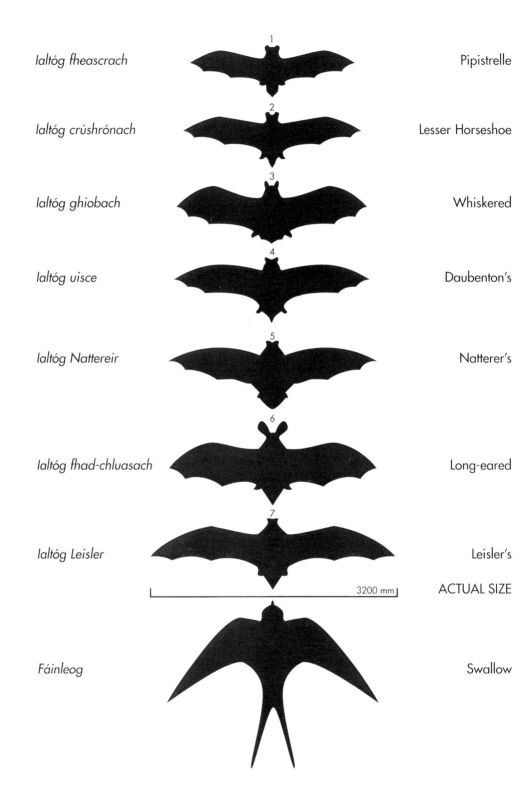

Ialtóg fheascrach	1	Pipistrelle
Ialtóg crúshrónach	2	Lesser Horseshoe
Ialtóg ghiobach	3	Whiskered
Ialtóg uisce	4	Daubenton's
Ialtóg Nattereir	5	Natterer's
Ialtóg fhad-chluasach	6	Long-eared
Ialtóg Leisler	7	Leisler's

3200 mm ⎤ ACTUAL SIZE

Fáinleog	Swallow

CHAPTER 5

Order Lagomorpha – Hares, Rabbits and Pikas

Behold the ever-tim'rous hare
Already quits the furzy shade,
And o'er the field, with watchful care
Unseen will nip the sprouting blade.
Samuel Thompson (1766-1816)

The earliest of the Lagomorpha appeared in the fossil record of central and eastern Asia about 55 million years ago. It is not entirely clear which other mammalian order contains their closest relatives. The many lines of evidence from modern Lagomorpha show little agreement as to who are their nearest relations. The rodents, the carnivores, the tree shrews and the ungulates all have competing claims that are not yet resolved.

There are two modern families of Lagomorpha, pikas and hares including rabbits and they evolved at about the same time. The hares first evolved somewhere in Asia and then spread to, and became very successful in, North America from about 30 million years ago. By about 5 million years ago they were also widespread and successful in Europe and Asia. The pikas e.g. tailless hares, by contrast, arose in Eurasia about 30 million years ago. They spread outwards to North America and western Europe about 5–10 million years ago.

Characteristics

The lagomorphs are small herbivores. The smallest species of pika weighs about 100g and the largest of the hares weighs up to about 5kg. The arrangement of the teeth resembles that of rodents. Lagomorphs have a large chisel-like incisor tooth in each side of the upper and lower jaws. However, they also have an additional small peg-like incisor, located behind the large incisor in each upper jaw only. This is a crucial feature for distinguishing skulls of lagomorphs from those of rodents. There are no canine teeth. The tooth row, like that of other herbivores, has a long gap, called a diastema, between the incisors and the cheek teeth. The incisors and cheek teeth have open roots and grow continuously throughout life. This serves to replace the cutting and grinding surfaces that are continuously being worn away. Lagomorphs can move their jaws forwards and backwards, as well as from side to side, as they grind their food.

The limbs of pikas are relatively short and their bodies are relatively plump. The bodies of rabbits and hares are narrower and the legs are longer. They are faster and more efficient runners than the pikas. The front feet always have five fingers while in some species there may be only four on the hind-foot. They tend to walk on the soles of their feet when moving slowly, but raise the 'wrists' and 'heels' to run on their fingers and toes when moving at speed.

The digestive system is relatively long to cope with the difficulties in digesting plant material. The digestive strategy of lagomorphs includes a fermentation step, by which microorganisms digest the plant cellulose, mainly in the caecum, a specialised blind-ending side-chamber, located towards the hind end of the gut. Since this digestion of cellulose takes place when the food has almost passed through the gut, lagomorphs have evolved an unusual process in order to absorb the products of digestion. They pass the food through their gut for a second time. This is called refection, literally eating again, or coprophagy which means eating faeces. This is not as gruesome as it sounds, since the material passed for recycling is soft and quite unlike the hard fibrous pellets produced when the faeces are finally discarded.

The brains of lagomorphs are generally moderately developed. In many species the parts which process information from the eyes and nose are particularly prominent. This has probably evolved due to the intense predation to which lagomorphs are subjected under natural conditions.

Diversity

The modern Lagomorpha is not a very diverse order and all are small or medium-sized herbivores. However, they are an important component of many terrestrial animal communities. They may account for 30–50% of the total biomass of animals in particular areas. There are only two families of lagomorphs. The Ochontidae contains the pikas (14 living species) and the other, the Leporidae, includes the hares and rabbits (49 living species).

Finding out more about hares and rabbits

The rangers of Dúchas The Heritage Service of the Department of Arts, Heritage, Gaeltacht and the Islands (RoI) or of the Environment Service of the Department of the Environment (NI) will be able to provide information on hares locally. They will be especially glad to hear of sightings of brown hares, on which information is scarce. Members of coursing clubs are a valuable source of information on the distribution of hares. The resource list at the back of this book gives wildlife organisations that publish information on mammals, including rabbits and hares. The mountain hare and the brown hare may be compared in the display of specimens from Letterkenny in the Natural History Museum, Dublin.

Rabbit – *Coinín*
Oryctolagus cuniculus, Linnaeus 1758

This is the original Norman conqueror, since Ireland's thriving wild rabbit populations are the descendants of domestic rabbits first introduced by the Normans in the 12th century.

The names

The scientific description of the rabbit was written by the Swedish biologist Linnaeus in 1758, based on a specimen from Germany. The generic name is derived from Greek and means the digging (*oryctos*) hare (*lagos*). The specific name is Latin for rabbit. The Irish name *coinín* may be derived from the old English cony. Originally the term cony was applied to adults only, while the young were known as rabbits. The burrows were originally known as a cony earth. This changed to conygarth and in Irish became *coinicéir*. The term rabbit warren eventually became the common name for the burrow system. Placenames referring to rabbit warrens or conygarths (*coinicéir*) are quite common in Britain and Ireland. This is clearly due to the importance of rabbits for meat and fur production in medieval times. There are many place names in Ireland which either incorporate *coinín*, cony, *coinicéir* or warren e.g. Kylenagonneney (Co Limerick), Coneyburrow (Co Kildare), Coniker (Co Laois), Warrenpoint (Co Down). Male rabbits are known as bucks, females are called does, and the young are kittens.

Identification and characteristics

The rabbit is smaller than the hare. The total length from nose to the tip of the tail is about 50cm including 7cm of tail. It has long hind-legs. The hind-feet are usually between 7.5 and

9.5cm long. There is little obvious difference in size between the sexes, but male rabbits are about 10% heavier than females. Adult males weigh up to about 2kg, females 1.4–1.8kg. The profile of the head is more round in males, and that of females is more angular. Rabbits have long slender (6–7cm) ears but they are shorter than the length of the head.

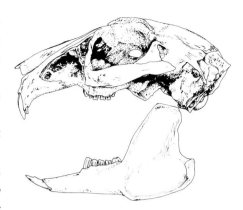

The most common coat colour is greyish brown, but slate-grey, fawn and partially to totally black individuals may be seen. The upper surface of the tail is black. Rabbits usually moult their coat once a year. The eyes are large and set in the side of the head, so their field of vision is particularly wide, almost 360°. Their sense of smell is well developed and they have a variety of glands, under the chin, in the skin and around the anus which are used to signal identity, social status and territorial information. The chin gland is particularly used to mark objects, or other animals, in the rabbit's home range. Their hearing is extremely sharp. They are not particularly vocal, although they have a piercing distress or alarm scream. They also signal danger by thumping the ground with their hind feet.

Rabbits are herbivorous and have extremely sharp teeth, 28 in all. There is a pair of large chisel-like incisors in the upper and lower jaws but in addition there are two smaller incisors behind the larger pair in the upper jaw. The presence of this second pair distinguishes the skulls of rabbits (and hares) from those of rodents.

Rabbits move with a series of intermittent leaps when relaxed or a series of bounding leaps when running at high speed.

Distribution and population density

The rabbit originated in the area of the Iberian peninsula and northwest Africa. It has spread both naturally and through man throughout western Europe, as far east as Poland and to southern Sweden and Finland in the north. It is absent from Italy and most of the Balkan countries. It has also been introduced to many other countries such as USA, Chile, New Zealand. In Australia it has become a major pest.

Rabbits may be particularly destructive on small or isolated islands. They have two main effects: firstly, they may directly destroy habitats by overgrazing, and secondly they may allow higher numbers of predators to exist, which might then contribute to the extinction of other native prey species.

It is not clear if rabbits were present in

Ireland before the ice ages. They certainly were present in Britain. However, they became extinct in these regions. Hares are illustrated in the Book of Kells but rabbits are not. They were not reintroduced to Britain until Norman times when they were an important domestic animal. They were also introduced to Ireland with the Norman settlement. They were originally confined to warrens, from which predators were excluded and to which extra food was supplied. Warrens were often established on islands. The earliest references to rabbits in Britain or Ireland are to warrens on Lambay Island in 1191 and in Connacht in 1204. There are also early records of coney-warrens at Ballysax (Co Kildare) in

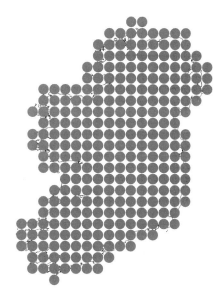

1282, in Ardmayle (Co Tipperary) and Rosslare (Co Wexford) about the same period.

Rabbits probably became established in the wild soon after their introduction and became locally numerous over the next two hundred years. The spread was partly due to new agricultural practices, which created more favourable habitats, and to man's increasing interest in predator control. Domestic and wild rabbits formed the basis of an important skin-export industry in the 17th and 18th centuries. Over two million skins were processed annually for export and in the 1870s most of the rabbit meat in the Manchester market came from Ireland.

In Ireland today, the rabbit is found all over the country in a wide variety of habitats from the coast to upland moors. It is extremely difficult to estimate the size of a rabbit population. It may be necessary to walk along a predetermined route and count rabbits feeding in the evening at least twenty times before a reliable average figure can be calculated. Even then, such counts carried over a long period are really only useful to indicate whether the population is increasing or decreasing. If a true census is needed then different approaches, much more effort and more sophisticated computations are required. Population density of rabbits varies throughout the year and is highest in September and October. Densities may range up to 15 per hectare in winter and up to 40 per hectare in late summer. In populations of rabbits, death rate rather than birth rate seems more sensitive to population density. The mortality of rabbits in their first year varies from about 50% up to 90% from year to year and in different habitats. Adult mortality varies from 30% to 50%. The key factors causing death of adult rabbits are predation, viral diseases, food supply in autumn and the weather in winter. Foxes, stoats, badgers and mink prey on rabbits but there is no reliable information on their impact on rabbits in this country.

Habitats, diet and habits

The rabbit is a creature of short grass habitats from sea level up to the treeline. It may be extremely common on lowland pastures. The most favoured habitats, such as coastal machairs, grassy cliff tops, dry heathlands and agricultural pastures, include areas of short grasses in association with cover and secure refuge areas, such as bramble patches or gorse. Rabbits appear to avoid extensive tracts of coniferous forest but may use forest edge as refuge areas.

They feed mainly on grasses and particularly like short, soft species. They may have a significant impact on the local plant communities and may be the most important agents in maintaining close-cropped swards that are used by other species such as the chough, a bird which forages for invertebrates on grassy areas maintained by rabbits. In areas where large populations of rabbits are dramatically reduced or eliminated, grasslands may be rapidly invaded by woody scrubland species. Rabbits also eat a variety of other plants and the composition of the diet depends to some extent on habitat. Rabbits will feed on agricultural crops such as young stages of cereals, root crops and tree seedlings and saplings, particularly in winter. This can cause serious economic loss.

Rabbits are mainly nocturnal, but may be active by day, particularly at dawn and dusk in spring and summer. In populations that are not subjected to intense hunting, rabbits may be active throughout the day. The rabbit passes its food through its gut twice, which allows more complete extraction of carbohydrates, proteins and vitamins. Soft faeces produced during the day are eaten and excreted for the second and last time when the rabbits are foraging at night.

Social organisation

Rabbits live in extensive burrow systems called warrens. At low densities, rabbits live in pairs. In large warrens, the population may consist of a number of discrete social groups organised in hierarchies of males and females. Dominant males father most of the kittens; dominant females have priority of access to the best nest sites. Groups tend to defend their core areas within the warren. Males mark the boundaries of their territories by displaying in parallel runs along the margins and excavating shallow paw-scrapes. Boundaries are also marked with urine and faecal pellets laced with secretions from the anal glands. These pellets are darker than the usual type.

Rabbits are rarely found more than 400m from their warren. Home ranges of rabbits are therefore rather small and depend on population density and food supply. They vary from about 0.5 to 2ha. Particularly in expanding populations, rabbits may nest above ground in dense cover.

Reproduction and life-cycle

Rabbits may breed throughout the year, but the main breeding season extends from about January to August. It may be shorter in years of food shortage or bad weather. The length of the breeding season is also affected by population density and is shorter in overcrowded warrens.

Most pregnancies occur between April and June. Female rabbits do not ovulate spontaneously; eggs are released in response to mating. Males are attracted by the scent of a female in heat and the courtship may be quite frantic, involving squabbles and chases between a female and her suitor. There are also threat displays and more protracted fights between competing males. The fights may involve kicking with the hind legs or boxing with the fore-legs. It is likely that high-ranking males mate with more than one female. It is not clear if females mate with more than one male. They may, however, mate at about weekly intervals even when pregnant.

Rabbits born early in the year may breed in that same year. Breeding females usually produce three to seven litters a year. The gestation period is about 30 days and females mate and conceive their next litter within 24 hours after delivery of the previous one. The litters are born in specially dug burrows called nest-stops, which are generally somewhat removed from the main warren. The mother lines the nest-stop with soft fur that she plucks from her body. The litter size generally varies from three to seven, is usually about five, but may be as many as ten. Litter size is affected by a number of factors, the most important of which are the age and general health of the mother and time of year. When populations are extremely high, social stresses and population density may suppress reproduction.

The young (kittens) are born without fur and with their eyes closed. They are usually left unattended in the nest-stop, the entrance to which is carefully concealed by the mother when she leaves. The mother is never far from her litter but she only visits the nest to feed them. This occurs for about five minutes at night and most kittens are only fed once every 24 hours. The young grow rapidly and appear above ground after about 18 days and are weaned after about 24 days. Mortality of young rabbits may be as high as 90% in their first year. Few rabbits survive beyond 5 years of age. By five months of age substantial numbers of juvenile rabbits have freely dispersed from the territory in which they were born. Young males are more likely to disperse, and they travel greater distances than females. The young females that remain in their native territory are more likely to breed successfully as yearlings than those which disperse. Male and female littermates appear to disperse independently and it is quite unusual for a dispersing brother and sister to settle in the same location.

Watching rabbits

Rabbits may be seen almost anywhere in the country. Warrens are usually found on slopes in well-drained sites and may be quite extensive. Landowners will usually be aware of the location of warrens on their property. The most obvious signs of rabbits are their faecal pellets that may be quite abundant in the vicinity of a warren. They are often found in conspicuous piles, particularly when used as scent markers, often in association with scrapes in the earth. Close-cropped short grass areas are also usually indicative of the presence of rabbits. The openings to the burrows are quite variable, depending to some extent on the frequency of use, and may range from 10–40 cm in diameter.

Clear footprints of rabbits are not usually seen except where the bare earth is muddy. There are five toes on the fore-foot (but the fifth toe is set well back and often does not make an impression) and four on the hind-foot. In general, therefore, only four claw marks show on a footprint. Sometimes the pads of the feet leave an impression about 2cm across and about 3cm long. Only in very soft mud is the full impression (about 12cm long) of the hind foot likely to be found, showing the large difference between fore- and hind-feet. Although they are smaller, it is difficult to distinguish the tracks of rabbits from those of hares.

Environmental impact and management

The rabbit is an important prey species and in Ireland forms an important part of the diet of foxes, stoats and badgers. However, these predators have little or no impact when set against the rabbit's potential for reproduction. It is classified as a pest and may be shot at any time of year.

In one sense at least the rabbit is a man-made pest. It originally spread slowly from the western Mediterranean area during historic times. Its current invasive and pest properties are because the wild rabbits in most countries are descended from domestic stock that was originally selected, by the Romans, for high reproductive rates. The rabbit therefore may become locally abundant and cause significant damage to agricultural crops and young forest plantations although the cost is not well quantified in this country.

Myxomatosis, since its introduction, has had a significant impact on rabbits. The myxoma virus, isolated from a South American species of rabbit and spread by the rabbit flea, was released to control rabbits in Ireland in the early 1950s. It was first reported from Carlow in 1954. Myxomatosis is a highly specific disease and the early strain of the virus was highly virulent and killed more than 99% of infected rabbits. Since then co-evolution of the virus and the rabbit has led to the appearance of less virulent strains of virus and more resistant rabbits. The disease is now endemic in rabbits and outbreaks regularly occur, in different populations, usually in late summer. Another viral disease, rabbit viral haemorrhagic disease, has recently spread throughout most of Europe and is devastating rabbit populations in certain areas. Mortality of up to 90% of adults has been reported. However, many rabbits in Britain and Ireland appear to have some immunity to this disease, which suggests that a less virulent form of the virus may already be present in the rabbit populations. This disease was first identified in domestic rabbits in Britain in 1992 and in Ireland in 1996. It has already appeared in wild rabbits in Britain but is not spreading as rapidly as predicted. It may be expected to reach wild populations in this country in the near future.

Brown hare – *Giorria gallda*
Lepus europaeus, Pallas 1778

The brown hare was introduced to Ireland in the 19th century. Its current status is uncertain.

The names

The scientific name derives from the Latin for European (*europaeus*) and hare (*lepus*). The scientific description is that of the German zoologist Pallas, based on a specimen from France, dating from 1778. The Irish name acknowledges the recent addition of this species to our fauna and means foreign (*gallda*) hare (*giorria*). Indeed the brown hare in Ireland was often known as the English hare or the thrush hare, the latter a reference to its more speckled coat. The Irish word for hare is itself derived from small (*gearr*) deer or game animal (*fia*).

Identification and characteristics

There has been virtually no study of this animal in Ireland, so most of the account of this species is derived from work undertaken elsewhere. Like most species of hare, the brown hare is much larger than the rabbit. The total length from the nose to the tip of the tail is about 65cm, including about 10cm of tail. There is little apparent difference in size between the sexes but female brown hares are about 10% heavier than males. Adult males weigh about 3.1–3.3kg, females 3.3–3.5kg.

The brown hare has long hind-legs. The hind-feet are usually between 12 and 15cm. The ears are long (about 10cm) and slender and are about as long as the head. If folded downwards they would reach to the tip of the nose. (The ears of the mountain hare are shorter than the length of the head.)

The coat is variable in colour but is generally yellowish brown in summer and reddish brown in winter with a greyish rump. They often have a mottled appearance and in the north of the country are referred to as thrush hares. The lower flanks are paler and the belly is white. Brown hares moult their coat twice a year, but, unlike the mountain hares, never show any trace of white in the winter coat. The upper surface of the tail is black. This is a main distinguishing feature between the brown and mountain hare, the upper surface of whose tail is generally white in winter. In summer, however, the upper surface of the tail of many mountain hares in Ireland becomes darker, making it possible to confuse the two species.

The eyes are large and set in the side of the head so their field of vision is particularly wide, almost 360°. The eyes are extremely good at detecting moving objects although their ability to discriminate between stationary shapes is poor. Their sense of smell is well developed and they possess a number of skin-glands that produce scents of social significance. Their hearing is extremely sharp. They are not very vocal but scream when distressed. They also have a number of faint clicking, purring and snorting sounds. They move with a loping gait when relaxed or a bound-like gallop when running at high speeds, up to 70km per hour.

The brown hare is generally considered to be larger than the mountain hare but the difference in size may be more apparent than real. It may be due mainly to the differences in their habitats in other countries. Mountain hares from grassland in Ireland are about as big as brown hares from grassland in Britain. The colour of the droppings is rather variable. They are about 1cm in diameter and are larger and more flattened than those of rabbits, but it is almost impossible to distinguish between droppings of brown hare, mountain hare and rabbit.

Distribution

The brown hare is distributed from central Asia westward through Europe. In Europe it extends from southern Scandinavia and most of Britain in the north, to the northern Mediterranean rim, excluding most of the Iberian peninsula. The brown hare is generally

considered to be less well adapted to more severe winter conditions than the mountain hare and thus, over most of its range, is absent from higher altitudes and latitudes. Across southern Europe it replaces the mountain hare.

In Britain the brown hare is largely a creature of mixed arable farmland and is absent from heather moors. Thus the brown hare is found in England and Wales, while the mountain hare is largely confined to Scotland.

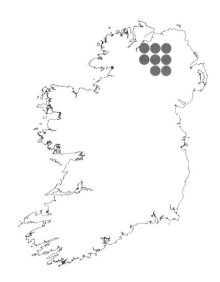

The brown hare is the more enigmatic of our two hares since its current status in most of the country is quite uncertain. This, the southern counterpart of the mountain hare, never apparently colonised Ireland naturally, but during the second half of the 19th and the early part of the 20th century, brown hares were introduced to many parts of Ireland. These included Lurgan (Co Armagh), Fermoy (Co Cork), Copeland Islands (Co Down), Cleenish Island (Lough Erne), Strabane and Barnscourt (Co Tyrone), Powerscourt (Co Wicklow) and Letterkenny (Co Donegal). The subsequent performance of these populations is poorly documented.

In the 1970s there were occasional reports of brown hares from Co Donegal and brown hares were still present there in 1981, but there have been no confirmed reports since the mid-1980s. It is still apparently found along the north coast from Lough Foyle to Carlingford Lough. It has also been reported from the border regions of Armagh, Tyrone and Fermanagh. There may also be a pocket in Co Down. Most data are from sightings only and there is an urgent need for information based on specimens. The most recent information on the distribution of brown hares has been collected in the early 1990s in general surveys or as part of the national badger survey. The distribution map shows the location of the 20km squares from which hares have been reported since 1989. This distribution map, however, must be considered provisional.

Habitats, diet and habits

In Britain the brown hare is particularly found in lowland areas which contain a substantial proportion of arable crops and open grassland. It is somewhat intolerant of high densities of livestock. The main foods in summer are herbs, grasses and the early stages of cereals and root crops. In winter, grasses, turnips and sometimes tree bark are the main food items. The hare passes its food through its gut twice, allowing more complete extraction of carbohydrates, proteins and vitamins. Soft faeces produced during the day are eaten and finally excreted during night-time foraging. Brown hares are mainly nocturnal but may be active throughout the day particularly at dawn and dusk in spring and summer.

In Britain there may be between two and four brown hares per hectare. There is little evidence of territorial behaviour. The home ranges of brown hares occupy about 300ha, which are partly shared with other individuals. Hares usually have daytime resting areas, in hedges, woods or shelter-belts, and a foraging area elsewhere which is used mainly at night.

When not foraging, hares rest in nests called forms. Hares may also excavate shallow burrows. These are often deep enough to conceal the hind part of the body of a crouching hare. Each home range may have a number of resting and feeding areas interlinked by conspicuous paths and trails. Brown hares are generally of a nervous disposition and are quite excitable and thus difficult to maintain in captivity.

Social organisation and reproduction

Brown hares are generally considered to be solitary but may regularly be seen in groups. These are most usually seen during the breeding season or in particularly rich feeding areas. Where home ranges overlap or when hares are in groups, a social hierarchy based largely on body size may decide priority of access to resources. In poorer habitats, when hares are at lower densities, they may be more solitary.

Brown hares are seasonal breeders. The breeding season extends from about February to October but may be shorter in years when food is scarce. When hares are in breeding condition the females do not ovulate spontaneously. Non-pregnant females mate at about seven-day intervals and eggs are released in response to mating. Males may increase their home ranges during the breeding season to increase the chances of encountering a breeding female. Males are attracted by the scent of females in heat. The courtship may be quite frantic involving squabbles between a female and her suitor. Males usually attempt to defend breeding females from the attentions of competitors. Aggression is quite marked and there may be protracted fights between competing high-ranking males. Subordinate males are less likely to stand and fight and may be chased away energetically. The fights may involve boxing with the fore-legs or kicking with the hind-legs. It is likely that high-ranking males mate with more than one female, but it is not clear if females mate with more than one male.

Hares do not usually breed until their second year and breeding females usually produce two or three litters a year. The gestation period is about 42 days. But unusually for mammals, females may mate and conceive their next litter before the current one has been born. The litter size varies from one to four but is usually three. The young hares (leverets) have their eyes open from birth and are fully furred. The mother does not spend much time with the leverets and although she will be close by, she only returns to feed them about dusk. Most leverets are only fed once every 24 hours. Over the first few days of life, they tend to hide in the nest while the mother is away. After a few days they tend to disperse and reassemble at feeding time only. They grow rapidly and are weaned after about 23 days. Mortality of young hares may be as high as 80% in their first year. Adults have a higher survival rate and may live to 7 years.

Hybridisation between brown hares and mountain hares

Brown hares and mountain hares share a common ancestor which lived about 2–4 million years ago. The two types of hare that evolved from this ancestor probably did so in populations that had become isolated from one another. As a result of different natural selective forces acting in the different populations, the two distinct types would have emerged as the populations diverged. If they became sufficiently different they might be considered to belong to two different species. Several processes conserve the genetic integrity of a species and prevent an individual from breeding with an individual from another species. These include behavioural and anatomical differences that either make breeding impossible or, if it occurs, prevent the production of fertile offspring. Otherwise, two populations would be unlikely to evolve into two species because interbreeding would act to prevent their further divergence.

Under normal circumstances meeting and interbreeding were most unlikely because brown and mountain hares were separated either by long distances or by living in different habitats. However, it appears that insufficient time has elapsed for barriers to reproduction to evolve, because brown hares and mountain hares are still capable of occasionally interbreeding and producing fertile offspring. They will readily do so in captivity. Female mountain hares will mate with brown males and produce viable and fertile offspring. Female brown hares are choosier and will not usually mate with male mountain hares. But if they are artificially inseminated with mountain hare semen they will also produce viable and fertile offspring. Natural hybridisation has certainly occurred in Sweden where brown hares were introduced in the 19th century. Genes of mountain hares have been detected in brown hares although the reverse has not so far been observed. It is not yet known if this process has occurred in Ireland. It would be most likely if male brown hares became isolated in an area with a high density of female mountain hares.

Population

Population density of brown hares is variable from year to year and in different habitats. Densities in Britain may range from about one to almost 150 per km^2. Warm springs and autumns are associated with population increase. Disease, particularly coccidiosis, is a major killer of brown hares. They are also susceptible to parasitic infection. Recently brown hares have died in large numbers in other countries from a viral disease known as European brown hare syndrome. Brown hares are vulnerable to grass–cutting machines and to agricultural pesticides. The fox is the main predator of hares particularly the leverets and immature individuals. Leverets may also be captured by stoats.

The lifespan of brown hares in Ireland is unknown. In other parts of its range the survival rate of adults is quite variable. On average 40% to 65% of adults dies each year and the maximum age is about seven years. There is no recent reliable information on which to base any estimate of the population of brown hares in Ireland.

Watching brown hares

See the section on the mountain hare for advice on watching hares.

Conservation and management

The status of the brown hare in Ireland is at present unclear. It appears to be patchily distributed throughout Northern Ireland but is generally considered to be absent from the

Republic. It is not an original member of our fauna and is of doubtful conservational value. The current conservation legislation makes no specific reference to the brown hare and it is thus subject to the same provisions as the mountain hare. It is, therefore, both a protected species in the Republic of Ireland and Northern Ireland and a game or quarry species, and may be hunted during the open season, under licence issued by Dúchas The Heritage Service of the Department of Arts, Heritage, Gaeltacht and the Islands (RoI) or the Environment Service of the Department of the Environment (NI). This usually extends from late September to the end of February. Hares may also be captured during the hunting season for coursing by muzzled greyhounds, in accordance with the rules of the Irish Coursing Club. In fact some of the original introductions of brown hares to this country were to provide hares for coursing purposes. The general view was that although the brown hares were faster than the mountain hares, they were not so agile in turning. The scarcity of brown hares means that probably very few are taken by hunting or for coursing. There are unconfirmed reports that brown hares from Britain or Europe are still being released in Ireland in small numbers.

Mountain (Irish) hare – *Giorria*
Lepus timidus hibernicus, Linnaeus 1759

The mountain hare is one of Ireland's longest-established mammals.

The names

The scientific description is that made by Linnaeus in 1859, based on a Swedish specimen. The scientific name is Latin and means the timid (*timidus*) hare (*lepus*). Mountain hares in Ireland are sufficiently distinct, by not having a white winter coat, to be regarded as a subspecies of the mountain hare. Its full scientific name thus has the extra piece, *hibernicus*, Irish, to acknowledge this fact. The Irish name is derived from *gearr* (short/small) *fia* (deer or game animal), perhaps indicating an ancient and long-established association with hunting. On some large estates hares were formerly reared in semi-captivity in hare parks or hare 'warrens'. The mountain (Irish) hare appears in a number of placenames such as Ballygirriha, the townland (*baile*) of the hare (*giorria*), Dromgurrihy, the hare's ridge (*drom*) (both in Co Cork) and Meenagarragh (Co Donegal), the smooth field (*mín*) of the hare (*giorria*). There is a rich folklore associated with hares, some of which is still to be found even in urban areas, although in a much-altered state. The Easter bunny is actually a hare. Male hares are sometimes known as jacks, while the females are called jills.

Identification and characteristics

Like most species of hare, the mountain hare is much larger than the rabbit. There is little obvious difference in size between the sexes, but females are about 10% heavier than males. Adult males weigh about 3kg, females 3–3.5kg. The total length from the nose to the tip of the tail is about 61cm, including 7cm of tail. The hind-feet are usually between 15 and 17cm long. The ears are long and slender but are shorter than the length of the head. This helps to distinguish it from the brown hare, whose ears are about as long as its head.

The coat is variable in colour, but is generally reddish brown in summer and grey–brown in winter. Hares moult their coat twice a year. In all other countries the summer and autumn coat is replaced by a white one such that the only pigmented parts in winter are the nose, eyes and the dark tips of the ears. This change in colour is controlled by a number of factors, including the length of the day in winter, air temperature and the presence of snow. In Ireland, mountain hares do not usually turn white in winter although there are occasional reports of a hare showing a partial or almost total colour change. In these few individuals the white patches are lost again when the coat is renewed in spring. The upper surface of the tail is generally pale, usually whiter in winter, and is quite conspicuous when the hare is running away. This is the single feature that absolutely distinguishes the mountain hare from the brown hare, but in summer the upper surface of the tail of many mountain hares in Ireland becomes darker, and so it is less easy to distinguish it from the brown hare.

The eyes are large and set in the side of the head so their field of vision is particularly wide, almost 360°. The eyes are extremely good at detecting moving objects, but their ability to discriminate between stationary shapes is poor. The sense of smell is well developed and the hearing is extremely sharp. Mountain hares are not very vocal but scream when distressed. They also have a number of faint clicking, purring and snorting sounds. The mountain hare has relatively few teeth, 28 in all. There are 16 in the upper jaw and 12 in the lower.

Hares move with a loping gait when relaxed and a bound-like gallop when running at high speed. No accurate measurements of the speed of the mountain hare from Irish populations have been made but speeds of up to 64km per hour have been recorded elsewhere. Since mountain hares in Ireland are somewhat larger than elsewhere, the figure for maximum speed may be an underestimate. Mountain hares do not rely only on their ability to run fast but are capable of changing direction suddenly to outwit predators.

Distribution

The mountain hare is distributed around the globe at northern latitudes, from Ireland and northern Britain through Scandinavia, northern Siberia, western Alaska, northern Canada and Greenland. There is also an isolated population in the European Alps. The mountain hare is generally considered to be better adapted to more severe conditions than the brown hare. Thus over most of its range it is found at higher altitudes and latitudes. It is replaced across southern Europe by the closely related European or brown hare (*Lepus europaeus*). In Britain, the mountain hare is largely confined to upland heather moors in Scotland. By contrast the brown hare is commonly found in England and Wales.

In Ireland the distribution of the mountain hare is most unusual. It is present in all counties and may be found at all altitudes from mountaintops to sea level. The oldest dated specimen of mountain hare from Ireland was excavated at Shandon (Co Waterford) and shown by radiocarbon-dating to be 28,200 years old. The mountain hare is thus one of the longest-established members of our fauna. It was present during the Woodgrange interstadial about 12,000 years ago. It is not clear if the mountain hare survived the last glaciation, about 10,500 years ago, because there is a gap of over 6000 years until the next oldest dated specimen. Even if it did not, it would have been one of the earliest subsequent colonists but how it would have reached the country has not yet been resolved. Bones of the mountain hare are relatively common in deposits dating from the early Mesolithic onwards. One of the earliest of these sites is Mount Sandel (Co Derry) dated to about 7000 years ago. Others were found at Newgrange and are over 5000 years old. The most recent information on the distribution of mountain hares was collected in the early 1990s in general surveys or as part of the national badger survey. The distribution map shows the location of the 10km squares in which hares have been sighted since 1989.

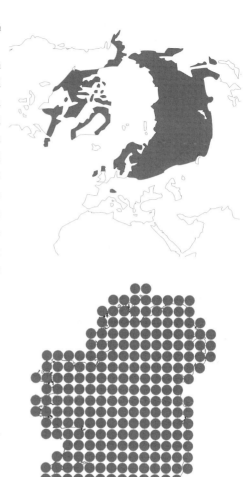

Habitats, diet and habits

The mountain hare is usually seen in open habitats. In Ireland it is found in a wide variety of habitats from coastal grasslands and salt-marshes to upland moors. Population densities, however, are quite variable. Mountain hares are more abundant on lowland permanent pasture and other short-grass, herb-rich habitats. They are less common on wet upland blanket bog in the west and northwest of Ireland. They feed on a variety of plant materials and the composition of the diet depends on habitat. In upland areas hares feed on a mixture of young heather, herbs, sedges and grasses and in winter will browse on bilberry, gorse and willow. They particularly favour heather moors managed for grouse. In lowland pastures grasses may comprise over 90% of the diet. Plantain, dandelions and other herbs are also favoured foods. The hare passes its food through its gut twice, allowing more complete extraction of proteins and vitamins. Soft faeces, produced during the day are eaten and finally excreted, as hard pellets, during night-time foraging. Mountain hares are mainly nocturnal but may be active throughout the day. They tend to be particularly active at dawn and dusk in spring and summer.

Home ranges of mountain hares depend on population density and habitat quality. These factors act mainly through food supply. Hares travel over larger areas on upland moorland (90–120ha in Scotland) than on lowland pasture (30–70ha on Bull Island, near Dublin). They usually have a daytime resting area and a foraging area elsewhere, which is used at night. In upland areas these may be up to 2km apart. When not foraging, hares rest in nests called forms. Hares may also excavate shallow burrows particularly in upland peaty areas. Each home range may have a number of resting and feeding areas that may be interlinked by conspicuous paths and trails. Mountain hares may regularly be seen in groups and four or five animals in fairly close proximity is not unusual. These groups may sometimes be quite large, particularly in rich feeding areas or during the breeding season. Where home ranges overlap or when hares are in groups, a social hierarchy or pecking order based largely on body size may decide priority of access to resources. In poorer habitats, where hares are usually found at lower densities, they may be more solitary.

Reproduction and life-cycle

Mountain hares are seasonal breeders. The breeding season extends from about January to September. It may be shorter in years when food is scarce. In good years in Ireland, breeding may be almost continuous. When hares are in breeding condition the females do not ovulate spontaneously. Eggs are released in response to mating. Males may increase their home ranges, during the breeding season in summer, as they search for females. Males are attracted by the scent of a female in heat. Events surrounding the courtship may be quite frantic. This involves squabbles between a female and her suitor, more protracted fights between competing males and energetic chases of subordinate males. The fights may involve boxing with the fore-legs or kicking with the hind-legs. It is likely that high-ranking males mate with more than one female, but it is not clear if females mate with more than one male.

Hares do not usually breed until their second year, but breeding females usually produce two or three litters a year. The gestation period is about 50 days and, in some cases, females may mate and conceive their next litter before the current one has been born. Thus a female hare may be pregnant with two litters of different ages. The litter size varies from one to four but is usually two or three. The young hares (leverets) have their eyes open from birth and are fully furred. The mother does not spend much time with the leverets and, although she will be close by, she only returns to them at feeding time. This occurs about dusk and most leverets are only fed once every 24 hours. For the first few days, they remain in the form while the mother is away. After a few days they tend to disperse a little and reassemble at feeding time. They grow rapidly and are weaned after about 21 days. Mortality of young hares may be as high as 80% in their first year. The lifespan of mountain hares in Ireland is not well known, The survival rate of adults is quite variable. On average 30–50% of adults die each year, but survival may be as low as 15%. The maximum age is about eight or nine years. See pages 94-95 for information on hybridisation of mountain and brown hares.

Watching mountain hares

One may expect to see Irish or mountain hares anywhere in the country, particularly on open grassland with adjacent cover. They may also be common on sand dunes. They were traditionally a typical feature of the Bull Island, in Dublin, but now are under severe pressure from uncontrolled dogs. They are common on the protected nature reserves of the Slobs near Wexford.

The best time of year to observe hares is during the early part of the breeding season in spring, when hares may be active most of the day and while the grass is relatively short. Hares are otherwise most active early in the morning and late in the evening. Clear footprints of hares are not usually seen, except where their paths run through muddy gateways. There are five toes on the fore foot although the fifth is set well back and often does not make an impression. There are four toes on the hind foot. In general only the claw marks of the feet show. Sometimes the pads of the feet leave an impression about 2cm across and about 3cm long. Only in very soft mud is the full impression (13–15cm long) of the hind foot likely to be found, showing the large difference between fore- and hind-feet. In winter the hind-feet are more heavily furred and leave a much wider impression in soft mud and snow. Hares tend to use the same pathways throughout their range. These are often most obvious where the paths cross field boundaries. Hare paths are sometimes difficult to distinguish from those used by foxes, but the hair entangled on wire or brambles may help to distinguish them. Hair fibres of the hare have a reddish brown base, darker central portion and paler tip. Fox hairs have a red base, dark centre and a red tip and are crinkly or fluffy, particularly if the underfur is present. The nesting sites or forms may be identified as shallow depressions in the vegetation. The droppings are greenish or brown about 1cm in diameter and are usually quite fibrous. They are indistinguishable from those of the brown hare and often from those of rabbits also. They are usually more scattered than those of rabbits, which are deposited in latrine scrapes on the boundaries between clans.

Population density

There is not sufficient information from enough sites in this country to develop a reliable estimate of the total population of mountain hares in Ireland. Furthermore, there is no reliable information on overall population trends. Population density of mountain hares is extremely variable, from year to year, and in different habitats. In other countries major fluctuations, occurring in regular cycles, are probably related to changes in food supply. Densities in Ireland may range from about one per km² on blanket bog in the west, to 5–7 per km² on lowland pasture in Kildare. When areas of bogland in the west of Ireland were converted to heavily fertilised pasture, the density of hares increased locally to over 30 per km². In particular locations, such as airports, hares may be found in large groups and at high densities. Groups of over 100 animals have been recorded at Aldergrove airport near Belfast. In other habitats, such as areas of mature heather in upland areas, density is much lower. The key factors determining population size are food supply in autumn, weather conditions in winter and predation. The fox is the main predator of mountain hares. Leverets and immature individuals are particularly vulnerable. Stoats occasionally kill leverets. Parasites and disease are also important mortality factors.

Conservation

The mountain hare is an original member of our fauna and worthy of conservation. It is an important prey species for both mammalian and avian predators. It may be locally abundant and cause some damage to young forest plantations, especially those containing broadleaf species, although this is not well quantified. It appears to be somewhat intolerant of sheep and cattle and generally tends to avoid grazing in their general vicinity. The impact on hare populations of the management of grassland for silage needs to be examined, since it is usually accompanied by a reduction in herb content of the grass sward. This has been suggested as a cause of the decline of the brown hare in Britain. This may also be relevant to the mountain hare in Ireland, since it occupies similar habitats to those used by the brown hare abroad.

It is a protected species in the Republic of Ireland and in Northern Ireland, but it is also classified as a game or quarry species and may be hunted, under licence issued by Dúchas The Heritage Service of the Department of Arts, Heritage, Gaeltacht and the Islands (RoI) during the open season. This usually extends from the last week of September to the end of February. Hunting of hares is totally prohibited, however, in the vicinity of the Wexford Wildfowl Reserve. Hares may also be captured, during the hunting season, for coursing by muzzled greyhounds in accordance with the rules of the Irish Coursing Club. A specific licence is required to course hares outside the hunting season. Hares used for coursing must be tagged prior to release and not used for coursing again. The effect of coursing on the subsequent survival of released hares is not known. The mountain hare is listed in the Irish Red Data book as internationally important and in Appendix III of the Berne Convention as a protected species, and in Annex V of the Habitats Directive as a species which may be exploited but not to the extent that its favourable conservation status is compromised.

CHAPTER 6

Order Rodentia – The Rodents

House, be still, and ye little grey mice,
Lie close tonight in your hidden lairs.
Padraic Pearse (1879-1916)

Over 40% of all mammalian species are rodents. They are the most successful order of mammals and over 1700 species are recognised. Their extraordinary success is due, unlikely as it sounds, to their jaws. Rodents exhibit an array of subtle variations in design features of the jaws and associated muscles, which permits an extraordinary diversity of gnawing actions. This allows exploitation of a correspondingly wide array of foods.

The first rodents appeared in the fossil record of North America about 60 million years ago. There are three main evolutionary lines within the surviving rodents characterised by different gnawing actions. The squirrel-like rodents (Sciuromorpha) arose about 30 million years ago and are now widespread except in Australia and Antartica. Although the mouse-like rodents (Myomorpha) also first appeared about 30 million years ago, they really became diverse only relatively recently. For example, the New World mice evolved about 10 million years ago. At about the same time the true mice and rats arose in SE Asia and colonised Eurasia. The most recent of this group to evolve are the voles, who first appeared about 3 million years ago and began to exploit the prairie and tundra grasslands which were then spreading. The third evolutionary line, the Hystricomorpha, probably arose in Eurasia about 30 million years ago and later spread to the Americas. It includes porcupines, guinea-pigs, etc. None of these is native to Ireland.

Characteristics

Modern rodents are, in general, eaters of seeds. Many, however, are omnivorous or herbivorous and some are insectivorous. Most rodents are small, between 10g and 2kg in weight, but some are as light as 6g (many species of mice) and the largest rodent, the capybara, is about as large as a pig, 50kg. Some extinct rodents were even larger. The largest that ever lived was found in South America. Its head was almost 70cm long and it was as big as a rhinoceros.

The teeth are the most characteristic features of rodents. Rodents have a large curved chisel-like incisor tooth in each side of the upper and lower jaws. This is a crucial feature for distinguishing the skull of a rodent from that of a lagomorph (rabbits and hares have a pair of small extra incisors behind the main upper teeth). The incisor teeth of rodents are self-sharpening. The front edge of the tooth is composed of hard enamel and the back surface is softer dentine. The dentine wears away faster than the enamel, thus always leaving a sharp edge. The incisors have open roots and continue to grow throughout life. There are no canine teeth and many of the premolars may also be absent. Therefore the tooth rows, like those of other herbivores, have long gaps between the incisors and the cheek teeth. The cheek teeth of some species such as voles also have open roots and grow continuously throughout life. This process maintains the height of teeth that are continuously being worn away at the cutting and grinding surfaces. The teeth may also have relatively high crowns to counteract the extreme abrasion. The grinding surfaces of the cheek teeth may have extremely complex series of sharp ridges and crests of enamel separated by valleys of softer dentine. Rodents can move their jaws forwards and backwards as well as from side to side as they grind their food.

The digestive system varies in different dietary specialists. Because of the difficulties in digesting plant material the digestive system in herbivores is relatively long and complex. The digestive strategy of rodents includes a fermentation step, in which microorganisms digest the plant cellulose, in a specialised chamber of the gut. This occurs in the colon and in the caecum, a blind-ending side-chamber located towards the hind end of the gut. Since the digestion of cellulose takes place when the food has almost passed through the gut, some rodents, like the lagomorphs, are obliged, in order to absorb this material, to pass the food through their gut for a second time. This is called refection, literally eating again, or coprophagy, which means eating faeces. This is not an entirely accurate description since the material passed for recycling is soft and quite unlike the hard fibrous pellets produced when the faeces are finally discarded.

The number of fingers and toes is quite variable. In some species there are five digits on each foot. However, in others, there may only be three on the fore-leg and four on the hind-leg. All the rodents found in Ireland have four digits on the fore-foot and five on the hind. Rodents have adapted to almost all habitats and have mastered almost all modes of progression. There are types that live above ground, that burrow, that live in trees or in water. They can run well, swim, climb, hop like a kangaroo or glide from tree to tree. The brain is moderately developed and in many species the parts which process information from the eyes and nose are particularly prominent.

Diversity

The order of rodents is the most successful and diverse of modern mammals. It contains 33 families. The order is divided into three sub-orders. The first is the Sciuromorpha, with about 400 species in seven families. These contain the squirrels, beavers, gophers, marmots and their relatives. The Myomorpha contains nine families including 1110 species of mice, rats, gerbils, mole rats, hamsters, dormice, jerboas and their relatives. The Hystricomorpha contains the porcupines, guinea pigs, capybaras and maras and is divided into about 195 species in 17 families.

Distribution

The living Rodentia are found in all the climatic zones of the world. They are widely distributed across the globe and are native to most land areas except Antarctica, New Zealand

and some Arctic and oceanic islands. Accidental transport or deliberate introduction has extended the current distribution of many species to regions well outside their natural range. Members of seven families of rodents are found in Europe, two of which, the Sciuridae and the Muridae, now occur in Ireland. The two Irish scurids are the red and grey squirrel; and there are five murids – the wood mouse, the house mouse, the black rat, the brown rat and the bank vole. Two species of lemmings went extinct here at the end of the last ice age.

Red squirrel – *Iora rua*
Sciurus vulgaris, Linnaeus 1758

The red squirrel has become extinct in Ireland at least twice. The current population is descended from individuals introduced from Britain during the 19th century. It appears to be in decline again at present.

The names

The red squirrel was first described scientifically by the Swedish naturalist Linnaeus in 1758 from specimens collected locally in Sweden. The generic name (*sciurus*) is derived from the Greek word for squirrel (*skiouros*) which is itself composed of the words for shade (*skia*) and tail (*oura*). The specific name (*vulgaris*) is Latin and means common. The Irish name means red (*rua*) squirrel (*iora*). There do not appear to be many Irish place names associated with the red squirrel.

Identification and characteristics

This is the smaller of the two species of squirrels now found in Ireland. The total length from the nose to the tip of the tail is about 40cm, including 18cm of tail. The hind-feet are usually between 5 and 6cm long. The weight of individual red squirrels may vary by as much as 10% depending on the time of year and food supply. Squirrels are at their lightest in spring. There is little difference in size between the sexes. Adult females weigh 240–350g and males 250–390g.

The overall colour appears brown, but may vary from greyish brown through dark brown to chestnut red. The underside is creamy or white. The summer coat is chestnut brown and the bushy tail is chestnut to pale buff coloured. The tail hair is moulted in late summer, usually in July and August, and the general autumn moult takes place in September and October. The winter coat and tail are thicker. The winter coat ranges from dark grey or brown through ginger to deep red, while the tail is usually dark red or brown. The ear tufts are small and pale in summer, but are moulted in September and October and the winter tufts are thick and brown and quite conspicuous, giving the impression of pointed ears, quite unlike the appearance of grey squirrels.

The sense of touch is vital to squirrels and they have special sensory hairs, which are called vibrissae, above and below the eyes, under the chin and on the nose (whiskers). They also have vibrissae on the fore-legs, the feet, the underside of the body and at the base of the tail. These are used to assist navigation through the trees. Like all agile animals that live in trees, their eyesight is good. The eyes are large and set in the side of the head so their field of vision is particularly wide. Their sense of smell is well developed but their hearing may not be particularly sharp. They mark particular locations with secretions from mouth glands and with urine.

They can run quickly up and down tree-trunks and leap from branch to branch using their tail for balance and steerage. They often attempt to avoid observation by scurrying round to the far side of the tree-trunk. Red squirrels spend less time on the ground than grey squirrels. On the ground they move in a jerky irregular run or in a series of bounding leaps often interrupted by brief periods spent sitting upright scanning the surroundings. They are good swimmers. Red squirrels are quite vocal and have a number of calls usually heard during aggressive interactions with other squirrels. Body postures and tail flicking are also used in communication.

Like most rodents, red squirrels have relatively few but extremely sharp teeth. There are 22 teeth in all, 12 of which are in the upper jaws. Gnawing is carried out by the two pairs of incisors at the front of the jaws.

Distribution and population density

Tree squirrels first appeared about 25 million years ago in North America and soon spread to Asia and Europe. The red squirrel probably first appeared about 3 million years ago. It is found across most of Europe and Asia and extends down through eastern China and parts of Japan.

The red squirrel has probably been a member of Ireland's fauna since prehistoric times. If that is so, it may have gone extinct during the last ice age, about 10,500 years ago. If so, it could have become re-established in the early postglacial period. Suitable habitats would have developed by about 9000 years ago. But by then Ireland would have been isolated from Britain, so it is not clear if it recolonised the

country naturally or whether it was introduced by man. It has not, in any case, been recorded from archaeological sites due probably to its small size and fragility and the preoccupations of archaeologists, who are more usually interested in the remains of humans and domestic animals.

The earliest historical reference is from about AD 655. In any event, by medieval times red squirrels were apparently sufficiently abundant in Ireland to support an export trade in pelts. This trade persisted until the mid-17th century. Some time during the 18th century, the red squirrel underwent a dramatic decline, during the extensive clearance of woodland. By the end of the century it was considered to have become extinct. Between 1815 and 1876, red squirrels were reintroduced from England and released in at least ten sites here. These were Ashford (Co Wicklow), Lucan (Co Dublin), Birr (Co Offaly), Garbally (Co Galway), Castleforbes (Co Longford), Multyfarnham (Co Westmeath), Toome (Co Antrim) and Ravensdale (Co Louth). It spread rapidly during the late 19th century into 18 counties and by the early 20th century was re-established in the expanding forests in all counties.

In Ireland, red squirrels are found throughout the country, and although in most places their density is low, they may be locally common. Their distribution is more limited and local along the western and northern seaboards. The distribution of red squirrels has been monitored several times since the 1970s and is currently under investigation. The distribution map indicates the 20km squares in which red squirrels have been recorded since 1990. The maps indicate the approximate current distribution of the red squirrel. It may be expected to occur in suitable habitats in the areas indicated, although its distribution may be somewhat patchy. There may be changes in distribution along the edges of the expanding range of the grey squirrel. Population density of red squirrels is extremely variable from year to year and between different locations even in the same year, the key factors being the abundance of food in autumn, weather conditions in winter and disease.

Habitats, diet and habits

In northern Europe and Asia the red squirrel is mainly found in coniferous forests of spruce and pine. In western and southern Europe the red squirrel is also found in mixed broadleaf woods. In Ireland, they are found in a wide variety of habitats that provide an adequate supply of seeds. These range from coniferous forests to mixed forests, broadleaf woods and parks, particularly if grey squirrels are not present. They feed on a variety of seeds, berries, fruit and fungi and they spend about 70% of their active periods searching for food. In times of extreme cold weather they may go without food for up to two days but they do not hibernate. In coniferous forests, their main stronghold, seeds are eaten all year round, supplemented by conifer buds and shoots in winter and spring. In summer substantial amounts of bark may be stripped from trees. Squirrels often remove bark from the growing tips of branches that then wilt and are subsequently snapped off by the wind. In autumn, fungi are added to the diet. In broadleaf woods the diet of red squirrels is more variable and includes hazelnuts, beech mast, berries, fruit, buds, bark, fungi and acorns. The seasonal differences in amount and quality of available food means that squirrels are at their heaviest in autumn and winter and lose weight during spring and summer.

Red squirrels are generally active from dawn until dusk, but in summer they are most active in the morning and evening. In winter, when days are short, there is only one main activity period in the day. Red squirrels are mainly inhabitants of the tree canopy and spend most (85%) of their foraging time feeding high in the trees in all seasons and habitats. Red squirrels hoard food in caches at various locations on the ground throughout their home range. This is called 'scatter hoarding'. Scatter hoarders bury food items singly or in small numbers at many locations within their range. A red squirrel may hoard over 2000 food items when food is abundant in late summer and autumn. This behaviour is an important factor in the dispersion of the seeds of many trees. It is likely that grey squirrels may find much of the food hidden by red squirrels. This is because grey squirrels normally spend more time foraging on the ground.

Red squirrels also collect fungi from the forest floor and cache them on the branches of trees near where they emerge from the trunk. It is unlikely that squirrels remember the location of these food depots and they probably relocate them by smell. The pattern of recovery of hoarded food depends on the availability of other food within the animal's home range. Hoarded food may be an important component of the diet. Fungi tend to be eaten soon after storage but these and hoarded seeds might sustain a squirrel for from 50 to 80 days.

Home ranges of red squirrels depend on their population density and food supply. The ranges vary from about 3 to 12ha and are larger in deciduous than in coniferous forests. The home ranges of males are generally larger than those of females, particularly in summer. The home range may have a core area, which is used almost exclusively by a particular individual. While a number of males and females may occupy the same general area, the home ranges of animals of the same sex do not show extensive overlap. There is a greater degree of overlap between the range of a female and that of a male than with that of another female and vice versa. In locations where the home ranges of several individuals overlap, a social hierarchy or pecking order may decide priority of access to resources. Squirrels may have a number of nests or dreys throughout their home range. These are made of twigs and are roughly spherical, about 30cm in diameter; the central hollow is lined with grass and leaves. They are usually located in a forked branch, close to the main trunk, about 5m from the ground, but hollow trees are sometimes used. Summer dreys are often open platforms; the winter or maternity dreys are enclosed.

Reproduction and life-cycle

Red squirrels are seasonal breeders and the timing depends on latitude and altitude acting through climate and food supply. In Ireland, the breeding season extends from about December to the following September but may be shorter in years when food is scarce. Access to food seems to be the critical factor in determining the lifetime reproductive success of females. Under-weight females are often without a regular home range and will not breed. Females with a home range in food-rich areas are usually heavier, live longer, produce more litters and leave more surviving offspring.

During the breeding season the females come in heat for about one day during the fertile period. It is not clear how many fertile periods occur during the breeding season. Males are attracted by the scent of a female in breeding condition. Events surrounding the courtship are quite frantic, involving fights between competing males and energetic chases of the female. It is not known if the female usually mates with more than one male while she is in heat. If adult females become fertile in winter, then they may produce two litters, one in spring (February to April) and a second in summer (May to August). The litters may be as large as six, but three is more usual. Yearling females produce one litter in summer. After mating, a female usually builds a drey. This is a spherical structure of twigs, leaves, and bark and is lined with grasses or moss. Gestation lasts for about 39 days and the young, weighing between 10 and 15g each, are born blind and naked. They are weaned after about nine weeks. Adult females do not mate again until their first litter is weaned. If a female produces two litters in a year, the young from the first litter tend to disperse when the second is born. Otherwise the litter may over-winter with the mother in her nest.

Mortality of young squirrels may be high. About 80% of young red squirrels disappear from the population, by death or dispersal, during their first winter. The second winter of life is also a critical period for red squirrels. Heavier individuals might live for a further four years, lighter ones for only about half as long. Females tend to live a little longer than males, and some survive for up to six years, but two years is more usual.

Studying red squirrels

Red squirrels are more difficult to observe than grey squirrels because they do not usually forage on the ground and are increasingly associated with large tracts of coniferous woodland. Signs of their feeding activity usually reveal the presence of squirrels in an area. Squirrels split the shells of hazelnuts cleanly, unlike other rodents, which gnaw a hole to get at the kernel. They strip the scales relatively cleanly from conifer cones and often leave piles of scales and cores at particular locations, such as stones or tree stumps or around the bases of trees. The core of the cone is left with some ragged strips hanging off (grey squirrels apparently strip the cones more cleanly). When red squirrels strip bark it is often left hanging from the branch or trunk in spirally twisted ribbons (deer tend to remove bark in straight strips by ripping it upwards). The droppings are about 12mm long and 8mm in diameter. Squirrel footprints have four toes on the front-leg and five on the larger hind-foot.

It is not always possible to distinguish between the feeding signs of red and grey squirrels, so a positive sighting is required. A good pair of binoculars is recommended for observing wild squirrels and a magnification of about 8x40 or 7x50 provides the best compromise between adequate light transmission and ease of use. In urban areas it may be possible to observe red squirrels at relatively close range. Red squirrels may still be seen in many urban parks, such as the National Botanic Gardens and St Anne's Park in Dublin. They are readily seen at Avondale and in other forests of County Wicklow, and indeed in any Scots pine or cone-bearing spruce forest. They are present in Killarney National Park and throughout Munster. They are scarcer along the western and northern seaboards, particularly in Connacht, where they have a more patchy distribution. The local rangers of Dúchas The Heritage Service of the Department of Arts, Heritage, Gaeltacht and The Islands (RoI) or of the Environment Service (NI) or the foresters of Coillte will be able to provide information on the status of red and grey squirrels.

Conservation

Red squirrel populations in Ireland and Scotland, which were supplemented from translocated English red squirrels in the 18th century, prospered in the early part of the 20th century, but then began to decline again. The recent decline has continued also in England and Wales so that the red squirrel is now extinct in most areas of its former range in these two countries. As a long-standing member of our fauna, the red squirrel is worthy of conservation. Although it may be so locally abundant as to cause considerable damage to Scots pine forests, its future prospects give cause for concern.

There is much debate regarding the impact of grey squirrels on the red squirrel, which has disappeared from parts of its former range. Although the spread of the grey squirrel and the decline in the red squirrel were noted about the same time, it not clear if and how the grey affects the occurrence of the red. In a number of areas, red and grey squirrels coexist in fairly close proximity. It may be that in areas where the red squirrel declined for any of a number of reasons such as disease, food or habitat loss, the grey moved in and, in some cases at least, prevented recolonisation by red squirrels. On the other hand, the larger, more prolific, aggressive and more omnivorous grey squirrel may compete directly with reds already in residence. A key factor in Britain appears to be the presence of oak trees in woodland. While acorns may be eaten by both species of squirrels, they are not easily digested by and are slightly toxic to red squirrels. Grey squirrels, on the other hand, find them quite palatable. This means that, in mixed woodland, grey squirrels compete directly with red squirrels for hazel nuts and then later switch to acorns, a resource not available to the red squirrel. When hazel crops are poor or if hazel is removed, then the reproductive rate of red squirrels is depressed, increasing the likelihood of replacement by greys.

While the expansion of coniferous woodlands will increase the area of suitable habitats, they will be unlikely to provide a secure refuge unless of adequate size. It seems that reds are most secure in tracts of coniferous woodland over 2000ha in area, particularly if the density of large-seeded broadleaf trees is low and there are no corridors of broadleaf trees to allow invasion by greys. In fragmented woodland, male red squirrels are forced to occupy larger home ranges, while females appear to be restricted to isolated copses and woods. In such habitats their home ranges may be smaller than usual. Tree-lines in hedgerows may provide important corridors for dispersal and exchange of animals between small tracts of woodland.

Grey squirrel – *Iora glas*
Sciurus carolinensis, Gmelin 1788

The grey squirrel is becoming the typical squirrel of parks and gardens and is held in some affection in urban areas. It is the third most recently arrived mammal in this country, having been first released here early in the 20th century, and it is rapidly colonising the country.

The names

The grey squirrel was first described scientifically by the German naturalist Gmelin in 1788 from specimens collected in Carolina, USA. The generic name is derived from the Greek word for squirrel which is itself composed of the words for shade (*skia*) and tail (*oura*). The specific name (*carolinensis*) is Latin and means of Carolina, in reference to where the original specimens were collected. The Irish name means grey (*glas*) squirrel (*iora*).

Identification and characteristics

This is the larger of our two species of squirrel. The total length, from the nose to the tip of the tail is about 48cm, including 22cm of tail. The hind-feet are usually longer than 6cm. Thus, they are much larger than red squirrels. There is little difference in size between the sexes. Adults weigh about half a kilogram, females 400–720g and males 440–650g. The weight of grey squirrels varies by as much as 25% depending on the time of year and food supply. They are at their lightest in spring.

The overall impression of their colour is brownish grey but the upper fur, flanks and feet may have a chestnut tinge, particularly in summer. The underside is pale or white. The winter coat is grown between September and December and is thicker and more yellow. The winter coat is moulted from April to July. The tail is bushy and grey and tail hairs have indistinct brown–black bands and a white tip. The hair of the tail is moulted and renewed in August and September, the winter tail being darker. The ear tufts are small and quite inconspicuous, unlike in the red squirrel. Like most rodents, grey squirrels have relatively few but extremely sharp teeth. There are 22 teeth in all, 12 of which are in the upper jaw. Gnawing is carried out by the two pairs of incisors at the front of the jaws.

Like all agile animals that live in trees their eyesight is good. The eyes are large and set in the side of the head so their field of vision is particularly wide. Their sense of smell is also well developed but their hearing is not particularly sharp. They mark particular locations with secretions from mouth glands and with their urine. Their sense of touch is well developed and they have an array of sensory bristles, known as vibrissae, at various locations on the face (where they are known as whiskers), on the 'wrists' and 'ankles' and at a number of other locations on the body. These vibrissae allow them to detect objects before they come into more solid contact with them. They can thus adjust their limbs, at the last moment, to make secure contact with branches. They can run up and down tree trunks and leap from branch to branch using their tail for balance and steerage. They often attempt to avoid observation by scurrying round to the far side of a trunk. On the ground they move in a hesitant, irregular run or in a series of bounding leaps often interrupted by brief periods spent sitting upright scanning the surroundings. Grey squirrels are quite vocal and have a number of calls usually heard during aggressive interactions.

Distribution and population density

The grey squirrel is native to the species-rich, broadleaf forests of the eastern states of the USA and Canada from the Gulf of Mexico to the Great Lakes and from the eastern edge of the prairies to the Atlantic coast. This squirrel has been introduced to several European locations including Ireland, to Australia, South Africa and also within North America. It has generally proved to be a successful coloniser and spreads rapidly in a number of habitats. It is now widespread in Ireland, Britain, parts of Italy, South Africa and Vancouver in western Canada.

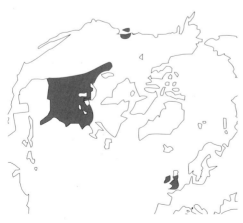

The Irish population is mainly founded on a group of squirrels introduced from England in 1911 to Castle Forbes in Co Longford. It has now colonised at least twenty counties towards the eastern side of the country and there is no doubt that it will eventually be found in all counties as has occurred in England and Wales. The distribution of grey squirrels has been monitored several times since the 1970s and is currently under investigation. The distribution map indicates the 20km squares in which grey squirrels were recorded since 1990. The boundaries of the range of the grey squirrel are continually changing. Within the current distribution, grey squirrels may be expected wherever the habitat is suitable, but throughout the range, the distribution may be somewhat patchy. Population density of grey squirrels varies from year to year and with location. The key factors are the abundance of food, particularly acorns, in autumn and the weather conditions during winter. Densities may range from about two to eight per hectare in broadleaf woodland.

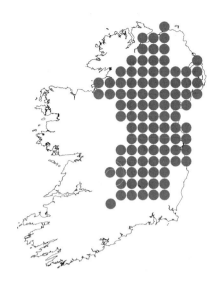

Habitats, diet and habits

In North America, grey squirrels are typically found in broadleaf woodlands. In Ireland they are found in a wide variety of habitats which provide seeds of broadleaf trees. These range from hedgerows and suburban gardens through parks to broadleaf and mixed forests. Seeds and fruit are the major component of the diet in winter and spring. Grey squirrels particularly like acorns, beech mast, hazelnuts and pinecones. In summer and autumn, buds, flowers and bark may be eaten. They are active from dawn to dusk and spend about 60–70% of their active periods searching for food. They forage mainly on the ground, especially in the winter, but in summer they tend to spend more time feeding in the canopy. In times of extreme weather they may go without food for up to two days but do not hibernate. Grey squirrels are relatively opportunistic feeders and will raid vegetable gardens, orchards or bird tables if within their range. They will eat root crops such as swedes as well as cereal shoots and grain. Grey squirrels often remove bark from the growing tips of branches and stems of trees, to gain access to the sugar-rich sap that saturates the soft tissue under the bark. The damage caused by peeling off the bark produces wilting and the affected branches may subsequently be snapped off by wind. Evidence of this damage is often seen under trees in parks in summer.

Home ranges of grey squirrels depend on population density and food supply but range from about 4 to 8ha. Males may increase their home ranges in summer to about 12ha. Where home ranges overlap, a social hierarchy may decide priority of access to resources. Squirrels may have a number of nests or dreys throughout their home range. These are usually located at varying heights in a forked branch, sometimes close to the main trunk but often at some distance along the branch. Summer dreys are open platforms built of twigs, but winter or maternity dreys are enclosed. The dreys are about 50cm in diameter, roughly spherical, made of twigs, with the central chamber lined with leaves and grass.

Reproduction and life-cycle

Grey squirrels are seasonal breeders. The breeding season extends from about December to July, but may be shorter in years of food shortage. Males are attracted by the scent of a female in breeding condition. Events surrounding the courtship are quite frantic, involving fights between competing males and energetic chases of the female. It is not clear if the female mates with more than one male while she is on heat. If winter breeding is possible, adult females usually produce two litters, one in spring and another in summer. Yearling females produce one litter. Females build dreys after mating. These are spherical structures composed of twigs, leaves and bark and lined with grasses or moss.

Gestation lasts for 44 days. The young weigh about 15–18g and are blind and naked at birth. They are weaned after about nine or ten weeks. Adult females do not mate again until the first litter is almost weaned. The average litter size is three but may range from one to seven. Mortality of young squirrels may be high. About 70% of young grey squirrels disappear over their first winter. Females tend to survive longer than males and may live for up to seven years but few animals live longer than three years (two breeding seasons).

Watching grey squirrels

Signs of feeding activity usually reveal the presence of squirrels in an area. Squirrels split the shells of hazelnuts cleanly, often leaving a little notch at the top. This distinguishes them from other rodents that gnaw a hole to get at the kernel. Grey squirrels strip the scales cleanly off conifer cones and often leave piles of scales and cores at particular locations such as stones or tree stumps. (Red squirrels also strip the scales of pinecones but usually leave ragged strips hanging off. Some birds are also less tidy removers of the seeds.) When grey squirrels strip bark it is often left hanging as spirally twisted ribbons (Deer also remove bark from trees but do so in vertical strips and, unlike squirrels, eat it for the minerals it contains.)

The droppings of grey squirrels are about 12mm long and 8mm in diameter. Squirrel footprints have four toes on the front leg and five on the larger hind foot. It is extremely difficult to distinguish between the feeding signs of red and grey squirrels, so a positive sighting is required. A good pair of binoculars is recommended for wild populations and a magnification of about 8x40 or 7x50 provides the best compromise between adequate light transmission and ease of use.

The local rangers of Dúchas The Heritage Service of the Department of Arts, Heritage, Gaeltacht and The Islands (RoI) or of the Environment Service (NI) or the foresters of Coillte will be able to provide information on the status of red and grey squirrels. They will also be interested to hear of sightings of grey squirrels, particularly at the edges of their current ranges.

Impact on the environment

The grey squirrel is either loved or hated. In the areas where it occurs it is the squirrel most likely to be seen by most people, because it has colonised suburban areas. Particularly in the greater Dublin area, it has learned how to raid bird tables and it has a tendency to forage on the ground. In Ireland and Britain the grey squirrel has rapidly become a pest, unlike the situation in its homeland or in South Africa, though a recently introduced population in Italy is also giving cause for concern. It can cause considerable damage to broadleaf forests and is subject to attempts to control numbers. It is, however, an extremely resilient species and, although an alien, has now firmly established itself as part of our fauna. There is no information on the genetics of the grey squirrel in Ireland. British populations are quite variable due probably to the multiple origins of the original founder stock.

See page 111 for a discussion on the impact of grey squirrels on the red squirrel population.

Bank vole – *Luch rua/Vól bruaigh*
Clethrionomys glareolus, Schreber 1780

Until quite recently voles were absent from Ireland. The bank vole is Ireland's only vole and one of the latest additions to the land mammals. It was first discovered, in the 1960s, in north Kerry. It was certainly introduced and is now found throughout about half the country.

The names

The scientific description of the bank vole is based on specimens from the island of Lolland in Denmark and was written by Schreber in 1780. There is some confusion about how Schreber derived the scientific name. The generic name is from Greek, either *clethria* (a hole or nook) or *klethra* (an alder-grove) or *klethron* (a bolt), in combination with *mus* (mouse). The first two possibilities refer to the preference of this animal for dense cover. The third is presumed to refer to the fact that, unlike other voles, the teeth of the bank vole have roots that anchor the teeth in the jaw. The specific name is Latin and is a combination of *glarea* (gravel) and *-olus* (little). This presumably is a reference to the type of habitats where the original specimens were found. An appropriate Irish name might be *luch rua* (red mouse) although *vól bruaigh* (bank vole) is also used.

Identification and characteristics and characteristics

The bank vole is a small rodent. It is about the same weight as a mouse but is a more compact animal. The total length of the body from snout to tip of tail is about 15cm, of which 5cm is tail. Adult males weigh about 25g, females 22g. The head is short and round, with a rather blunt nose. The tail is shorter than that of a mouse. It is about half as long as the head and body combined. The eyes and ears are small. The fur is a chestnut red or brown on the upper surface and buff–grey underneath. Juveniles are grey–brown. Like most rodents, bank voles have rather few teeth, 16 in all, eight in the upper jaws and eight in the lower.

The sense of smell is important to bank voles. Males and females have a number of special scent glands used to mark territories. There are four toes on the fore-foot and five on the hind. The footprints are slightly smaller than those of the wood mouse are but it is difficult to distinguish between them.

Bank voles emit a limited range of squeaks and also a chattering sound. Mothers and young communicate by ultrasound, frequencies too high for the human ear to hear. Breeding adults may also communicate using ultrasound.

Distribution and population density

The bank vole is widespread in upland regions of Europe except Spain and Greece. It extends as far north as Lapland and into western Russia. It is also widespread in Britain and has been there since at least the Iron Age.

It is Ireland's most recent mammalian arrival and was first discovered in County Kerry, in 1964. It was almost certainly introduced here in recent times, probably accidentally, somewhere on the south side of the Shannon estuary between 1925 and the 1950s. Irish bank voles are genetically quite similar to one another, as might be expected if the founder population was extremely small and recent. It has steadily been expanding its range at the rate of between 1 and 4km per year. Range expansion seems to be related to the availability of suitable habitat. By the early 1990s, the bank vole was found in all the counties of Munster and was moving into Leinster and had crossed the Shannon into Galway. Its distribution has been most closely studied in the southwest of the country. The current distribution along the edges of its range is less well known but is currently under investigation. The distribution map shows the 20km squares in which bank voles have been recorded since 1990.

Habitats, diet and habits

Bank voles are usually found in habitats where there is dense undergrowth. They inhabit woodlands with a thick shrub layer and may be found in young coniferous woods, areas of scrub or in rank grassland and hedgerows. They do not regularly inhabit areas with little or no ground cover but will cross short areas of open space. Thick hedgerows probably act as important dispersal corridors for the bank vole. They are active by day and night but particularly so at dawn and dusk. They appear to be less active at night during winter. Bank voles use regular surface pathways through their home ranges. They also excavate burrows and construct underground nests that they line with leaves, moss, grass, feathers or wool.

The bank vole is largely vegetarian and a wide variety of food is eaten. Berries, bulbs, fruits, seeds and fungi are eaten as available. In winter, they will sometimes strip the bark from young trees, including some conifer species, to reveal the edible tissues beneath, which they prefer. Leaves of woody plants and grasses are also taken. Although it feeds mainly on the ground, it a very agile climber and may forage in hedges and small trees. It also eats invertebrates such as insects, larvae, snails and earthworms. In late autumn and winter, bank voles store seeds in small caches usually near their pathways or underground in their tunnels.

Reproduction and life-cycle

Bank voles are seasonal breeders but occasionally they may breed all year round if food supply is adequate. They usually begin to breed in April and continue until September or October. Bank voles are usually well dispersed in suitable habitat during the breeding season and females usually occupy individual home ranges which may extend in area from 0.1 to 0.5ha. The home ranges of males are generally larger, usually cover from 0.5 to 1.5ha and often overlap those of several females.

Female bank voles release their eggs only after mating has occurred, unlike females of most species, which ovulate spontaneously. When population densities are high, female voles tend to produce and rear fewer pups. The first pregnancy of the year lasts for about 18 days. Bank voles may produce a litter every four weeks and litter size ranges from one to seven, depending on the age, size and condition of the mother. Pups usually weigh about 2g and are naked and blind at birth. Their mother feeds the young for about 18 days. Females can become pregnant with the next litter before the first one has been weaned. The duration of the second and subsequent pregnancies of the season depends on the number of young currently being fed and can be as long as 23 days.

Young bank voles disperse soon after weaning to find territories of their own. Bank voles born early in the season may themselves breed later in the summer. Most of the overwintering population consists of young born that year. Very few bank voles survive through two winters. They may live for up to three years in captivity, but it is unusual for an animal to exceed about 20 months in the wild. The average life expectancy of a newborn bank vole is less than four months.

Studying bank voles

Signs of bank voles' feeding activity can often reveal their presence in an area. One of the best indications that bank voles are in the vicinity is revealed by the characteristic clean-edged hole they gnaw in hazelnuts. By contrast, wood mice leave a jagged hole with scratches along the edge while squirrels split the nuts open. Bank voles eat the flesh of rosehips, not the seed (whereas wood mice eat the seeds and discard the flesh). Bank voles split the fruit of the ash-tree to remove the seed (whereas wood mice gnaw a hole in the side). The droppings of wood mice and bank voles are rather similar but, at about 3–4 mm long and slightly less than 1mm in diameter, those of the bank vole are slightly smaller. The colour of their droppings varies, depending on the diet, and so is not a reliable method for identifying the presence of bank voles.

The only practical way to see a bank vole is to use a live-trap to catch one. The animal should later be released at the capture site. Live-traps consist of two parts. The animal enters via a tunnel that contains a trapdoor operated by a tripwire system that closes and locks the door as the vole moves down the tunnel. The tunnel leads to a nestbox compartment in which the vole is retained. Plastic mousetraps marketed as humane traps conform to this basic design and, although they are not very resistant to the gnawing activities of rodents, with modification they would be suitable for use in the field. The principal modification required is a larger nest chamber with improved ventilation. The trap should be baited with a mixture such as muesli and chopped apple. This can be laid at the entrance to the tunnel and also within the nest chamber to provide for a captured vole. It is advisable to empty a sprung trap into a large clear plastic bag to view the catch and to avoid unpleasant surprises such as confronting an angry rat or stoat.

The local branch of Birdwatch Ireland may have information on locations of roosts of birds of prey where food pellets may be collected to examine for the presence of small rodents. The local rangers of Dúchas The Heritage Service of the Department of Arts, Heritage, Gaeltacht and The Islands (RoI) or of the Environment Service (NI) or the foresters of Coillte will be able to provide information on the status of bank voles. They will also be interested to hear of sightings of bank voles particularly at the edges of their current ranges.

Impact on the environment

The bank vole is becoming more abundant in Ireland and future expansion of its range seems likely as afforestation increases. Population densities of bank voles vary greatly depending on weather, food supply and time of year. Bank vole populations in Ireland are usually at their lowest in spring. Numbers build up to a peak in autumn and, in good-quality habitats, there may be as many as 30 or more per hectare.

In Scandinavia populations of bank voles may undergo regular fluctuations with a cycle of four years. In this they resemble the lemmings, to which they are related. In more southern countries, including Ireland, such regular changes do not apparently occur, although dramatic fluctuations may occur from time to time. Such irregular rapid increases in population density locally may be accompanied by substantial damage to young trees, as competition for other food becomes severe. The result is that the bank vole may occasionally become a pest locally in forest plantations, damaging seedlings or young trees by bark stripping.

On the other hand, bank voles may become an increasingly important element in the diet of a number of predatory mammals and birds. Bank voles have been detected in the scats of foxes from southwest Ireland. They may also comprise up to 35% of the diet of the endangered barn owl. (Birds of prey and owls do not pass the indigestible parts of their prey through their gut, but regurgitate hair and bones in compacted pellets. Examination of these pellets can reveal the presence of bank voles in a bird's diet. The three cheek teeth of bank voles, found in such pellets, are relatively flat-topped; the top grinding surface somewhat resembles a zigzag and the teeth have two roots each.) The bank vole is not specifically mentioned in either the domestic or international conservation legislation that applies to Ireland.

Wood mouse – *Luch (luchóg) fhéir*
Apodemus sylvaticus, Linnaeus 1758

The wood mouse is one of Ireland's most common mammals. It has been present in Ireland for at least 8000 years. Mice transported to Ireland during the Viking and subsequent invasions have apparently supplemented the Irish population from time to time.

The names

A specimen from Sweden provided the basis for the scientific description of this species by Linnaeus in 1758. The first part of the scientific name is derived from the Greek *apo* (away from) and *demos* (home) to distinguish it from the house mouse, which lives in closer association with humans. The second part of the name, *sylvaticus*, is Latin and means 'of the woods'. In Ireland it is often confusingly referred to as the field mouse. The Irish name translates as the grass (*féar*) mouse (*luch/luchóg*). To add further confusion, the pygmy shrew is often referred to by the same Irish name. The wood mouse gives its name to Gortnalughoge, the mouse's (*luchóg*) field (*gort*) in County Donegal and Inchnalughoge, the mouse's meadow (*inch*), in County Clare, for example.

Identification and characteristics

The wood mouse has an alert, inquisitive air and has the habit of leaping into the air when startled. It has large eyes and ears and a long tail. The fur is dark brown or chestnut-brown on its upper surface and a whitish-grey on the underside. There is usually a yellow-brown spot or patch on the throat. Juvenile wood mice are grey. The body length from nose to tip of tail is about 16–19cm in males and 15–18cm in females. The length of the head and body combined ranges from 9 to 10cm while the tail length ranges from 7 to 9cm. The hind feet are relatively large (2–3cm), and are longer than those of the house mouse. Adult male wood mice weigh about 20–27g, females 17–24g. Wood mice on our offshore islands tend to be larger and heavier than those on the mainland, indicating their capacity to adapt to local environments.

Rodents have, in comparison with other mammals, a low number of teeth. The wood mouse has only 16 teeth in all, eight in the upper and eight in the lower sets. The four broad sharp incisors at the front of the mouth carry out the gnawing action.

Distribution and population density

The wood mouse is widespread in wooded areas of Europe and western Asia. It is found almost everywhere in Britain and Ireland, including most islands. The earliest record in Ireland is of a tooth found at Clondalkin, near Dublin in a site that showed evidence of Mesolithic humans, and dated to about 7600 years ago. Although the wood mouse has a long history in Ireland, it is likely that it was repeatedly introduced unwittingly by man. Some wood mouse populations show genetic relationships with those of northern Europe and are

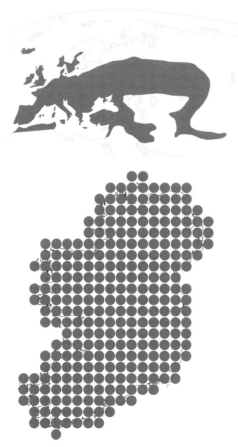

descended from individuals that came ashore from Viking longships. Irish wood mice are more like those in the Hebrides, Iceland and Norway than they are like Scottish mice. The genetic variability of Irish wood mice also indicates that they are long established and were introduced here many times.

There has been no systematic survey of wood mice in Ireland. Current information is derived from a range of local studies and occasional records and reports. The distribution map shows the 20km squares in which wood mice were recorded in the 1990s. Population densities of wood mice vary greatly depending on weather, food supply and time of year. In good-quality habitats in early autumn there may be as many as 20–90 per hectare (yew forest), 3–24 per hectare (oak wood), 6–45 per hectare (beech woods) and 0–20 per hectare (coniferous woodland). Population density is lowest in early spring, when there may be as few as one mouse per 2ha.

Habitats, diet and habits

The wood mouse is highly adaptable and is found almost everywhere except in water-saturated areas. It is found in woodlands, hedgerows, in long-grass pasture, arable crops, blanket bog, heather, coastal grasslands, sand dunes and gardens. It may be found up to altitudes of about 1000m on mountains. On areas of short-grass pasture, most wood mice are found along field boundaries in both winter and summer. In Britain the most abundant small rodent of grassland is the field vole. Although this vole does not occur in Ireland, the wood mouse has not taken over this niche and is not very common on grassland. During the summer, however, they may be common in cereal fields, although the population drops dramatically when the crop is harvested. Farm buildings, in general, seem to be of little importance to wood mice, though they may occasionally colonise unoccupied buildings in summer. They are rarely found in buildings in winter, particularly if house mice are present.

Female wood mice usually occupy individual home ranges during the breeding season, which may extend in area from less than 0.1 to 1ha. It is not clear if males share overlapping home ranges, though male ranges often overlap those of several females. They may, therefore, extend from less than 0.1 to about 3ha, although most are less than 1.5ha. The size of the home range of a male depends on a number of factors, including food supply, habitat type and his general vigour. Wood mice are mainly nocturnal and have two active spells each night, the first soon after dusk. In winter, there may be only one active period per night. Wood mice use regular pathways through their home ranges and also excavate an extensive burrow system that may be up to 3m long. They make underground nests that they line with shredded vegetation. They may also build nests above ground.

The wood mouse is essentially a seedeater – seeds usually occupy about 70% of the diet – but in reality it is an opportunistic omnivore. Its diet largely depends on what is available and includes invertebrates with some plant material. Acorns, seeds, grain, blackberries, elderberries, other fruits, fungi, bulbs, buds and grass flowers have all been identified in the diet. It is a very agile climber and forages in hedges for fruit and buds. It also eats invertebrates such as earthworms, insect larvae and snails. Invertebrates form an important element of the diet at certain times of the year, and wood mice in coniferous woodland rely particularly on invertebrates. In late autumn and winter, wood mice store seeds in small caches, usually near their pathways or underground in their tunnels. In good years, when seed production is bountiful, there may be sufficient to sustain the mice throughout most of the year. When food is scarce and temperatures are low, wood mice may become torpid and sluggish for part of the day. They lower their body temperature by 10°C or more during these periods and thus reduce their energy requirements.

Social organisation, reproduction and life-cycle

The social organisation of wood mice populations is somewhat variable in different places and at different times of the year. Wood mice may nest communally in winter but, during the breeding season, the females become less tolerant of one another. Wood mice are seasonal breeders but occasionally they may breed all year round. They usually begin to breed in April and continue until September or October. When in breeding condition, the females come on heat at about four- to six-day intervals. Pregnancy lasts for about 20 days. The young weigh about 1–2g and are naked and blind at birth. Their mother feeds them for about 22 days. Wood mice usually produce two or three litters a year, but sometimes as many as five. If females become pregnant with the next litter before the previous one has been weaned, implantation may be delayed so the next pregnancy will be longer than the first. The litter size is usually four or five but may be as many as 11. Litters of wood mice born early in the season may suffer high mortality but some individuals may develop sufficiently to breed themselves later in the summer. Individuals breeding in their second year of life usually maintain the populations. Most of the overwintering population consists of young born that year. Very few wood mice survive from one summer to the next.

Studying wood mice

Signs of feeding activity are often a clue to the presence of wood mice in an area. One of the best indications that wood mice are in the vicinity is the characteristic jagged-edged hole with marginal scratches that they gnaw in hazelnuts. (By contrast, bank voles leave a clean hole and squirrels split the nuts open.) Wood mice eat the seeds of rosehips and discard the flesh. They remove the seed from ash-fruit by gnawing a hole in the side, unlike bank voles who tend to split the seed. Wood mice may feed on snails by gnawing through the shell outwards along the coils, starting from the spire. Piles of discarded shells may sometimes be found. Shells opened by wood mice are often under cover. Thrushes are also important predators on snails but they use anvil stones on which they smash the shells, so it is possible to distinguish snail shells left by wood mice from those left by thrushes by the pattern of damage and the absence of an anvil stone near by. The droppings of wood mice and bank voles are rather similar but those of the wood mouse are slightly larger, at about 4–4.5mm long and about 1mm in diameter. The colour varies, depending on the diet.

The only practical way to see a wood mouse is to use a live-trap to catch one that may later be released at the capture site. (See page 121 in the section on bank voles for advice on how to use a live-trap.) The local branch of Birdwatch Ireland may have information on locations of roosts of birds of prey where food pellets may be collected to examine for the presence of small rodents.

Impact on the environment

Because so few species of small rodent occur in Ireland, the wood mouse is an important prey species for a number of predators. It is a significant component of the diets of a variety of carnivorous birds and mammals such as the long-eared owl, barn owl, kestrel, fox, stoat, pine marten, badger and domestic cat. It may comprise up to about 70% of the diet of the long-eared owl and the barn owl. Owls prey heavily on populations of wood mice in cereal fields at harvest time.

Wood mouse populations respond rapidly to an increase in food supply. For example, numbers of wood mice increase rapidly in areas of set-aside land or on conservation headlands where herbicide application is reduced or abandoned. The wood mouse may occasionally become a pest locally, by removing planted seed. It may also colonise outhouses and become a pest of stored grain or animal feed. It is extremely common in stored hay and straw. Because of its omnivorous habits, the wood mouse is liable to be poisoned by eating foods containing insecticides, herbicides and molluscicides. The practice of burning straw can temporarily reduce numbers locally.

House mouse – *Luch thí*
Mus (musculus) domesticus, Linnaeus 1758

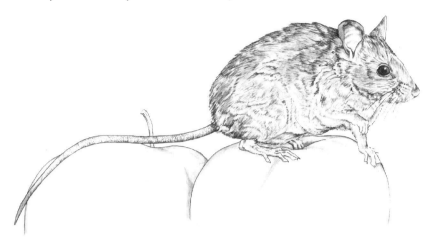

The house mouse is one of our most common and familiar mammals.

The names
Linnaeus first described the house mouse from a Swedish specimen in 1758. The house mouse is somewhat variable across Europe, Asia and Africa and there is some debate as to whether there is only one species occupying this vast area. The variation is used to divide the species into four sub-species. Some consider that these four types are so distinct that there may in fact be four separate species of house mouse. The scientific name is derived from Latin. The generic name *mus* means mouse. On the view that there is only one species, the specific name is formed from *mus* (mouse) and *-culus* (little). So, loosely translated it means the little mousy mouse. The type present in western Europe is then given the extra name *domesticus* (domestic or related to the house). If, on the other hand, the western European type is considered to be a separate species it is known as *Mus domesticus*. The Irish name is a direct translation of the English name, the mouse (*luch*) of the house (*thí*).

Identification and characteristics
The fur is usually grey–brown on the upper surface and slightly paler on the underside. However, there is considerable variation in coat colour. For example, many house mice in the greater Dublin area have a buffish coat. Females are slightly larger than males. The size of house mice also varies between locations. Adult males weigh about 13–25g, females 14–30g. The body length from nose to tip of tail is about 16–18cm in males and 15–18cm for females. The length of the head and body combined ranges from 7 to 9cm, while the tail length ranges from 7 to 8.5cm. The ears and eyes are relatively smaller than those of the wood mouse. The

structure of the retina of the eye is best suited to conditions of low light or darkness. The snout is pointed and the whiskers are long. The tail is about as long as the head and body combined. It is scalier than that of the wood mouse and resembles that of a rat. The eastern European form has a shorter tail.

Rodents have rather fewer teeth than other mammals. House mice have 16 teeth in all, eight each in the upper and lower sets. There are no canine teeth. Each of the upper incisors, viewed from the side, has a characteristic notch just behind the cutting edge. The first molar tooth in the skull has three roots (that of the wood mouse usually has four). These distinguish the skull from that of the wood mouse. There are four toes on the fore-foot and five on the hind. The hind-feet (1.5–2cm) are distinctly smaller than those of the wood mouse.

House mice are quite curious but also extremely suspicious of new objects within their territories. They scurry about in short bursts, often pausing and standing on their hind legs to scent the air. They tend to avoid moving across exposed areas and generally run along covered trails. If they must cross open spaces, they tend to run close to walls. Scent is extremely important to house mice and they are well-equipped with glands on the face, feet and genital area which are used to scent-mark key features of their home range. The saliva and urine also contain important scents. Scents convey information as to identity, sex, breeding condition and social rank. House mice have a wide repertoire of vocal communications, some audible to humans. Young mice (pups) communicate with their mother using ultrasound, high-frequency squeaks above the range of human hearing.

Distribution and population density

The house mouse probably originated, between 1 and 2 million years ago, in the grassy steppes of what are now Iran and Turkestan in central Asia. It lived in rock crevices and fed mainly on seeds of grasses and other plants. It developed a close association with human settlements and extended its range along with humans. It was in the Middle East about 10,000 years ago, reached central Europe about 4000 years ago and was recorded in north-western Europe less than 3000 years ago. A rodent of this type is now found over most of Europe, Asia, the Americas, Australasia and southeast Africa.

The species found in Ireland, *Mus (musculus) domesticus*, is found in western Europe and extends as far east as eastern Germany. It is also found along the eastern coastal regions of the Adriatic and in Greece, Romania and Turkey and in North Africa. It is replaced in Scandinavia and eastern Europe by *Mus (musculus) musculus*. In the narrow zone where *M. m. domesticus* and *M. m. musculus* meet, hybrids between them are found.

It is not certain when the house mouse reached Ireland. It was certainly present in Britain during Roman times, but may have

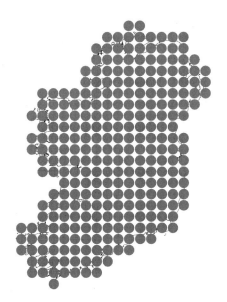

arrived with settlers as early as the Iron Age. It was clearly well established in Ireland by the 7th century and is now found almost everywhere in Ireland, including most inhabited islands. Population densities of house mice vary greatly, depending on location, food supply and time of year. Indoors, in food stores, there may be the equivalent of thousands per hectare. Outdoors, populations may reach up to 50 per hectare in summer.

Habitats, diet and habits

The house mouse is probably restricted in its use of habitats by the presence of competitors. In Ireland, as throughout most of its range north of the Mediterranean area, the house mouse lives indoors during the winter. It is most usually found in buildings and warehouses. It is rarely found far from buildings in Ireland except on some offshore islands. The house mouse avoids open habitats, but may be found in fields or hedgerows close to buildings particularly in summer. It can tolerate a wide range of temperatures and has colonised both central heating ducts and cold meat stores. On uninhabited islands it tends to live under open-field conditions.

There is substantial genetic variation within and between local populations of house mice in Ireland. At high densities in confined spaces, social hierarchies operate in house mouse society. In less confined spaces, house mice are more obviously territorial. Home range size varies with population density and ranges from about 5m^2 in confined conditions up to 400m^2 in fields. House mice living outside tend to move into buildings in late autumn and winter.

House mice are mainly nocturnal and have two active spells each night, the first soon after dusk, the other just before dawn. House mice use regular pathways through their home ranges but may also excavate an extensive burrow system in soft earth. The positioning and design of nests are highly variable and may be quite complex.

The house mouse probably evolved as a seed-eater. It then exploited the developing human settlements. This reduced competition with other small rodents and provided a constant source of food and shelter. The house mouse is now an opportunistic omnivore and its diet largely depends on what is available. It particularly likes cereals but will eat almost anything that is easily digestible. Mice in outside populations will also eat invertebrates such as insects and their larvae. When a wide variety of foods is available house mice tend to take a little of each, but when choice is restricted they eat from 3–4g of a single food per day.

Social organisation, reproduction and life-cycle

The social organisation of house mice populations is somewhat variable in different places and at different times of the year. In some locations the whole population behaves as a random breeding unit. In others the population may be highly structured into semi-isolated breeding groups. A range of scents that act as badges of membership signals affiliation to these groups, into which immigrants are not readily accepted.

House mice are unusual in that their breeding season is not controlled by day-length. Females come on heat at four- to five-day intervals throughout the year, unless pregnant. Given suitable conditions indoors, house mice will breed all year round and may produce up to ten litters in a year. They usually begin to breed outdoors in April and continue until September or October. They may produce litters at five-week intervals. Females build a nest of grass, paper or other suitable fabric. Pregnancy lasts for about 20 days. The litter size ranges from five to eight. The young weigh from 0.8 to 1.5g at birth. They are born blind and naked and are fed by their mother for about 16 days. There is little or no paternal care. If females become pregnant with the next litter before the previous one has been weaned, implantation may be delayed. The next pregnancy will then be longer than the first and may last 36 days. There are many social controls on reproduction, many of them operating through information contained in scents. If a male joins an all-female group, they will all quickly come into breeding condition. On the other hand, if a strange male takes over a social group, his odour blocks any pregnancies currently in progress. Female house mice are capable of breeding at as young as six weeks and certainly by 8–12 weeks of age. Males do not usually breed before 18 months. Populations can build up rapidly and increase six- to eight-fold in a season.

The house mouse is an important prey species for a variety of carnivorous birds and mammals such barn owl, kestrel, fox, stoat, and domestic cat. Most of the annual mortality, however, is probably due to cold. Mice outdoors rarely live through two winters, though house mice indoors may live for more than two years.

Studying house mice

House mice often defecate and urinate at particular locations, which may accumulate a substantial pile of droppings and smell strongly – a distinct, stale, musty, mousy odour. Droppings are about 6mm long and 2–2.5mm wide. Mouse droppings are variable in colour but do not crumble when crushed. This distinguishes them from bat droppings. Traces of their gnawing may found on the casing of electrical cables. The size of the bite marks may be used to distinguish the damage from that caused by rats. Mice also tend not to completely consume each food item. Thus, partly eaten food particles are usually evidence of the presence of house mice.

Even people interested in wildlife would usually prefer not to study house mice at large in their own homes, but pet mice are a useful way to study mice without unpleasantness. The strains of laboratory and pet mice are derived from wild house mice introduced to breeding programmes that were set up in the early 1900s. This avoids the risk of contraction of diseases that must always be borne in mind when coming to close contact with wild animals or their products.

Management and control

House mice are prepared to eat almost anything. As a result, almost nothing is safe from their nibbling. Among the more apparently unpalatable materials which they attack is electrical insulation. Where there are high-density populations in attics there is often damage to the electrical wiring. The house mouse may become a pest of stored grain or animal feed, not only because of the amount of food it consumes, but also due to contamination by its urine and faeces. The opportunities for contamination of stored products are substantial. Each mouse may produce as many as 50 faecal pellets each day. The bacterial disease leptospirosis, (Weil's disease) which infects kidneys and liver and is a threat to humans, is one of the major diseases carried by house mice.

Methods of control range from a variety of mousetraps to chemical poisons. The active agent of the poisons is usually an anticoagulant. There is evidence that resistance to some poisons and bait-shyness, both of which are inherited traits, are spreading in house mouse populations. This is evolution in progess.

Brown rat – *Francach donn*
Rattus norvegicus, Berkenhaut 1769

The brown rat is also known as the common rat, and it is much the commoner of our two species of rat.

The names

The scientific description of the brown rat was written in 1769 by Berkenhaut from specimens taken in Britain, where it had become a pest since the early part of the 18th century. Its scientific name is Latin. *Rattus* simply means rat, and the specific name *norvegicus* (Norwegian) is based on the mistaken view at the time that this species had originated in Norway. The Irish name also indicates the belief that this rat arrived from abroad (correct) but this time from France (*Francach* meaning French), probably during the Norman invasion (incorrect). *Donn* means brown. There are a number of placenames in Ireland that refer to rats, but the black rat is probably meant.

Identification and characteristics

The brown rat is larger and more bulky than the ship (or black) rat. The head and body together may measure as much as 28cm. Adult males weigh from about 270 to 500g, females 250 to 400g.

Despite its name, the brown rat shows some variation in coat colour but is generally grey–brown above and pale grey on the under surface. Some individuals are black all over, so colour is not a useful guide in distinguishing it from the black rat. The tail is long and scaly and is covered sparsely with fur. The scales are arranged in rows, giving the appearance of

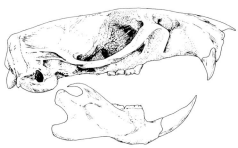

between 160 and 200 rings on the tail. The tail is thicker than that of the black rat and usually shorter than the length of the head and body combined – often as much as 20% shorter. In its normal posture the head is carried much lower than the back, giving the rat its characteristic hump-backed appearance. There are four toes on the fore-foot and five on the hind-foot. Rats move with a variety of gaits. When moving slowly they almost waddle. They usually travel using a brisk scurrying walk or run. At higher speed they may use a bounding run.

Brown rats have the low number of teeth typical of rodents. There are 16 teeth in all, eight each in the upper and lower jaws. These consist of a pair of chisel-like incisors at the front, separated by a long gap from three pairs of molars at the sides of the mouth. There are no canine teeth.

Brown rats' senses of smell and hearing are very sharp – though their ears are relatively small – but their eyesight is poor and works best under conditions of low light. They have an extremely sophisticated communication system that relies mainly on scents and sound. They have an array of glands on the face, the feet and the genitals and the anus. Brown rats are quite vocal and use a range of sounds that are audible to the human ear. They also use ultrasound (sound pitched too high for humans to hear) for communication between mothers and young and between males and females. They have a variety of piping calls, screams, whistles and shrieks. Their true range of sounds only becomes apparent if a bat detector (see page 41) is used to lower the frequencies sufficiently to be detected by the human ear. Their sense of touch is also extremely well-developed and they are well-endowed with whiskers. There are other sensory hairs all over the body. This allows them to navigate through complex unlit environments. When in their home territory they navigate as much by touch as by any other sense.

Distribution and population density

The brown rat is widespread in Europe, southern and central Asia, China, Japan and in the tropics except at low altitudes. It probably originated in eastern Asia or China and was spread by man along trade and commercial routes. It reached Ireland and Britain in the early 18th century (about 1722), aboard ships originating in Russia or eastern Europe, and by 1730 had become a serious pest in Dublin. From this time onwards numbers of the already established black rat declined due, it is believed, to competition from the

invading brown rats. The brown rat is now found all over Ireland and on many of the offshore islands and is our most troublesome mammalian pest.

Population densities of the brown rat vary greatly depending on weather, food supply and time of year. Populations tend to be highest in autumn and winter but will have declined to their lowest by spring. Adverse weather conditions are probably the major factor controlling populations of the brown rat. Rats are preyed on by a number of other species such as foxes, dogs, cats, stoats and barn owls. Most of these, however, are reluctant to tackle a fully grown rat, so the juveniles are highly vulnerable. The brown rat is the principal food of the barn owl throughout most of Ireland.

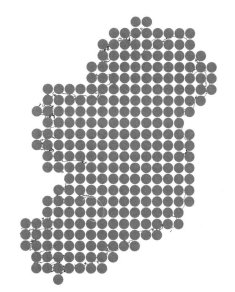

Habitats, diet and habits

Brown rats are highly adaptable and opportunistic animals. They prefer to exploit habitats where food is particularly abundant due to human activities. Brown rats are found in industrial and commercial buildings, on farms, on refuse tips, in sewers, along inland waterways and on the coast. They may also be found in hedgerows, particularly in summer and autumn, when they may forage among cereals and root crops. Brown rats are likely to be found in any area close to human habitation where food and cover are suitable.

Brown rats are social animals and spend considerable time investigating and grooming one another. The complexity of the social organisation of brown rats depends on population density and food supply. Clans defend territories containing areas of high-quality resources such as food and nest sites. When population densities are low, animals range over greater areas and males occupy more or less exclusive territories. Residents are quite intolerant of strangers. When population density rises, because of better food supplies, the residents become more tolerant of one another. This is probably because it is more difficult and less necessary to maintain exclusive rights to the food resource.

Brown rats are good diggers and excavate extensive burrow systems in banks or hedgerows. They are also proficient swimmers, jumpers and climbers. They are almost exclusively nocturnal, but will forage by day when food is freely available. Other circumstances such as nocturnal predation or the pressure of overcrowding may also force animals to become more diurnal (active in the daytime).

Brown rats develop detailed knowledge of their environment. They use regular pathways through their home ranges. These may be seen as runs worn through vegetation, along walls or other boundaries. Where the fur comes in contact with solid objects a dark oily deposit is left. In buildings this produces the characteristic greasy curved smears on main beams at points where they have to deviate to skirt roof joists.

Diet

The brown rat is omnivorous and will eat almost anything but is mainly vegetarian, preferring food rich in starch or protein. It will scavenge meat, fish, bones, bread and vegetable remains from refuse tips. It can be a major pest of stored food, fruit, seeds and cereals. On farmland, brown rats feed on cereals, root crops and silage. They will also take a variety of animal prey depending on location. These include earthworms, shore crabs, snails etc. They may also eat the eggs of ground-nesting birds. They usually take food items to a safe place to be eaten. They are generally wary of novel food items and rarely eat them in large quantities for some time. This habit makes the formulation of rodenticides difficult.

Reproduction and life-cycle

Brown rats can probably breed all year round in suitable locations where food supply is abundant. When in breeding condition, non-pregnant females come into heat at four- to five-day intervals. In general, most litters are born between March and November. Females construct a relatively large nest and may produce from three to five litters per year. Litter size depends on the size of the female and ranges from three to ten. The first pregnancy of the year lasts for about 22 days. The young (pups) weigh about 5-6g and are blind and naked at birth. Their mother feeds them for about 22 days. Males are not involved in rearing the litter.

Females can become pregnant with their next litter before the first one has been weaned. The second and subsequent pregnancy of the season depends on the number of young currently being fed and can be as long as 29 days. Members of small litters usually grow faster than do those of larger litters, and brown rats are usually capable of breeding at about 12 weeks of age. Mortality is high and about 90% of animals do not survive into their second year. They may live for up to three years in captivity.

Studying brown rats

There is probably more known about the behaviour of the brown rat than any other mammal. The laboratory rat is a specially bred strain of the brown rat. It has been the mainstay of the psychology and animal behaviour laboratory for decades. While observing wild rats is something of a minority interest, it is a useful starting point for the novice interested in animal behaviour. Brown rats are mainly nocturnal but in areas where food is abundant they may be active during the day. Grain stores and refuse tips are good areas for studying brown rats. They may often be observed for long periods from a concealed location, unless startled by movements or loud, unusual noises.

The droppings of brown rats are cylindrical, rounded at one end and tapered at the other and are usually dropped in groups. They are about 15–20mm long and about 5–6mm in diameter. The colour varies with the composition of the diet and the time since the droppings were produced. They are usually pale brown when produced and become darker with age. There are four toes on the fore-foot and five on the hind-foot. The footprints are somewhat star-shaped and are best seen in soft mud. The print of the hind-foot is almost twice as long as that of the fore-foot. There is usually a mark made by the tail as it drags over the surface of the mud. There are usually well-worn continuous narrow pathways leading to and from entrances to burrows and along linear features of the habitat. Solid objects along the pathways may be covered with a dark oily substance transferred from contact with the hair. This smear may often be seen looping round obstructions, such as roof beams inside buildings. Mounted specimens of both brown and black rats are on display in the Natural History Museum, Dublin.

Management and control

The brown rat is widespread in this country and may be locally abundant. It can be a serious pest of stored food by damaging bags and contaminating it with urine and faeces. It may be a serious predator of eggs of rare or endangered ground-nesting birds.

It harbours a number of pathogens (organisms that cause disease) that may be transmitted to humans. These include *Toxoplasma*, *Salmonella*, *Leptospira* (which causes Weil's disease), *Yersinia*, *Cryptospora*, and the organisms which cause Q-fever and Hantaan fever. Up to 50% of rats in some populations may carry *Leptospira*, which is excreted in their urine. This bacterium causes leptospirosis, which may be fatal to humans. In suitable habitats, particularly fresh water, these bacteria may survive for over a month. So, where there are high densities of rats, contamination of watercourses may be substantial, and anglers, canoeists and participants in other water sports should be aware of the potential risk.

Control of the brown rat is frequently required, especially in cities and towns, around farm buildings and where food storage and preparation occurs. Rats are neophobic, which means that they are extremely wary of new experiences, particularly foodstuffs. This characteristic is hereditary and can only be overcome by the use of poisons that act long after the food has been eaten, even after several feeding bouts. This strategy attempts to overcome the rats' ability to learn to avoid strange or unpleasant flavours. The main active ingredients of rat-poisons are slow-acting anticoagulants. However, such is the reproductive rate of rats that widespread use of these early poisons resulted in the selection of resistant strains of rats that required development of a second generation of anticoagulants. Signs of resistance to these are now also becoming apparent. In several populations, resistant rats are undersized, indicating that they have not completely adapted to the poisons. However, in some populations exposed to poisons, the resistant individuals are large and also appear to prosper when the poisons are not used. This makes them extremely difficult to control. It seems that the evolutionary battle between the chemist and the rat will continue into the foreseeable future. The best approach to control is through appropriate hygiene management, particularly the restriction of access to food and shelter.

Black rat – *Francach dubh*
Rattus rattus, Linnaeus 1758

The black rat, which was implicated in the spread of the Black Death in Europe, is one of our rarest (if not the rarest) land mammals. There has been no evidence of its breeding in Ireland for some years.

The names

The black rat is also known as the ship rat. Linnaeus first described the black rat in 1758 from specimens taken in Sweden. Its scientific name uses the Latin for rat (*rattus*) for both parts, which makes it the ratty rat. The Irish name reveals the original view that rats arrived from France (*francach* meaning French). *Dubh* means black, so the Irish name means literally the black French one. In Ireland there are relatively few placenames which refer to the rat, but examples are Lachtnafrankee in Co Waterford which means the stone of the rats (*Leacht na bfrancach*) and *Oileán na bhfrancach*, rat island, a fieldname in Co Cork. These almost certainly refer to the black rat, since the names predate the arrival here of the brown rat.

Identification and characteristics

The black rat is smaller, more slender and more lightly built than the brown or common rat (*Rattus norvegicus*). The combined head and body length is usually less than 24cm. The tail is thin and at least as long as, if not 30% longer than, the length of the head and body combined. Adult males may weigh up to about 250g, but are usually less than 200g; females are smaller and weigh about 130–190g.

Despite its common name, the black rat is somewhat variable in colour throughout its range. It varies from completely black to brown with a grey or creamy white belly. The head is more pointed and the whiskers are longer than those of the brown rat. The eyes and ears are relatively large compared to those of the brown rat. Rodents have relatively few teeth and the black rat, like the brown rat, has 16 teeth in all, eight each in the upper and lower sets. They include a pair of chisel-like incisors at the front separated by a long gap from three pairs of molars at the sides of the mouth.

Distribution

In continental Europe the black rat has been found in association with the earliest human habitations. However, it appears that its populations in Europe have ebbed and flowed and it may have gone extinct many times. It probably originated in the Far East in India or the Malay peninsula. The black rat was one of the earliest animal equivalents of a weed. It was one of the first mammals to be spread by man along trade routes from India to Egypt. It is now widespread in Europe south of Scandinavia, North Africa, southern and Southeast Asia, China and Japan. It is also still widespread in the tropics. Throughout its current range it is largely confined to coastal regions. It colonised Britain during the Roman occupation and it has been found in an early Christian site in Rathmullen, Co Down. The first historical reference in this country is an illustration in the Book of Kells (8th or 9th century). It seems to have become scarce or extinct in northern Europe during the Dark Ages (AD 500–700) perhaps due to climatic deterioration. It was reintroduced to northern Europe along trade routes opened up by the Vikings, but, surprisingly, it is absent from Viking sites in Ireland and did not apparently reappear here until medieval times. There are further references and specimens from the 11th and 12th centuries in Ireland. It then became common and widespread in these islands and was associated with human habitations.

The human population of Europe was devastated numerous times by the Black Death during the Middle Ages. It is generally believed that this was bubonic plague caused by the bacterium *Yersinia pestis*, which was transmitted by fleas carried by the black rat. The Black Death reached Britain and Ireland relatively later than other European countries. The first major outbreak occurred in Ireland in 1348, but there are earlier accounts of what may have been plague from 664 AD. Irish towns were devastated by plague at intervals between 1348 and the 1650s. Between the 14th and 16th centuries, black rats in northern Europe were substantially larger than they are now. This may have been due to the lack of competition from similar animals or by adaptation to the somewhat colder climate of the time. In any case, black rats prospered until the arrival of the larger brown rat in the early eighteenth century.

In former times the populations on ships could be extremely high: as many as 1700 were captured on one ship in the port of London at the end of the 19th century. During the 1930s it is reported that over 14,000 black rats were killed in Dublin

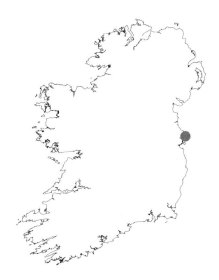

port and its environs, but the infestation rates of ships declined markedly during the 1950s due to improved ship design and more vigilant pest control both on ships and ashore. Throughout the second half of the 20th century, the shore populations came under increased pressure from improved rodenticides to which they are particularly vulnerable. In addition the recruitment of individuals from ships was almost eliminated.

Its numbers have declined in Ireland in this century, and it may now survive here only on Lambay island, off the coast of Dublin. It is occasionally found in ports, where it probably lands off ships. The most recent black rat caught on a ship here was found in Cork harbour in 1990. It is now in the collection of the Department of Zoology, University College Cork. The most recent authenticated record of the presence of the black rat living in the wild in Ireland was the finding of its bones in the food pellet of a short-eared owl on Lambay island in 1988.

Habitats, diet and habits

In wild populations throughout its original range, the black rat is largely tree-living. Outside its original range, it is rarely found far from buildings, except on islands where there are few competitors or predators. In fact, its apparent dislike of open spaces serves to limit its dispersion from small isolated populations. In Ireland, it is only likely to occur on visiting ships or in warehouses and adjacent buildings in ports. It particularly favours cavity walls, lofts and attics where it can climb about in seclusion.

Ship rats live in groups which tend to be intolerant of intruders. Individual rats appear to be relatively sedentary and rarely travel more than 100m from a particular location. They are almost exclusively nocturnal, except when food is scarce. They use regular pathways through their home ranges and leave characteristic greasy blotchy smears on main beams of roofs at points where they have to deviate to skirt roof joists. The black rat climbs well and although it is also a good swimmer it does not appear to swim as regularly as the brown rat. It is extremely agile and can climb along suspended cables, and overhead electricity wires. It does not appear to tolerate the presence of brown rats and in competitive situations usually loses out to its larger relative.

The black rat is opportunistic and will eat almost anything but prefers fruit and other vegetable matter such as grain and seeds. However, like the brown rat, it is extremely suspicious of new potential food items. Black rats studied on an uninhabited island in the

Hebrides had a varied diet that included seeds, leaves, larvae of flies, caterpillars, beetles, earwigs and scavenged sea birds, but there is no information on the diet of the Lambay island population.

Reproduction and life-cycle

Black rats can probably breed throughout the year in suitable locations, but most litters are born between March and November. They may produce from three to five litters per year. The first pregnancy of the year lasts for about 21 days. The young (pups) are born blind and hairless, and weigh 4–5g. Their mother feeds them for about 20 days. Females can become pregnant with the next litter before the first one has been weaned. The second and subsequent pregnancies of the season depend on the number of young currently being fed and can be as long as 29 days. Litter size depends on the size of the female and ranges from three to ten. Black rats are capable of breeding at about 15 weeks of age. Mortality is high and about 90% of animals do not survive into their second year. They may live for up to three years in captivity.

Studying black rats

Even the enthusiast is unlikely to see a black rat in Ireland, except perhaps on Lambay. Mounted specimens of both black and brown rats are on display in the Natural History Museum, Dublin. Pest control companies or environmental health departments are the best sources of information on recent sightings of black rats.

Management and control

The black rat is a candidate for the title of the most destructive and dangerous mammal, apart from man, on the planet. Although it is extremely rare in this country, no conservation action is likely to be taken, partly because of the general antipathy of people towards rats, and partly because of its potential as a nuisance and a health hazard. It can locally become a major pest of stored food, fruit, seeds and cereals, and it causes substantial damage to a wide range of agricultural crops in the tropics. Population densities of black rats vary greatly depending on weather, food supply and time of year but are rarely likely to be high except very locally. However, in countries where black rats are abundant, they are difficult to control due to a combination of neophobia – a fear of new food items such as would be used as bait to deliver poisons – and the development of resistance to the chemicals used as rodenticides.

CHAPTER 7

Order Cetacea – The Whales and Dolphins

Who first discovered whales upon our coast
Such quantities as Britain cannot boast;
Ev'n Donegal produces equal store
To what is found on Greenland's foreign shore.
James Sterling (1701-1763)

About 50 million years ago, in the Eocene period, a group of mammals – who were descended from a group of hoofed mammals that were also the ancestors of the modern cattle and horses – began to become progressively aquatic. These animals were carnivorous and superficially resembled otters, although they are in no way related to them. Eventually these animals invaded the water so completely that they lost most obvious traces of their land-dwelling origins. These mammals were the direct ancestors of the Cetacea, the whales and dolphins. Evidence of the earliest of the true whales comes from Pakistan about 50 million years ago. Recent research in this area has unearthed a fine series of fossils that represent several stages in the transition from a fully terrestrial to a largely marine lifestyle.

Diversity

Living cetaceans fall into two main groups, the Mysticeti (the baleen whales) and the Odontoceti (the toothed whales). The Mysticeti includes all the large whales from the largest of all, the blue whale, which may weigh as much as 160 tonnes, to the relatively small minke whale which weighs about 10 tonnes. There are currently eleven species in this group. Some of the Mysticeti (Baleen whales) have a series of grooves in the throat. These species are sometimes collectively known as Rorquals. The Odontoceti, with 68 species, is more diverse and includes the sperm whales, the narwhal, the beaked whales, the porpoises and the dolphins.

Characteristics

Cetacea exhibit many advanced and unusual features. They are among the most highly evolved mammals of all. That is to say that selection for a totally aquatic existence means that they have become more different from the earliest mammals than almost any other living type. Their fore-legs have become broad paddles. The fingers have become longer and developed extra joints and they are enclosed entirely within the skin and do not develop claws. There is no external sign of the hind-limbs. These have become so small that in some species they exist as small bony structures under the skin or even deeper within the body. The tail has been redesigned, flattened from side to side but with fin-like structures, the flukes, which are horizontal. By contrast, the tail fins of fish are vertical.

The skull is quite unusual. The nostrils form the blowhole and have come to lie on top of the head rather than at the end of the snout. This has required a major reorganisation of the shape and location of certain bones of the head. In the Odontoceti the head is relatively symmetrical and the blowhole consists of the two nostrils. In the Mysticeti the skull is more irregular and there is a single blowhole. The jaws are also different in the two groups. This is related to the way in which they feed. Adult Mysticeti have no teeth. Teeth do begin to develop briefly in the foetus but then they disappear. Instead, these whales have a series of triangular plates, fringed with bristles, suspended from the outer margin of the upper jaw. These are composed of a tough, flexible substance called baleen, sometimes known as whalebone. The sides of the lower jaw of Mysticeti are not rigidly fused together as in our chin, for example. This allows an enormous gape when they open their mouths, to engulf huge volumes of water from which they filter small swimming planktonic organisms. The food items retained by the mesh formed by the baleen fringe are then licked off and swallowed.

The Odontoceti have teeth, usually in the upper and lower jaws but, in some species, in the lower jaw only. The teeth are usually relatively simple conical structures. They vary from two to about 260 in the different species. In most species the teeth are used to catch individual items of prey. But in those species with few teeth their main purpose seems to be as weapons in fights between males. The lower jaws of the Odontoceti are fused together. The Odontoceti or toothed whales also have an enlarged fatty structure derived from the upper lip. This is the melon and is situated in a bony depression in the skull, above the beak and in front of the nostrils, to form what superficially appears to be the animal's forehead.

Most cetaceans communicate by sound and some species have extremely complex 'songs' which are still being decoded by zoologists. Some if not all species of Odontoceti employ sonar to navigate and they locate prey by interpreting sound reflected from objects in the environment, as bats do in the air. A few species seem to be able to stun their prey by zapping them with a pulse of sound, the sonic equivalent of a laser weapon. Cetaceans have relatively large brains and the part of the brain that processes information from the ears is well developed.

Most cetaceans are capable of diving to considerable depths and remaining submerged for a relatively long time. They have a number of anatomical and physiological devices which allow deep diving. Their lungs and windpipe are so arranged as to reduce the risk of nitrogen dissolving in their blood. This can occur under the pressures experienced in deep water. (Nitrogen bubbling out of the blood as a diver comes to the surface produces the highly dangerous condition known as 'bends' in humans.) Furthermore, cetaceans can carry substantial amounts of oxygen stored in their muscles as they dive. This oxygen is bound to special carrier proteins, myoglobin, similar to haemoglobin, which transports oxygen in blood.

Myoglobin is a brownish protein but there is so much present in muscle that whale flesh appears almost black.

All these modifications have to be packaged inside a body that swims efficiently. Therefore all cetaceans are rather similar in general external appearance. They are all streamlined, with few if any external projections. There are no earlobes. The genitals of the male are retracted and even the nipples of the female are located within closed pockets and are only everted when the calves are being fed. Almost all hair has been lost, except around the snout in some species. To compensate and to improve insulation, cetaceans have a thick fatty layer of blubber under the skin. Water provides buoyancy. Therefore, unlike in land mammals, the load-bearing strength of leg bones does not limit the size of cetaceans. For this reason, cetaceans are in general larger than their ecological equivalents on land. For example, the largest marine grazer, the blue whale, is about 30 times larger than the African elephant, the largest herbivore on land.

Distribution

The Cetacea are widely distributed across the globe. Most live in the sea but some species such as the river dolphins may spend most or all of their lives in fresh water. Many species, particularly the larger whales, are widely distributed and are migratory. Others are more restricted in distribution. Of the 79 living species, 31 are found in European waters. Twenty-four of these have been stranded or washed up on Irish coasts or have been recorded from Irish coastal waters.

Studying whales and dolphins

The south and west coasts of Ireland are some of the best places in Europe to see cetaceans. Headlands or cliffs are good searching areas. It now is clear that many species may be seen there throughout most of the year. The former impression that cetaceans were relatively scarce in Irish waters during the winter was due more to the behaviour of the observers than of the observed. It takes a certain dedication to spend hours on an exposed windy site on a cold day waiting for a whale or dolphin. A high vantage-point makes viewing easier and binoculars (7x or 10x) are essential. You need to spend at least two to three hours to have a reasonable chance of seeing a cetacean of any sort. The light is best for viewing whales' blows early in the morning or late in the evening. Patience is essential and expect many disappointments. Watching from a boat is often more rewarding than from land.

The Irish Whale and Dolphin Group is dedicated to the study, conservation and dissemination of knowledge of cetaceans in Irish waters. It collects and collates information on Irish cetaceans and regularly publishes an informative newsletter. The contact address is c/o Zoology Department, University College, Cork. The resource list at the back of this book lists several books and articles on cetaceans, and the National Museum in Dublin has exhibits of interest, including complete whale skeletons.

Conservation

Many species of cetaceans, especially large whales, have been hunted by man, in some cases almost to extinction, all over the world. Whaling stations in Europe in the 19th and early 20th centuries usually operated at different times of the year as the whales migrated north or southwards. There were even whaling stations in Ireland, operating on Iniskea and in Blacksod Bay in County Mayo between 1908 and 1915 and, briefly, between 1920 and 1922.

In view of the danger to whale species, whales are now protected. Some species have been protected for many decades, and there has been a general ban on whale-hunting since 1985, although small numbers of particular types of whale are allowed to be taken by traditional methods in some parts of the world.

In 1991 Ireland declared that all cetaceans would be absolutely protected within the Irish fisheries limit, that is, up to 320 km from the coast. This was Europe's first whale and dolphin sanctuary. The Shannon estuary has been designated a Special Area of Conservation (SAC) because of its resident population of bottlenose dolphins.

The northern right whale –
Fíormhíol mór na Bioscáine
Eubalaena glacialis, Muller 1776

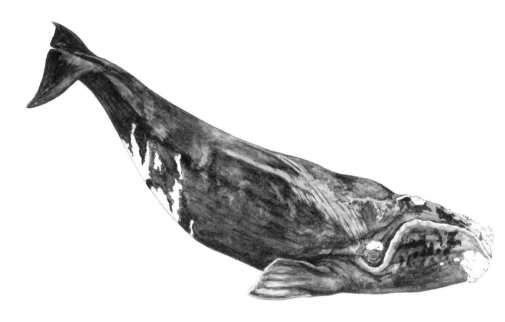

This whale was the first target of organised commercial whaling because it was relatively tame, easy to kill and easily manipulated to shore using small boats. It is now extremely rare in Irish waters.

The names

The right whale is a relatively slow swimmer and is so oily that it floats when dead. Therefore it is relatively easy to kill and difficult to lose. Furthermore it provided a good yield of oil (about 20 tonnes) and baleen (about 1 tonne). It was thus the 'right' whale to hunt, and this is where its common name comes from. This whale was well known to, and described by, the classical writers of the Greek and Roman periods. The first scientific description was that of the German naturalist Muller in 1776. The scientific name is a combination of Greek *eu* (right, good or correct) and *balaena* (whale) and Latin *glacialis* (relating to ice – although in fact it is the related bowhead whale that is truly an Arctic species). Northern right whales are found in the North Atlantic and North Pacific. A related species, the southern right whale, *Eubalaena australis*, is found in the southern oceans. The prevailing view is that there are two

146

species of right whale, the northern and the southern, although it has been suggested that there are in fact three separate species or indeed only one. This whale is known as *fíormhíol mór na Bioscáine* in Irish. This may be loosely translated as the true or right (*fíor*) whale (*míol mór*) of Biscay (*na Bioscáine*), a reference to the long tradition of hunting this species that began in the Bay of Biscay.

Identification and characteristics

The northern right whale is one of the largest whales found in the waters around Ireland. In the North Atlantic adults measure 14–17m long and may weigh between 40 and 80 tonnes. The females are generally larger than the males. The body appears rather plump and dumpy, since it has a relatively broad girth. There is no dorsal fin. The flippers are large, broad and spade-like with an almost straight outer edge. The broad curved tail is deeply notched and its trailing edge is concave. The overall colour is generally uniform, blue–black or dark brown with a variable number of white or pale blotches on the belly. Pale brown and albino individuals have occasionally been reported.

The head is particularly large, almost one-third the length of the body. The snout, viewed from above, seems disproportionately slender. The upper jaw is remarkably narrow and arched, while the broader lower jaw is markedly bowed. There are a number of pale horny growths, 'callosities', on the head, and a particularly large one on the tip of the snout. This is known as the bonnet. Although callosities are generally pale, they range from whitish through yellow to red. They are usually infested with a variety of external parasites such as barnacles, worms and whale lice. The mouth, in profile, is arched upward, well above the level of the eye and then curves downward so that the corner of the mouth is located below and behind the eye. Thus the sides of the lower jaws are higher than the front of the mouth. Viewed from the side, the line of the mouth appears to be curved in a grimace. There are between 200 and 270 baleen plates hanging down from the sides of the upper jaw in the mouth. The plates range in colour from dark grey, through dark brown to black. They are narrow, about 2–2.5m long and have a dense fringe of extremely fine bristles. There are no throat grooves.

The nostrils are quite separate and form two blowholes that are relatively far apart. The most characteristic feature of the northern right whale is the blow, which is unusual in that it consists of two sprays forming a V-shape. These often rise as high as 5m. When swimming slowly, this whale blows about once per minute. Before long dives, usually about 10–20 minutes, the tail flukes are usually lifted well clear of the water. It can, however, remain submerged for up to an hour. This whale is quite vocal and produces a range of grunts and moans mainly in the frequency range 0.15–2 kHz. Most of the communication seems to operate over short ranges and they tend to be more vocal at night.

Distribution

The northern right whale is a creature of shallow inshore waters, mostly within about 20 miles of the coast. Its range is indicated by the hatched area on the map of the world. It lives

in both subpolar and warm, temperate coastal waters of the northern hemisphere roughly between 30° and 60°N. It is now so rare that most of our knowledge of its distribution comes from historical whaling records. It is found in the North Atlantic as well as on the eastern and western edge of the North Pacific. The North Pacific populations are not well known but probably include only a few hundred individuals. The stocks in the North Atlantic are also small. The best-studied population is that of the western North Atlantic, which currently contains about 300–500 animals, most of which have been individually identified. This population ranges along the eastern seaboard of the USA and Canada, from the Gulf of Mexico to Labrador.

There are very few right whales in the eastern North Atlantic and this population may be close to extinction. They formerly wintered in substantial numbers in the Bay of Biscay, along the Iberian coast and as far south as the Azores. They migrated along the European coast from their wintering grounds to their summer feeding grounds off Spitzbergen (Svalbard) and Norway in the Arctic. This was one of the first species to be commercially hunted. By the 12th century an important whaling industry was established in the Basque country around the Bay of Biscay. At the height of the hunt, right whales were being taken at a number of whaling centres in western Europe. Northern right whales move through the waters off the west coast of Ireland from about May to October. Only eighteen northern right whales in total were landed at a whaling station in Mayo, however (mostly caught in June), and none after 1910, so this species has been in decline in these waters for a long time. The map shows where migrating right whales may be expected. No strandings have been recorded in Ireland for at least two hundred years, if ever. Only two sightings have been made since 1970.

Diet

As is true of most baleen whales, the right whale tends to be a seasonal feeder and migrates to the productive sub-polar waters at higher latitudes in summer. It is a specialist in terms of both food collection and diet. It is a skimmer and swallower. It usually feeds at the surface of the water or just below it but it occasionally feeds on the seabed. It appears that most food is caught during long dives (up to about eight minutes). It catches food by swimming slowly with its mouth open through the swarms of planktonic animals, mainly the small (3–4mm) crustaceans known as calanoid copepods. Right whales do not have expandable throat grooves like the other baleen whales but they compensate by having a larger baleen filter formed by long plates attached to the arched jaw.

Reproduction and life-cycle

Relatively little was known of the biology of this species until fairly recently. Most of our current information is derived from study of the individually identified animals in the population of the western North Atlantic. The northern right whale is a moderately social animal and is generally found in small groups, although many recent sightings have been of single whales.

In the western North Atlantic, courtship activity is most likely to be seen in summer and autumn but usually not in the nursery areas, although males may visit from time to time. Male–male aggression is apparently not very common during the breeding season and females are polygamous, mating with several males. Calving occurs in winter in the waters off the southern coast of USA, along the coasts of Florida, Georgia and Carolina and, formerly, in the Gulf of Mexico. The mother-and-calf pairs move north in spring and spend the summer in traditional, relatively secluded, nursery areas. Females often return to the same nursery area each year and most calves tend to use the nursery in which they were reared. The young are weaned after about 12 months, when they are back in the feeding grounds, often in the area where they were born. Females probably breed for the first time when they are about ten years of age. Not all females breed every year and there is usually a three- to five-year interval between births. The average lifespan is not known.

The breeding system in the eastern Atlantic is poorly understood. The precise locations of calving grounds are unknown but they are probably at the equatorial end of their range, in the warmer waters off the coast of north-west Africa and in the Bay of Biscay. There have been very few sightings of cow-and-calf pairs in the eastern North Atlantic in recent years. The problems of finding mates in a population with so few scattered individuals are considerable.

Studying the northern right whale

This species is extremely rare in Irish waters. No specimen has been stranded on the Irish coast during the 20th century. Only two sightings at sea have been reported since 1970. The most likely places to see northern right whales of the Atlantic population are off southern Nova Scotia and in the Bay of Fundy in eastern Canada, and in Cape Cod Bay, USA. In these locations northern right whales appear to be quite tolerant of observers and some information on their biology and social organisation is beginning to emerge. Right whales are relatively slow swimmers and shallow divers. They are much more agile and acrobatic than their shape suggests and often indulge in energetic displays on the surface.

Conservation

The northern right whale, once widespread in the North Atlantic and North Pacific, was the first species of great whale to be systematically hunted. Indeed the earliest records of systematic whaling date from the 11th century in the Bay of Biscay. Apart from ease of capture, right whales yielded large volumes of oil. The long baleen plates were also extremely valuable and used for production of whalebone. (Whalebone, despite its name, is not bone at all. It is a tough flexible material consisting largely of the protein keratin. It was used mainly as a reinforcing support material in such articles as corsets and umbrellas, for example. In the Middle Ages it was also used in the manufacture of powerful crossbows.)

By the 1750s, within a hundred years of the onset of the American whaling industry, northern right whales had become extremely scarce in the Atlantic. Attention then turned to the Pacific stock and removal of over 20,000 animals between 1800 and 1900 also brought this population almost to extinction. The related species, the southern right whale, was also similarly exploited. Between 1800 and 1900 the American whaling industry alone removed over 60,000 animals. The pressure from the whaling fleets of several nations was so severe that within about 70 years, by 1835, it was no longer worth hunting exclusively. By the end of the 19th century it had been driven almost to extinction. The right whale is now very rare and is probably one of the most endangered large whales in the world. The entire North Atlantic population numbers only a few hundred individuals.

All right whales have been completely protected since 1935, but southern right whales were still being taken illegally by Soviet whalers until the early 1970s. The world population of right whales may now be as low as 2000. Continued total protection of this species is vital. The southern right whale may be responding to protection, and populations are increasing in the waters of Argentina and South Africa. The news of the northern right whale is less encouraging. Even the largest population, that in the western North Atlantic, is slow to show signs of recovery and numbers about 500 individuals. It has been suggested that mortality due to collisions with ships and entrapment in fishing gear is significantly retarding the recovery of the northern right whale. Their coastal habitats are also under threat of degradation by industrial activities, ship traffic and pollution.

Humpback whale – *Míol mór dronnach*
Megaptera novaeangliae, Borowski 1781

Humpback whales, although relatively rare in Irish waters, are perhaps the best known of the large species of whale, because of their acrobatic displays and their 'song'.

The names

The humpback whale acquired its name from the habit of arching its back before it dives and the manner in which it flexes the spine as it submerges. Many other whales flex their back to a similar extent, but it is exaggerated in the humpback whale because the dorsal fin is raised on a platform of blubber. The humpback had acquired a scientific name, coined by the German naturalist Borowski in 1781, long before a proper scientific description was available. He gave it its Latin specific name derived from *nova* (new) and *anglia* (England) in recognition of whalers' descriptions from New England on the eastern coast of the United States where it was common. The species was eventually formally described using a specimen that was stranded in Germany in 1846. The generic name is Greek, from *megas* (huge) and *pteron* (wing), referring to its huge flippers, and is perhaps a more apt description than the common name. The Irish name means the hunchback (*dronnach*) whale (*míol mór*).

Identification and characteristics

The humpback whale has a long, moderately slender body. The females are larger than the males. Like other baleen whales, humpbacks from the southern hemisphere are slightly larger than their northern counterparts. Adult females measure between 12m and 17m long, males between 11.5m and 15m. Humpback whales may weigh up to 35–40 tonnes. The skin is black or grey on the back and is paler or even white underneath. The amount of white is variable and ranges from patches on the throat to the entire underside.

The dorsal fin is located on a slight hump about one-third of the body length forward from the tail. Although it is usually small, less than 30cm tall, this hump can be very variable in size and shape and is often scarred. It can therefore be used to help distinguish between individual humpbacks. The pectoral fins (flippers) are mainly white and extremely long, up to about one-third the length of the body. They are the most characteristic features of the humpback. There is a series of knobs along the front edge of the flippers. The tail flukes are broad with a black dorsal surface. The tail has an obvious central notch and the trailing edges of the flukes have an irregular shape. The undersides of the flukes may range from all white at one extreme to all black on the other. They often have intricate pigmentation patterns and a series of scars. Much of the information we have on the social organisation and reproduction of this species is available because scientists can identify individuals from sightings or photographs over many years. The pigment pattern and the shape of the edge of the flukes may be used to identify individuals in much the same way that fingerprints are used for humans. Humpback whales usually show their flukes before a long dive.

The head occupies between one-quarter and one-third of the body. Viewed from the side, the head appears slim, although it is quite broad and it has a central ridge leading to the paired blowholes. The head is covered with a series of knobs or 'tubercles', many of which have sensory hairs. There is a particularly large knob near the tip of the lower jaw. The mouth contains between 270 and 400 baleen plates on each side. These plates are relatively short. The longest are about 70–100cm long and 30cm wide and the bristles along the margin are relatively coarse. There are between 12 and 36 widely spaced grooves on the throat and they extend back as far as the navel. The blow is broad and diffuse and rises to about 3m. Typically humpbacks blow every 20–30 seconds for about three minutes before a deep arched dive, which brings the tail flukes clear of the water. They may remain submerged for three to about 30 minutes, although dives normally do not exceed 15 minutes.

Humpback whales are extremely active and energetic and engage in an extensive repertoire of acrobatic manoeuvres in both the feeding and breeding areas. They slap the water with their pectoral fins or tail and often leap clear of the water, executing a backward flip before crashing back onto the surface (this is called breaching). These whales have the most complex set of sounds of all whales. They produce sounds ranging from long drawn-out snores and moans to high-pitched chirps and whistles (0.5–2 kHz). They also produce higher-frequency clicks (2–7 kHz). The complex sound sequences produced by males are often termed 'songs'. These songs have particular themes or 'tunes' that consist of repeated phrases in a particular sequence. The songs are produced by males only and are almost exclusively made on the breeding grounds. They are probably used to attract females. Members of local populations all have a similar song, although the general theme may vary from year to year. The songs can probably be heard by other humpback whales more than 100km away. Humans appear to have an extraordinary affinity for the song of the humpback whale, which is now one of the most instantly recognisable of all natural sounds. This whale, as a singer, has the distinction of being the star performer featured on a disc that holds the record for the largest number of copies produced in a single pressing.

Distribution

The humpback whale is one of the most widely distributed and wide-ranging of all mammals and is found in most oceans, roughly between 80°N and 80°S, usually close to coasts. Its range is indicated by the hatched area on the world map. This is one of the most migratory of whales. Humpbacks appear to migrate in winter from the polar regions (40° to 80°) to the equatorial end of their range in the tropics (0° to 30°) to calve and mate, returning to higher latitudes in summer. There is a migratory route off the west coast of Ireland used by whales travelling between Iceland and the Caribbean. Six humpback whales were landed in Mayo between 1908 and 1914, but none were caught between 1920 and 1922. They appear to be at home in shallow waters and humpbacks rarely become

stranded alive on shore. There have been only five confirmed strandings on Irish coasts, two about the turn of the 19th century and the latest at Tralong Bay (Co Cork) in 1992. This was a juvenile female that had not yet grown its baleen and had therefore not yet been weaned. There have also been a few sightings of this species off the southwest coast since 1966. The stranding sites are indicated by closed circles on the map of Ireland.

Diet

In spring, summer and autumn, humpback whales are found on their feeding grounds at high latitudes (40° to 80°). Since their prey is both highly mobile and patchily distributed, foraging humpback whales must often travel long distances between feeding areas, which are usually close to coasts. Humpbacks normally feed on swarming or shoaling prey within 50m of the surface. They lunge through the shoal with their mouths open. They engulf a large volume of water containing numerous prey which they filter from the water using their baleen sieves. They have a varied diet. In the southern hemisphere the most common prey are small crustaceans, mainly euphausids, collectively called krill. They also take small shoaling fish or shoaling squid. In the northern hemisphere small shoaling fish such as herrings, capelin, and anchovies also form an important part of the diet.

Humpbacks have a number of different hunting techniques depending on the prey type. One of the more spectacular involves bubble netting. The whales approach the fish from below and, swimming round them, blow sprays of bubbles (bubble nets) to herd the fish into a tight shoal. These are then engulfed as the whales lunge vertically through the shoal.

Social organisation, reproduction and life-cycle

Humpback whales are generally seen singly or in small groups, usually of fewer than five individuals, although large aggregations can be seen on the feeding grounds. Apart from mother-and-calf pairs, the membership of these groups is quite unstable. The small group size has been attributed to the relatively low risk posed by predators – so there is no need for the protection afforded by membership of large groups – and the patchy distribution of food, which means that areas of suitable food are relatively small and could not normally support large groups. Where food occurs at greater densities, as in shoals of herring, for example, then group sizes may be much larger and co-operative herding of prey and feeding can be seen. There appears to be little overt aggression on the feeding grounds, and groups of more than twenty males may often be seen feeding together. Humpbacks may be in vocal contact with many other members of the species that are considerable distances away and not in visual range. For example, songs, which are usually made by males on the breeding grounds, probably to impress females and to intimidate other males, may carry for at least 20km, whilst the lower frequencies may be audible up to 150km away. For this reason, it is hard to analyse the social organisation of whales, as just observing obvious groups is probably not sufficient.

The breeding areas of whales seen in Irish waters (those of the northeastern Atlantic population) are probably located off the coast of northwest Africa. (The northwestern Atlantic population breeds in the Caribbean Sea.) Associations between adult males and adult females on the breeding grounds are usually short-term, lasting only hours or a few days at most. Aggregations on the feeding grounds may last longer but they do not necessarily persist through the long migration to the breeding areas. In the northern hemisphere calves are born mainly in January and February. Mating also takes place about this time (gestation takes about 11–11.5 months). Although some females may mate soon after the birth of their current calf, most females that have just given birth are unlikely to conceive until the following winter or even the winter after that. Courtship is a promiscuous, protracted, noisy and energetic business. During the breeding season, competition between adult males for access to females may be intense, and aggressive bouts of barging and jostling are frequently seen. A considerable amount of intimidation is also carried on through the bouts of singing. Single calves are the norm and they measure about 4–4.5m and weigh about 2 tonnes. They are weaned after about five to ten months. In the North Atlantic, females first breed at about five or six years of age and probably produce a calf at two-year intervals. It is unlikely that the same male fathers successive calves produced by a female. Males probably mature at about the same age as females but are unlikely to breed until they are about ten. The lifespan of humpback whales is certainly 45 years but may be as long as 90 years.

Studying humpback whales

Humpback whales are now relatively rare in Irish waters, although they may occasionally be seen. For example there were two sightings each in 1993 and 1994 off the south and west coasts. The western Atlantic population appears to be responding to the protection afforded since the ban on whaling. It is now a mainstay of the whalewatching industry and in summer humpbacks may be seen at many locations on the eastern US and Canadian seaboard and then in the Caribbean in winter. Only five humpbacks are known to have been washed ashore during the 1900s. The National Museum has a complete skeleton of a humpback whale and a 1:12 scale-model on display. This skeleton, from a specimen stranded at Enniscrone (Co Sligo) in 1893, is best viewed from the first-floor gallery.

Conservation

The humpback whale is relatively easy to catch compared to the other large rorquals (blue, fin and sei whales), but it was never a prime target as long as larger and more valuable whales were abundant. The North Atlantic stocks did not come under severe pressure until the late 19th and early 20th century. But inevitably the humpback was eventually hunted almost to extinction and had become rare by 1920. The remaining stocks in the South Atlantic then became more profitable and came under attack in the 1930s, and over 100,000 were taken in the southern hemisphere between 1900 and 1940. The Pacific whales avoided intensive hunting until the 1960s.

Protection by the International Whaling Commission was belatedly given in the North Atlantic in 1956, the southern hemisphere in 1963 and the North Pacific in 1966. Subsistence hunters took small numbers of whales annually under permit. Thus about ten were taken annually in Tonga until 1978 and about 15 annually in Greenland until 1985.

The humpback appears to be a very resilient species and many of the populations are showing signs of recovery, in some cases by up to 10% per year. For example, the northwestern Atlantic population now contains over 5000 whales and may be as large as it has ever been. But they are still scarce in the eastern North Atlantic. The main threats now appear to be boat traffic and entanglement in nets of inshore fisheries. A joint programme involving fishermen and biologists has dramatically reduced deaths due to incidental catches in fishing gear off the coast of Canada. Southern populations, particularly those off the coast of Australia are also recovering satisfactorily. There is insufficient information on which to base a reliable estimate of the current status of the population in the eastern North Atlantic.

Fin whale – *Míol mór eiteach*
Balaenoptera physalus, Linnaeus 1758

Although it is not generally known, the fin whale, the second largest of the whales, is also the second largest animal that ever existed. It is mainly a deep-water species but is occasionally found in the coastal waters around Ireland.

The names

Linnaeus scientifically described the fin whale in 1758 from a specimen from Spitzbergen (Svalbard Archipelago, Norway). It was at first considered to be a close relative of the right whale. In 1804 Lacepede placed it in a new genus to distinguish whales with throat grooves (such as the fin whale) from those without them (such as the right whale). The generic name is based on Greek, *balaena* (whale) and *pteron* (wing). The specific name is based on Greek, *phusalis* (wind instrument or puffed-up). The common name refers to the relatively large dorsal fin. The Irish name means the great (*mór*) beast (*míol*) with a fin (*eiteach*). It is also sometimes known as *droimeiteach*, which also refers to the dorsal (*drom*) fin (*eiteach*).

Identification and characteristics

Fin whales have a long, slender, streamlined body. The females are larger than the males. In the northern hemisphere, adult females usually measure about 20.5m long and males about 19m, although the sexes may reach 22m and 24m respectively. In the southern hemisphere fin whales are usually about 1m–2m longer. Fin whales weigh between 50 and 70 tonnes.

The asymmetric coloration of the fin whale is characteristic. It is generally dark grey to brown above and is paler or even white underneath. Only in the fin whale is the right side of the lower lip and palate white and the paler area extends further up the right flank. Many individuals have a greyish white chevron on each side of the head with its apex near the eye. There is also a pale stripe curving upwards from the base of the flipper, although it can be difficult to see clearly. Where visible, the shape and pigmentation of the chevron can be used to identify individuals, particularly from high-quality photographs.

The dorsal fin is small, up to 60cm tall, and often slopes backwards. It is located at about two-thirds of the body length back from the head. There is an obvious ridge along the back behind the dorsal fin. The pectoral fins (flippers) are rather small and the tail flukes are broad and distinctly notched. The undersides of the flippers and the tail are white. The body is flattened from side to side from the dorsal fin backwards and there is a prominent ridge running along the back from the dorsal fin to the tail.

The head occupies about one-fifth to one-quarter of the body. There is a V-shaped ridge on top of the head running from just behind the tip of the snout to the paired blowholes. The mouth contains between 260 and 480 baleen plates on each side. These are relatively short. The longest measure about 70–90cm long and are 20–30cm wide. They show the same asymmetric coloration as the head. They are generally dark grey except those at the front on the right hand side, which are creamy-white. The bristles on the plates are quite soft. There are between 56 and 100 throat grooves. The blow forms a shape like an inverted cone and often rises as high as 6m. The dorsal fin appears quickly after the animal blows. Fin whales usually blow two to five times at 10–20 second intervals before rolling into the dive. Long dives usually last from five to 15 minutes but dives to over 250m lasting as long as 25 minutes have been recorded. The flukes do not usually break the surface as the whale submerges. Fin whales occasionally breach by emerging almost completely from the water before crashing back onto the belly or flank. Sei and blue whales also breach in this way.

Fin whales communicate by a series of short moans (20 Hz) that are frequency-modulated, in other words, they change frequency as they are emitted. They also emit clicks that may be used for echolocation. They also use longer lasting (30 seconds) rumbles (1-3 Hz).

Distribution

Fin whales are found throughout all oceans roughly between about 20° and 80°N. There are a number of populations in each ocean basin although there may be exchange of individuals between some of them in the same hemisphere. The world distribution is shown by the hatched area. Fin whales tend to migrate to the higher latitudes in the summer and return to more temperate waters to breed in winter, but they are not such committed migrants as humpback whales, and some populations of fin whales are largely sedentary. For example, the population in the Mediterranean is resident all year round. The fin whale was and probably still is, despite a considerable whaling industry, one of the most abundant and widespread of the large whales in the North Atlantic.

Records from the Mullet peninsula (Co Mayo) whaling industry, which operated intermittently between 1908 and 1922, suggest that fin whales were once relatively common in Irish waters. Four hundred and thirty-five fin whales were landed in Mayo between 1908 and 1914 and 157 were caught between 1920

and 1922. In recent years sightings of fin whales in Irish waters have been more frequent and a group of twenty was seen off the coast of Cork in 1979. A fin whale was washed up at Ahabeg (Co Cork) in 1989 and another at Ballyheigue (Co Kerry) in 1994, where the skeleton is now on display. The dark circles indicate the stranding sites in Ireland.

Diet

Fin whales are fast swimmers (up to 35km/h in sprints) and may dive as deep as 200m. The feeding strategy and diet of fin whales appear to be variable. They feed on krill (small crustaceans, mainly copepods) and small shoaling fish such as herring, capelin and mackerel. They also eat cod and squid. Resident populations such as that in the Mediterranean appear to feed on fish throughout the year. Individuals in migratory populations spend about four months in the summer on their feeding grounds at high latitudes near the polar regions. They may be seen in large temporary groups, containing up to a hundred individuals, in particularly rich feeding areas such as those off the west coast of Iceland. They feed on the surface and filter food animals from the water using their baleen sieves.

A fin whale captures its prey by swimming towards it at high speed, rolling onto its right side and scooping sideways. The roll before the final lunge, which turns the paler white flank towards the prey, suggests that the prey may have good vision. When the mouth is open about 5–20 tonnes of water enter per second. When the mouth is at full gape, the joint between the front of the lower jaws separates with a loud crack. It has been suggested that this noise reverberating back along the jaw bones scares the prey towards the back of the mouth preventing their escape while the mouth is closing and the water is pumped out through the baleen plates. They may require over 1 tonne of food per day.

Reproduction and life-cycle

Fin whales are generally seen singly or in small groups of between three and ten. There is little evidence of long-term stable relationships between group members. There seems to be some segregation of the sexes and age groups during the migrations north and south.

The precise locations of the breeding grounds in offshore waters are largely unknown. The breeding grounds of the eastern Atlantic population are probably around the Canary Islands.

Births are generally thought to occur in warmer waters in winter. However, investigation of pregnant fin whales captured or found in Irish waters suggest that conception and birth may occur as late as spring and summer: a near-term foetus was found in a female captured in July and a new-born calf was stranded in Co Down in June. Gestation takes about 11 or 12 months and a single calf, measuring about 6–6.5m long and weighing about 1.75 tonnes, is produced at two- to three-year intervals. The young are weaned after about seven months, when they are on the feeding grounds.

Fin whales breed for the first time at about six to ten years of age depending on the status of the population. Before they became scarce they did not usually breed until they were about ten, but breeding begins at six or seven currently in many populations. A decrease in the age of puberty is usually characteristic of populations that are recovering from a reduction in size. Where population density is low there may be more food available to each individual and the normal social relationships that regulate reproduction may be relaxed. Fin whales may apparently live for over 90 years.

Conservation

This is one of the species that was most over-exploited in the North Atlantic by the commercial whalers of Scandinavia. Fin whales are fast swimmers but when high-powered harpoons and fast steam-driven whaling ships were developed in the 1860s they at last became vulnerable to whalers. The populations in the North Atlantic were the first to be depleted. For example, almost 600 were landed in Co Mayo between 1908 and 1922. After the North Atlantic populations were almost exhausted, attention turned, in the early 20th century, to the vast populations in the southern hemisphere, and when the blue whales became scarce in the 1930s the fin whale became the main target of the Antarctic whaling industry. Catches exceeded 25,000 per year when exploitation was at its most intense. The decline in stocks of capelin during the 1970s further depressed the population.

It was protected in the southern hemisphere in 1976, followed soon after by the North Pacific. The only fin whaling now taking place is the aboriginal catch from the small population off west Greenland. The recovery of fin whales in the various regions of the North Atlantic appears to be variable, but the entire North Atlantic now holds about 50,000 individuals. It will be many decades before the populations in the southern hemisphere and in the North Pacific recover to their former numbers, if they ever do.

There have been no systematic surveys for large whales in Irish waters but there are estimated to be about 700 fin whales in the waters off the west of Ireland and Scotland. This figure, however, could be as high as 1300 or as low as 350. About 300-500 are resident off our northwest coast.

Studying fin whales

Fin whales are regularly seen off the south and west coast. There were two sightings each in 1993 and 1994. It is now likely that a proportion of the large unidentified whales seen off the south-west coast in recent years are fin whales. Fin whales can be seen more frequently at other locations in the North Atlantic, particularly on the northeastern seaboard of the USA. The fin whale is more likely to be seen in Irish waters in summer than in winter. They do not usually approach very close to the coast so the best locations from which to search are high headlands or cliffs overlooking a fast-flowing channel between the mainland and an island or rock. (See page 144 for more advice on whale-watching in general.) Fin whales appear to be largely indifferent to boats. They occasionally breach. Up to two-thirds of the body may emerge from the water as they jump at an angle of about 45° before re-entry with a belly flop. Occasionally they may twist in the air and crash back on their sides.

At least twelve fin whales have been washed ashore in Ireland during the 20th century. In addition to the skeleton on display at Ballyheigue (Co Kerry), the National Museum also has a complete skeleton of a fin whale and a 1:12 scale-model on display. This skeleton was recovered from a specimen stranded in Bantry Bay (Co Cork) in 1862. It is best viewed from the first-floor gallery.

Blue whale – *Míol mór gorm*
Balaenoptera musculus, Linnaeus 1758

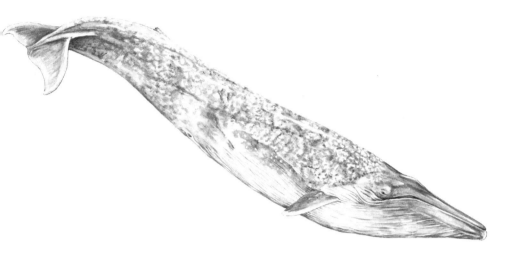

The blue whale is not only the largest of all the whales but is also the largest animal ever to have existed on earth. A large adult may weigh as much as twenty-five African elephants.

The names

The generic name is a combination of the Greek words *balaena* (whale) and *pteron* (wing). The specific name is Latin but it is not clear if it jokingly means "little mouse" or alternatively "muscular". The subspecific name of the pygmy blue whale is Latin, *brevi* (short) *cauda* (tail). The Irish name means blue (*gorm*) whale (*míol*, literally beast, *mór*, big).

Identification and characteristics

Blue whales weigh about 130 tonnes. Females are larger than males – adult females measure about 26m long, males about 24m. As in other species, blue whales from the southern hemisphere are slightly larger than their northern counterparts. The largest blue whale ever recorded was a female, from the Antarctic, which measured 33.5m long and weighed between 190 and 200 tonnes.

The skin is bluish grey, stippled with grey or off-white. The mottling patterns appear to be unique and individual animals can be identified from good-quality photographs. It is often called sulphur-bottom because in the colder polar waters its underside becomes coated with diatoms (microscopic plants), mainly of the genus *Cocconeis*, which give it a yellowish tinge.

Blue whales have a long, robust, yet streamlined body. The dorsal fin is relatively tiny (0.4m high) and is much closer to the tail than in other whales. It is clearly located about three-quarters of body length back from the head. The shape of the fin is variable from almost rounded through triangular to almost hooked. The flippers are long – about 15% of the body-length – have pointed tips and are pale or white underneath. The tail flukes are broad, triangular and slightly notched and they are sometimes lifted clear of the water before a long dive. The head occupies about one-quarter of the body. The mouth contains between 270 and 400 baleen plates on each side. The baleen plates are totally black and are relatively short and broad – the largest are about 1m long and 50–60cm wide. The bristles on the baleen are also black and roughly oval in cross-section, although they may be grey in old individuals. There are between 55 and 90 throat grooves that end at about the level of the navel.

The blow is narrow and often rises as high as 9m. Blue whales make a number of brief shallow dives (as many as twenty) before a deeper dive that may last up to 30 minutes. The back remains relatively low as it rolls into the deep dive and the tail flukes reach or just break the surface. The small dorsal fin does not appear until well after the blow. Blue whales do not usually dive much deeper than 100m. The communication system is not well understood. Blue whales emit low-frequency moans (1-3 Hz) that can travel over 150km under certain oceanographic conditions. They also are reported to use ultrasonic pulses or clicks (20–30 kHz) when feeding. These are probably for echolocation.

It is now clear that there is another type of blue whale. This is the pygmy blue whale (*B. m. brevicauda*), which was first recognised in the early 1960s. The major differences are its smaller size (generally less than 22m); greater weight at the same length, foreshortened tail region, relatively shorter baleen plates and the anatomy of the skull. A major research effort using a variety of techniques (from genetics to acoustics) is currently in progress to find a reliable way to distinguish between the two types at sea.

Distribution

Blue whales are found in deep water along the edge of continental shelves in all the world's oceans, although they may come close to the shore in certain areas. There appears to be very little transfer of blue whales between the northern and southern hemispheres. The world range is shown by the hatched area.

Blue whales migrate annually between summer feeding grounds at high latitudes and winter breeding grounds in temperate to sub-tropical areas. Blue whales are usually the first species of baleen whale to reach the feeding grounds and are often seen close to the ice. In

the North Atlantic they range as far north as 80° and although the migratory routes of the western and eastern sub-populations are different, there may be some mixing in the high Arctic. As the sea ice expands in September, the whales then migrate southward for the winter, towards their breeding grounds, believed to be somewhere near the equator. The range of the pygmy blue whale is narrower. They do not migrate so far into the polar regions. There is one year-round resident population found in a productive upwelling region off California.

The blue whale was once relatively common in Irish waters. The eastern population formerly migrated along the edge of the continental shelf off the west coast of Ireland. Ninety-eight blue whales were landed between 1908 and 1914 in Co Mayo, and 27 were caught between 1920 and 1922. It is now rare in most areas. There have been few well-confirmed sightings near Ireland in recent years, but sensitive underwater recording equipment has detected blue whale mating calls off the north, west and south coasts near Rockall, the Porcupine Bank and south of the Fastnet Rock. Recently 30-50 individuals have been detected off the south coast. The site where a blue whale stranded is shown on the map of Ireland.

Diet

Blue whales feed almost exclusively on small planktonic crustaceans, collectively called krill (mainly euphausids and copepods) found in the upper layers of the water, usually within 40m of the surface. They are relatively selective feeders and tend to specialise in a limited range of species of euphausids and copepods. They probably feed mainly at dawn and dusk when the planktonic organisms migrate upwards to the surface layer of the water. They swim through the dense concentrations of plankton and gulp in mouthfuls of krill-rich water, which they filter using the baleen sieves. A blue whale may eat up to 5 tonnes of krill each day. Most of the feeding takes place for about 120 days at higher latitudes during the summer, when the food organisms are extremely abundant. While in warmer water, individuals of migratory populations apparently feed infrequently, even though plankton may be abundant. In areas with resident or largely non-migratory populations, individuals tend to feed all year round.

Reproduction and life-cycle

Blue whales are generally now seen singly or in small groups, but formerly they formed large herds particularly when in tropical waters in the vicinity of the presumed breeding grounds. Little is known of the current breeding biology of this species. Indeed, the location of the breeding grounds is yet to be discovered. Those of the eastern North Atlantic population are thought to be somewhere in the vicinity of the Cape Verde Islands off the northwest coast of Africa.

Calves are born mainly in November. The gestation period is about 11–12 months, and a single calf, measuring about 7m long and weighing 2.5 tonnes, is produced at two- to three-year intervals. The young are weaned after about seven months. Female blue whales reach breeding age at about five years of age; males probably do not breed until they are somewhat older. It appears that blue whales are now breeding at younger ages than formerly. This situation is often seen in populations that have been severely depleted. Blue whales certainly may live to about 30 years but some may survive for more than 80.

Conservation

Like other rorqual whales (those with throat grooves) such as fin and sei whales, blue whales can swim quite fast, up to 55 km per hour and thus were not always easy to catch. They also tend to sink when dead. When faster steamships and improved whaling technology were developed, blue whales then became the preferred target for whalers in all oceans. At the height of the slaughter, almost 30,000 were killed in one Antarctic season (1930–1). The recognition of the pygmy subspecies was briefly used as a loophole to continue killing blue whales in the Pacific. Blue whales were finally and belatedly given total protection in 1966. Recent information, however, has revealed that the whalers of the former USSR continued secretly to take both blue and pygmy blue whales until as late as 1972.

It is difficult to monitor populations of blue whales but there may once have been over 200,000 individuals in the southern hemisphere. Recent information suggests that there may now be less than a thousand (excluding pygmy blue whales) remaining. There is a long-term research programme currently in progress to obtain a good estimate of the size and status of the southern hemisphere population. The populations in the North Atlantic were the first to be depleted, particularly in the eastern area. There are no good estimates of the current size of the eastern North Atlantic population but there may be about 400 individuals and it is still clearly depleted. There are, however, encouraging signs that the populations in the central and western North Atlantic are increasing. The current world population is between 2000 and 5000.

Apart from man, blue whales have no significant natural enemies except perhaps killer whales and some species of shark. Killer whales can swim faster and certainly kill some blue calves. There is at least one documented case of a school of killer whales successfully attacking an adult blue whale. The usual escape route for a blue whale under attack from killer whales is to submerge to depths beyond the reach of its pursuers. Like most creatures that use low-frequency sound for communication, they are sensitive to acoustic disturbances (noise pollution).

Studying blue whales

Sightings of blue whales are now extremely unusual in Irish waters, although the species is not as rare as was formerly thought. Only a single blue whale was stranded in Ireland during the 20th century. Baleen plates from a blue whale may be seen in the Natural History Museum, Dublin.

Sei whale – *Míol mór an tuaisceart*
Balaenoptera borealis, Lesson 1828

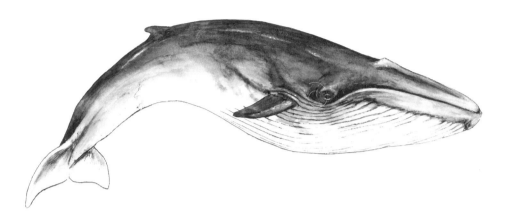

The sei whale is essentially a deep-water species. It is thought to be the fastest swimmer of all the great whales and can cruise at up to 55 km per hour.

The names

The sei (pronounced "say") whale takes its common name from the Norwegian *seje* (the pollock). This is because the whale and the pollock arrive near the Scandinavian coast at about the same time of year in search of the same plankton. The French zoologist Lesson first named the species in 1828, based on a description of a German specimen made by Cuvier five years earlier. The generic name is based on Greek, *balaena* (whale) and *pteron* (wing). The specific name is Latin – *borealis* means "of the north". The Irish name means the whale (*míol mór*) of the north (*tuaisceart*).

Identification and characteristics

Like the other species in the genus *Balaenoptera* (blue, fin, Bryde's and minke), sei whales have a long, slender body. It is, however, a little more stockily built than the fin whale. As with other baleen whales, the females are larger than the males. Individuals from the southern hemisphere tend to be larger than those from the northern oceans. In the North Atlantic adult males typically measure about 14m while females are about 14.5m long, but some may reach up to 17m. Sei whales can weigh up to 30 tonnes. The sei whale is dark grey, but paler underneath the throat and belly. Both sides of the mouth are grey. The dorsal fin is relatively large (0.3-0.6m) and strongly sickle-shaped. It is slightly further forward than in other species and is situated a little less than two-thirds of the body length back from the snout. The pointed flippers are uniformly grey. They are rather small, about 10% of the body length. The tail flukes are broad but relatively small for such a strong swimmer. They are dark and slightly notched.

The head is slender with an arched forehead and occupies about one-quarter of the body. There is an obvious ridge running from the snout to the blowhole. The mouth of sei whales from the northern hemisphere contains between 300 and 400 (but usually about 340 in the North Atlantic) dark grey baleen plates on each side. The baleen plates have a metallic sheen and are relatively short, up to 78cm long. The fringes of the baleen are quite fine and pale. There are between 32 and 62 (usually about 50 in the North Atlantic) throat grooves and they end well before the navel. The external appearance of the sei whale closely resembles that of the Bryde's whale and it is only since the late 1960s that the two species have been reliably separated in the records of the catch and sightings. The diagnostic feature used to separate them is the number of ridges on the head. Bryde's whale has three; the sei has only one.

The blow forms a shape like an inverted cone and rises as high as 3m. When swimming at the surface or before a shallow dive the sei blows every two to three minutes. It blows five or six times at 30–40 second intervals before a deeper or longer dive, of 10–20 and sometimes even 30 minutes. Sei whales slip under the water without much fuss. They neither arch their backs nor expose their tails as they dive. They seldom breach, but leap from the water at a very shallow angle.

They are not particularly vocal but emit a series of metallic clicks that are possibly used for echolocation.

Distribution

Sei whales are found throughout the oceans, mainly offshore in deep waters roughly between 20° and 80°N. Their world distribution is shown by the hatched area. They do not extend as far into the polar regions as other baleen whales but generally follow the typical baleen migratory pattern between high-latitude feeding grounds and sub-tropical winter breeding grounds.

The distribution of the sei whale (and the related Bryde's whale) seems to be determined largely by water temperature. Sei whales are generally confined to water whose temperatures lie between 8° and 25°C (whereas Bryde's whales prefer warmer waters, over 20°C, and thus are not seen in Irish waters). Because of its temperature preferences, its movements seem less regular and geographically consistent than the other large baleen whales and it is occasionally found in large numbers in 'unusual' areas. There appears to be an onshore movement in summer and most sightings are made in summer and autumn, but they are probably present

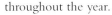

throughout the year.

This species was probably always less abundant than the fin whale. It may, however, be more common than sighting records would suggest, because of the difficulty in distinguishing it from closely related species such as the fin whale and, particularly, Bryde's whale. In the eastern Atlantic sei whales spend the winter off the coasts of Spain, Portugal and north-west Africa. They migrate to the area of Shetland, the Faroes and Norway in summer. Stranding sites are indicated by closed circles on the map of Ireland.

Diet

Sei whales feed mainly in the northern end of their range in summer. They have quite a varied diet and appear to feed on whatever is present in sufficient density. This includes krill (small crustaceans mainly euphausids and copepods), small shoaling fish and even small squid. The distribution of the copepods is patchy and irregular and this may explain the sudden local appearance and disappearance of sei whales. They feed either like other baleen whales, by gulping in large volumes of water containing prey, or by skimming their food off the surface rather as the right whale does. The prey is then filtered from the water by sieving it through the fringes on the baleen plates hanging along the margins of its mouth.

Reproduction and life-cycle

Sei whales are generally seen singly or in small groups. Little is known of their reproduction but breeding probably takes place at the equatorial end of the range in winter. The breeding grounds of the North Atlantic population are thought to be off the coast of southern Spain, Portugal and northwest Africa. Calves are born mainly in November and December. The gestation period is about 11 months and a single calf measuring about 4.5m long is produced at about two- to three-year intervals. The young are weaned after about seven months. Sei whales become mature at about eight years of age and may live for up to 60 years.

Conservation

Like other rorquals (whales with ventral grooves) such as the fin and blue whales, sei whales are fast swimmers and tend to sink when dead. Historically, sei whales were occasionally taken in net fisheries but were not a serious target for whalers until fast steamships and improved whaling technology were developed, but after that they became one of the species exploited by commercial whaling in western Europe, and they were hunted almost to extinction when blue and fin whales became scarce. By the early 20th century the population of sei whales in the North Atlantic was becoming seriously depleted. The attention of the whaling industry then turned to the southern hemisphere and the pattern of exploitation was repeated. When hunting blue and fin whales was no longer a profitable strategy, the sei whale became in the 1960s the main target of the Antarctic whaling industry. At its peak almost 20,000 were being killed annually.

As the population of sei whales declined, protective measures were introduced in the southern hemisphere in 1978. The last catches in the northern hemisphere were from Icelandic waters and there have been no catches since 1988. There are no good estimates of the population size of sei whales from anywhere in the world. There are about 17,000 in the northern hemisphere, most of them in the Pacific, while there are nearly 40,000 in the southern oceans.

In Ireland, sei whales were mainly taken in May and June at the Mullet peninsula whaling station (which operated between 1908 and 1922) on their northward migration. Eighty-eight sei whales were landed between 1908 and 1914 and three were caught between 1920 and 1922. A sei whale was washed up at The Old Head of Kinsale (Co Cork) about 1900 and another at Derrynane (Co Kerry) in 1914.

Studying sei whales

It is becoming apparent that sei whales are more common in Irish waters than previously thought. This is particularly true of the Celtic sea and the waters off the south and south-west coasts. It is likely that some of the unidentified large cetaceans reported from Irish waters are sei whales. For example, eight sei whales spent some time near the Old Head of Kinsale in November 1999. Baleen plates from the tip and side of the upper jaw of a sei whale may be seen in the Natural History Museum, Dublin.

Minke whale – *Droimeiteach beag/ Míol mór mince*
Balaenoptera acutorostrata, Lacepede 1804

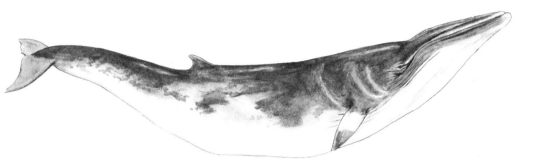

The minke whale is the smallest and commonest of the baleen whales found around the Irish coast.

The names

The scientific description, published in 1804, is based on a specimen from Greenland that was examined by the French naturalist Lacepede. The generic name is based on Greek, *balaena* (whale) and *pteron* (wing). The specific name is Latin, from *acutus* (sharp) and *rostratus* (beaked). The common name for this whale seems to be a corruption of the name of a Norwegian whaler, Meincke. He apparently had the profitable inability to distinguish between the large species which were permitted, and smaller ones, which were not, and regularly overestimated the size of whales, which might otherwise not have been captured. Thus individuals of this species, which is the smallest of the baleen whales, became known as Meincke's whales. It is also known as the common rorqual or the piked whale or the herring hog. One Irish name emphasises its relative size (*beag*) and its dorsal (*drom*) fin (*eiteach*) and refers to its general resemblance to the much larger fin whale (*droimeiteach*). The other Irish name is a direct translation of minke (*mhince*) whale (*míol mór*).

Identification and characteristics

The minke whale is the second smallest of all the baleen whales, although it may be up to 10m long. The females are slightly larger than the males. Adult females measure about 8.5m long, males about 8m. Minke whales weigh about 10 tonnes.

The skin is black, brown or dark grey and is paler underneath. The appearance of the minke whale apparently differs in some details in different regions of the world. The minke whale has a long, moderately slender body and a triangular head with a pointed snout. The head appears pointed viewed either from above or from the side. There is quite a sharp central ridge running along the centre of the head. The dorsal fin is relatively tall and located about one-third of the body length forward from the tail. The pectoral fins are relatively short and narrow up to 10–12% the length of the body. They are dark on the upper surface with a characteristic white band and white on the underside. The white stripe on the flippers is diagnostic of the minke whales in the northern hemisphere. (It is variable or often absent in southern populations.) The tail flukes are broad with white undersides. They are slightly curved and have a small central notch.

The mouth contains between 230 and 360 baleen plates on each side. The baleen plates are relatively short, about 20cm long and 12cm wide. In minke whales from the Atlantic, the baleen plates are usually creamy white with fine white bristles. There are between 50 and 70 (usually about 60) grooves or pleats on the throat which extend backward to a point between the flippers and the navel. There are two distinct, slit-like blowholes arranged in a V, the base of which is continuous with the head-ridge. The blow is low and rises to about 2m. It is quite diffuse and often difficult to see. Minke whales blow five to eight times at intervals of about a minute before they dive. The dive lasts up to 20 minutes and the tail is not usually raised out of the water as the whale submerges. Sometimes minke whales may rest with very little of the profile, the blowhole and the dorsal fin, visible above the water. The vocal repetoire of minke whales is not well understood. They emit a series of grunts and coughs (0.1–0.2 kHz) and a series of clicks (4–8 kHz) that may be used for echolocation.

Distribution

Minke whales are found throughout all the oceans in temperate waters. The hatched area on the world map indicates their global distribution. They usually approach closer to the continental shelf than other baleen whales. They are more common at higher latitudes, rarer in the tropics. Minke whales are not as migratory as the larger baleen whales, although in spring and early summer they are more likely to be found on feeding grounds at the polar ends of their range.

This is one of the most common whales in the North Atlantic and there are probably now between 70,000 and 100,000 still surviving in this population. Minke whales are regularly seen at sea off the west coast of Ireland or from headlands in the west but less often

in the Irish Sea. They often venture into bays or estuaries. There are also regular strandings of minke whales all around our coasts. They are reported to be most common in coastal waters in summer and autumn but may be seen all the year round. Sites where minke whales have stranded in Ireland are shown by dark circles.

Diet

Minke whales have the most varied diet of the baleen whales. They feed at the surface and filter food animals from the water using their baleen plates. They eat more fish than other baleen whales and in fact the main food items are small fish. These include the young of such species as capelin, sandeel, herring and cod. They also eat small squid as well as euphausid crustaceans called krill. In the southern hemisphere, minke whales feed almost exclusively on krill. Although they can exploit a range of prey, the decline in the populations of North Atlantic herring and capelin may have had an effect on their overall diet and their migratory behaviour.

They have a number of different hunting techniques, depending on the prey type. Sometimes they appear to herd or chase fish into a group before capturing them. They appear to drive prey from deep in the water to the surface before they attempt to catch them. They usually feed by rushing through a concentrated shoal of prey, gulping them in as they swim through. This may explain the presence of large haddock, cod and saithe in minke stomachs. The large fish may have been captured while they too were feeding on the same shoals of smaller fish. Minke whales have a rather complicated, four-chambered stomach and, although they are carnivores, they appear to use microbes to aid digestion of prey, much as ruminants, such as deer, use fermentation processes to digest cellulose from plants.

Reproduction and life-cycle

In the North Atlantic, minke whales appear to exist in three or four largely independent breeding populations. Minke whales are generally seen singly or in small groups, although larger feeding groups are sometimes seen, particularly at high latitudes.

The breeding grounds are found in temperate coastal waters towards the southern end of the range. In the North Atlantic, mating takes place between October and March, but mainly in February. The gestation period is about ten months and calves are born mainly in December and January. A single calf measuring about 2.5m long and weighing about 350kg is produced and is weaned after about six months. Minke whales produce a calf at one- to two-year intervals and it is not unusual for some females to be simultaneously pregnant and lactating. Minke whales are mature at about six years and may live for up to 50. Thus, under suitable conditions, the potential reproductive rate is comparatively high for a whale.

Conservation

The only predator of the minke whale appears to be the killer whale. Killer whales have been seen attacking minkes and remains of minke whales are frequently found in their stomachs.

Minke whales were originally considered to be too small to be worth exploiting, although they have been taken in small numbers in northern Europe since medieval times. However, they came seriously under pressure from commercial whaling from the 1920s, and with the decline in numbers of the larger whales, they began to be hunted more actively from about the middle of the 20th century. Non-national boats were hunting minke whales in Irish waters until 1976. There has been a moratorium on killing of whales since 1986, but small numbers continue to be killed, either by traditional fisheries or for scientific purposes, in Japan, Norway and Iceland. These latter two countries account for about 300 to 400 per year in the North Atlantic.

Minke whales appear to have increased since killing has been prohibited. This is particularly so in areas of the Antarctic, where blue whales were formerly abundant. It may be that minke whales are prospering by exploiting food resources that otherwise might have been used by blue whales. The population in the northern hemisphere, however, has still not recovered from the former persecution. It is estimated that there are about 80,000 minke whales currently in the northeast Atlantic.

Studying minke whales

Minke whales are found all round the Atlantic coasts and this is the whale most likely to be seen from land. They are usually found offshore but enter inshore waters in late summer and autumn. They are more likely to be seen off the west and southwest coasts, particularly in August and September, but are usually present between May and November. The best areas are headlands or cliffs overlooking fast-flowing channels between the mainland and an island or rock throughout the summer (see page 144 for general advice on watching whales). Some individuals may be semi-permanent residents in such locations throughout the summer. For example, they are regularly recorded in summer and autumn in the waters around the observatory on Cape Clear island and along the coast of Cork and Kerry. They may even be seen occasionally in Dublin Bay.

Minke whales often feed on surface-shoaling fish which are also targets for birds such as gulls and auks. It is worth observing feeding flock of gulls, since hunting cetaceans may also be in the vicinity. Watching from a boat is often more productive than from land. Minke whales are quite inquisitive and will often approach close to boats. They occasionally breach. Up to three-quarters of the body may emerge from the water as they jump at an angle of about 45° before re-entry, either with a belly flop or headfirst like a dolphin. They do not twist in the air as regularly as the other baleen whales.

The minke whale is the fifth most frequently stranded species on Irish coasts. There is an ear bone from a minke whale on display in the Natural History Museum, Dublin.

Sperm whale – *Caisealóid*
Physeter macrocephalus, Linnaeus 1758

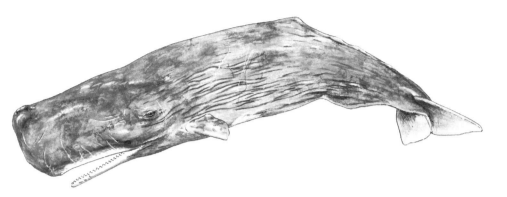

One of the most famous whales of fiction and perhaps fact, Moby Dick, was a sperm whale.

The names

The sperm whale was described and included in Linnaeus's classification of mammals in 1758, although he thought there were four different species. Since 1823 it is clear that there is only one living species of sperm whale and the type specimen is an individual which had been stranded at Berkhey in the Netherlands in 1598. The scientific name is derived from the Greek *physeter* (wind instrument or whirlpool), *macro* (big) and *kephalon* (head). The sperm whale gets its common name from the large reservoir of clear waxy liquid inside its head. This is called *spermaceti* (which means whale sperm, although in fact it is not sperm). The Irish name *caisealóid* is derived from the French name for sperm whale, *cachelot*, which is itself derived from the Gascon word *cachou* meaning big tooth.

Identification and characteristics

The sperm whale is the largest of the toothed whales. Males are much longer than females. A mature male is about 50% longer than a mature female. Adult males usually measure about 16m long but may be up to 18m; females are usually about 11m but may be up to 12.5m. Male sperm whales weigh about 65 tonnes, females about 20.

The sperm whale is usually dark grey but is paler underneath and on the head. There may be pale or whitish blotches on the flanks and the belly. Exceptionally, a sperm whale may be almost completely white. The skin often appears wrinkled and is usually covered with circular scars that are the healed wounds inflicted by the suckers on the arms of giant squid.

The dorsal fin is extremely reduced and appears as a rounded hump located about one-third of the body length forward from the tail. A distinct undulating ridge runs from this hump back to the tail. The pectoral fins (flippers) are short, broad and rounded with a series of knobs on the front edges. The tail flukes are broad and triangular with a deep central notch. The underside of the tail has a well-developed ridge or keel. The underside of the tail is always black, unlike that of the humpback whale, which usually has pale patches.

The sperm whale has a long squarish head which, in adults, occupies about one-third of the total body length. The skull is asymmetrical and larger on the right side. There is a large reservoir of clear liquid wax inside the head. This is used to control the buoyancy of the whale when it is at great depths. It may also be used as a lens to focus sounds emitted for echolocation. The liquid solidifies to a white waxy substance after death.

The lips and corners of the mouth are white. For an animal with such a large head, the lower jaw and the body seem decidedly undersized. The lower jaw is relatively narrow and slender and is markedly under-slung, not reaching the front of the snout. The lower jaw, when the mouth is closed, is almost hidden underneath and between the upper jaws. The mouth contains between 18 and 28 large, conical, slightly curved teeth on each side of the lower jaw. These teeth fit into sockets on the inner side of the upper jaw when the mouth is closed. The lower teeth may be up to 20cm long and weigh about 1kg each in large males; in females they are usually less than 10cm long. There are about 10–11 teeth in each side of the upper jaw, although they are small and barely visible above the gums in fresh specimens.

The blowhole is a longitudinal slit situated on a slightly raised area at the front of the head and is displaced to the left-hand side. The blow is broad and diffuse, rises to about 2m and is conspicuously directed forwards and to the left. Sperm whales blow about twenty times or more, at about 15-second intervals, before diving.

The whale flexes its back as it rolls into the dive and the hump and ridge on the back are exposed. The dive is almost vertical and the tail flukes flip well clear of the water. Sperm whales usually remain submerged for 10-50 minutes, depending on size. Larger whales remain underwater for longer. Sperm whales normally swim slowly (7–8 km per hour) at the surface but can sprint (at about 30 km per hour) for short periods.

Unlike other gregarious toothed whales, sperm whales have a relatively simple set of sounds, over the range 0.1–30 kHz, and do not usually emit whistles or squeaks. Regular series of evenly spaced clicks are probably used for long-range echolocation. Short, patterned series of clicks with variable spacing, termed codas, appear to be used to maintain contact with other whales. Similar codas are often found in different geographical regions and there is a strong suspicion that this may be due to the dispersal of individuals which grew up in the same social group. Beached whales have a distress call which is almost audible to humans. This often calls other members of the pod to assist the stranded whale and thus they may beach themselves also.

Distribution

The sperm whale has a more widespread distribution than all other cetaceans except the killer whale. Sperm whales are found throughout the deep temperate regions of the oceans roughly between the equator and 40°N and 40°S. Its range is indicated by the hatched area on the world map. The populations in the Atlantic, Indian and Pacific oceans are partially isolated from one another by landmasses and distance. Furthermore, the breeding seasons of the populations in the northern and southern hemispheres are six months out of synchrony.

Although they are widespread, sperm whales may be concentrated in particular regions within their range, particularly where colder water comes to the ocean's surface and where food is more abundant. Females and young males appear to undergo small-scale migrations to the equatorial end of their range in winter, returning to higher latitudes in summer. Large adult males tend to migrate further from the equator and are found closer to the poles in summer. Therefore for much of the year the adult males and females are living in different locations.

The larger males tend to appear off the western continental shelf of Ireland during their seasonal wanderings, particularly in late summer and autumn. They may sometimes enter inshore waters. Forty-eight sperm whales were landed between 1908 and 1914 and 15 more were caught between 1920 and 1922 by the County Mayo whaling industry. Sperm whales tend not to be found close to coasts and most of these were killed far out to sea, sometimes up to 400km from shore. There has been an increase in sightings and stranding of this species and in all, 28 sperm whales have been stranded on Irish coasts during the 20th century, 15 of these since 1980. Most of the sperm whales washed up in Ireland were adult males but a relatively young calf has also been stranded. The stranding sites are indicated by closed circles on the map of Ireland.

Diet

Sperm whales feed all year round. The diet varies somewhat with season and location. Overall, the main food item of sperm whales is squid, particularly individuals of large species, whose bodies, excluding the tentacles, are about 1m long. They also take species as small as 20cm long. They will often eat octopus and medium and large fish such as rays, smaller sharks, and a number of species of bony fish.

At the extreme north end of their range in summer, large males may feed almost exclusively on fish. A male may eat about a tonne of food per day, while females require about a third of a tonne per day. Their favoured feeding areas seem to be patches of ocean where cold nutrient-rich waters come to the surface. These are highly productive areas.

Sperm whales hunt mainly in deep-water trenches and may dive down to 3000m and remain underwater for up to an hour when hunting squid, which they swallow whole. They apparently control their buoyancy by cooling the spermaceti in their heads. As it becomes more solid, the density of the whale increases and it sinks. In deep, dark water they probably locate their prey by echolocation but, although their eyes are relatively small, they may also be able to see some of the prey which, like many deep-sea organisms, are bioluminescent and glow in the dark. When returning to the surface they pump more blood through the spermaceti. This melts the contents and makes the whale more buoyant. Although they can perform extremely deep dives, only about a quarter of dives are deeper than 500m. They sometimes hunt near the surface for small squid. When closer to the coast their diet is more varied and they eat fish.

Social organisation, reproduction and life-cycle

The sperm whale is a social mammal and groups of females and dependent calves and young males, under the leadership of a matriarch, are often seen. Female sperm whales are particularly interactive and co-operative and assist injured members of the herd. Many of the individuals in these nursery groups are closely related. Such groups are often termed matrilines since they largely consist of individuals related on the female side. It is unusual to see more than twenty individuals in such groups, but they may occasionally contain up to 50 individuals. Groups of sperm whales indulge in what can only be described as communal grooming. Groups of whales at the surface spend periods rubbing against and rolling over one another, abrading clouds of flaky skin in the process. There is also almost continuous emission of clicking sounds by schools of sperm whales. Some pairs of sperm whales may form long-term, semi-permanent associations. Occasionally, larger groups may form in areas with a high concentration of food. Younger sub-adult and smaller males tend to be found in bachelor herds and do not usually associate with the female herds.

In the North Atlantic population, breeding takes place in the temperate waters of the southern part of the range of the females, around 20°N. The nursery groups tend to remain there all year round. The breeding season appears to be rather extended and takes place probably between November and March, although the timing differs in different parts of the range. During the winter, one or more large adult males may be found in the nursery groups. The turnover of large males in these groups appears to be high. A large male may remain with a group of females for less than a day at a time. This is because he attempts to monitor the breeding condition of the females in all groups in the vicinity by cruising from one to another in search of oestrous females. This is a viable strategy, since it appears that most females in a breeding group tend to come on heat at about the same time.

The size difference in males and females suggests that dominant males may mate with more than one female if he can monopolise access to one or more nursery groups. It is assumed that competition between males is intense; many bear scars of wounds inflicted by teeth during fights. The large teeth seem to have little function in feeding and their primary role may be as weapons. There is, however, some evidence that males are able to assess one another and thus avoid the risk of serious injury. It is possible for scientists to estimate the size of a sperm whale from an analysis of their vocalisations, and it may be that the whales can do the same. After the breeding season the large males tend to become solitary again and often move northwards into the polar seas.

The gestation period is relatively long, about 14–15 months. In the northern hemisphere, calves are born mainly between April and July. Other females may assist the pregnant female during delivery of the calf. A single calf, measuring about 3.5–4m long, is produced. The milk of sperm whales is very rich and contains 35% solids (that of the dairy cow contains about 3–4%). The young grow rapidly and are suckled for usually two but sometimes up to three years. A female may not return to breeding condition immediately after she has weaned her calf, and calves are usually produced at four-year intervals. Young sperm whales tend to associate with a number of individuals within their social group, in addition to their mother. The social groups appear to adopt a babysitting strategy and a young calf is rarely left alone at the surface.

Females mature at about seven to ten years of age when they are about 8–9m long. Males, on the other hand, do not become fully mature until they are about 20 years and are 11–12m long. They do not attain their final adult size of 15–16m until they are about 40 years of age. It appears that sperm whales are now breeding at younger ages than formerly. This is typical of populations that are suffering overexploitation. Sperm whales may live for up to 60 years.

Conservation

The sperm whale has no major enemies apart from man and perhaps killer whales, which may prey on newborn calves.

A number of the body parts of sperm whales were valued highly, which made them a particular target of hunters. The spermaceti from the head yields oil that has been used as a lamp fuel and as a lubricating oil. The blubber and meat have been used as food. Ambergris, a deposit found in the intestine, was formerly used as a fixative in the manufacture of perfumes and cosmetics. Commercial whaling of sperm whales began in the north Atlantic in 1712 and they were extensively hunted for the next 273 years. For example, in the mid-18th century over 700 ships from North America alone were hunting this whale. Even as late as 1964, the annual world catch was about 30,000. Sperm whaling was finally totally banned in 1985.

There are probably now between one and two million sperm whales throughout their world range and there may be between 15,000 and 20,000 still surviving in the North Atlantic population.

Studying sperm whales

Sperm whales may occasionally be seen and are fairly common in small numbers in deep waters along the west and south coasts. They occasionally move closer to the shore in late summer and autumn. See page 144 for advice on whale-watching.

Watching from a boat is usually more rewarding than from land and sperm whales can sometimes be seen from fishing boats and from marine patrol aircraft. Some of the best viewing areas for sperm whales in the Atlantic are in the waters off the Azores. The 28 stranded sperm whales in Ireland were recorded from ten different counties stretching from Cork to Down. There are some teeth of a sperm whale together with a small lump of ambergris on display in the Natural History Museum, Dublin.

Pygmy sperm whale – *Caisealóid beag*
Kogia breviceps, De Blainville 1838

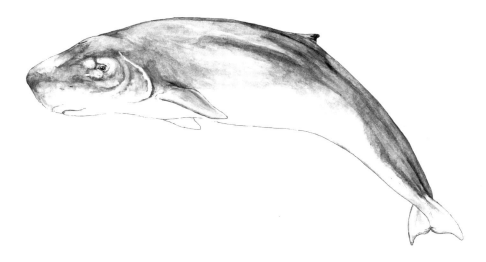

The pygmy sperm whale is one of Ireland's rarest whales.

The names

De Blainville first described this species in 1838 from a specimen found on the coast of South Africa. The derivation of the generic name *kogia* is not clear. The specific name is a combination of the Latin *brevis* (short) and *ceps* (headed). There has been much confusion as to the number of species of *Kogia*. It was finally generally realised in 1966 that there are two very similar species, the pygmy sperm whale and the dwarf sperm whale. The Irish name means the small (*beag*) sperm whale (*caisealóid*).

Identification and characteristics

Although a scaled-down version of the sperm whale, the pygmy sperm whale also superficially resembles a porpoise but there is no trace of a beak, that is to say, the snout does not extend conspiciously forward of the forehead. Males and females are roughly the same size, about 3-4m long, and weigh about 350kg.

The skin often appears wrinkled and is usually dark blue-grey on the back and on the upper surface of the fins and tail but is pale grey or white on the underside. The eye is almost completely surrounded by a pale or white patch. There is also a pale grey or white crescent-shaped vertical mark, called the false gill, between the eye and the flipper.

The dorsal fin is recurved and located at about the mid-point of the body or just behind it. The pectoral fins are relatively long, about 14% of the body length, and have tapering ends. The tail flukes are broad and triangular. The underside of the tail is pale.

The head viewed from the side appears squarish and occupies about one-fifth of the total body length. The head contains the *spermaceti* organ containing a waxy liquid that the whale uses to adjust its buoyancy. It is also used as a lens to focus sounds emitted for echolocation. The snout is short and the front is relatively flattened. In juveniles the snout is less rectangular and more pointed. The mouth resembles that of a shark. The lower jaw is short and is markedly underslung, not reaching the front of the head and is almost invisible, in side view, when the mouth is closed. The mouth contains between 10 and 16 small, narrow, inwardly curving teeth on each side of the lower jaw. These teeth fit into sockets on the inner side of the upper jaw when the mouth is closed. There are no functional teeth in the upper jaw.

The blowhole is situated on top of the head just in front of the eyes and is displaced slightly to the left. The blow is very low and diffuse. Pygmy sperm whales dive with little display, often sinking quietly almost without trace. Very little is known of their vocalisations but they produce clicks that are probably used for echolocation.

Distribution

Since it has only been apparent for the last thirty years that there are two kogia whales and they are rarely identifiable at sea, the extent of the range of the pygmy sperm whale is not

entirely clear. Most of our information is derived from strandings and fishery catches. The world distrubution is shown as the hatched area.

Pygmy sperm whales are found mainly throughout the deep-water regions of the warmer oceans, roughly between 20° and 40° N and 20° and 40° S. They are regularly found outside the continental shelf along the Pacific and Atlantic coasts of the USA, off South Africa, southeastern Australia, New Zealand, Japan and off the Iberian peninsula. There are no reliable estimates of the North Atlantic population. There have been only four strandings of pygmy sperm whales recorded in Ireland, one at Lahinch (Co Clare) in 1966, another at Barna (Co Galway) in 1985, the third in Co Mayo in 1999 and the most recent in Galway Bay in June 2000. One was seen at sea off the northwest of Ireland in 1982. The stranding sites are shown as closed circles on the map of Ireland.

Diet

Pygmy sperm whales are relatively slow swimmers. Information on the diet is derived from examination of the stomach contents of stranded specimens. This reveals that they hunt mainly in deep water but sometimes near the shore. The main food items of pygmy sperm whales are squid, octopus, crabs, shrimps and deep-water fish. One of the specimens stranded in Ireland had been eating squid.

Reproduction

Pygmy sperm whales are generally seen singly or in small groups of fewer than five or six. They probably breed in the general vicinity of the centres of population. Calves are born mainly between July and September but in parts of their range, births may occur also in winter. The gestation period is reckoned to be somewhere between nine and 11 months. The single calf measures about 120cm long. The calving interval is unknown, but some females have been found which were both pregnant and lactating.

Conservation

Pygmy sperm whales are too small to have ever been worth hunting commercially although small numbers have been taken in eastern Asia. They are occasionally captured accidentally in gill nets. There is no information on the current world population. In the more tropical part of the range strandings are quite frequent. In some areas many of these have plastic bags in their stomachs which may eventually cause the animals to starve to death since their digestion is impaired.

Studying pygmy sperm whales

Pygmy sperm whales are extremely infrequent visitors to inshore Irish waters, although their status off the edge of the continental shelf is less clear. Furthermore they are quite inconspicuous and often rest at the surface of the water with the tail hanging down. In such circumstances they are said to be calm and will tolerate the close approach of a boat. They do not appear to be particularly energetic and breach only occasionally. Beached specimens may often be misidentified as sharks at first glance. The skull of the specimen stranded at Lahinch in 1966 is on display in the Natural History Museum, Dublin.

Beluga/White whale – *Míol mór bán*
Delphinapterus leucas, Pallas 1776

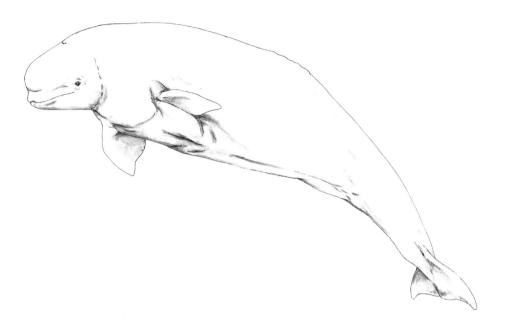

This is one of our rarest and most unusual cetacean visitors. It is a creature from the edge of the pack ice in the high Arctic.

The names
The beluga or white whale was first described by the German naturalist Pallas in 1776 from the skeleton of a specimen taken in a hunt off the coast of Siberia. The generic name is a combination of three Greek words, *delphinus* (dolphin), *a* (without) and *pteron* (wing), referring to its lack of a dorsal fin. The specific name is based on the Greek *leucos* meaning white. The common name beluga is Russian for white. This causes some confusion since it is also applied to the great white sturgeon, which is a fish, and to the caviar that is collected from it. Incidentally Moby Dick, a white whale in the novel by Melville, was not a beluga but a sperm whale. The Irish name means the white (*bán*) whale (*míol mór*).

Identification
Males are larger than females. Adult male belugas measure about 4.5m long and range from 4m to almost 6m; females are about 4m and range from 3.5 to about 5m. Adult males weigh about 1500kg, females about 900kg. There appears to be some variation in size between different locations.

The beluga is creamy white when adult although when newborn they are purple-brown and as the calves grow through their second year they become grey. The colour gradually fades until by about five or six years of age the animals are completely white. The beluga is a rather chunky whale with an obvious neck and a relatively small bulbous head. The profile of the forehead is rather steep and there is a very slight beak. The forehead contains an obvious melon (a deposit of fat and oils) that appears to change its shape when the animal is calling.

Unusually for whales, the vertebrae in the neck are not fused together and so the beluga has a wider range of head movements than other whales. There is no dorsal fin but there is a narrow ridge located about halfway along the back. This ridge is sometimes pigmented. The flippers are short and broad and are turned up at the ends more so in males than in females. The tail flukes have a deep notch. The mouth contains between eight and 11 pairs of strong, sometimes curved, conical teeth in the upper jaw. There are eight or nine pairs in the lower jaw. The blowhole is a transverse slit situated towards the back of the head just in front of the neck. Belugas blow at about 30-second intervals and swim relatively slowly at the surface. They are not particularly active at the surface except during the breeding season.

Belugas are extremely vocal. Their calls often carry out of the water. They have a relatively complex set of sounds and are sometimes known as sea canaries. They use the higher frequency clicks to detect prey or holes in ice by echolocation. The lower frequency calls, squeals, whistles and bells are used in communication with other whales. They become quite silent however if they hear killer whales in the vacinity. Their hearing is obviously well developed and their eyesight is good.

Distribution

Belugas are confined to the northern hemisphere, in the Arctic and sub-Arctic regions. They are widespread, but in discrete populations, in shallow coastal waters throughout the Arctic Ocean and extend as far north as 82°N. There is a small isolated population in the Gulf of St Lawrence and the St Lawrence River in Canada. They appear to be limited to waters cooler than about 15°C and rarely extend further south than 45°N. They may undergo extensive annual migrations in parts of their range. They spend the summer in Arctic and sub-Arctic coastal regions or estuaries. In winter they tend to migrate northwards towards the areas of advancing loose pack ice. They are excluded from areas only by ice so heavy that breathing holes are too widely scattered.

The current world population may contain up to 100,000 belugas divided into about fifteen largely separate populations. Ireland is well outside the normal range of the beluga. There are no records of strandings of belugas in Ireland and only one from

Britain, in the River Forth in Scotland in 1932. There have, however, been two authenticated sightings of belugas in Irish waters in the 20th century. The first was seen off the lighthouse on Clare Island (Co Mayo) in September 1948. More recently, in June 1988, a beluga visited Cork Harbour and was observed close to the seafront at Cobh. The sightings of belugas in Ireland are indicated by dark circles.

Diet

Belugas take a relatively wide range of prey. They feed both on the sea bottom and nearer the surface. They mainly eat squid but they also take octopus and crustaceans such as crabs and shrimps. They also take schooling fish such as capelin, cod, herring and salmon. They tend to migrate to the northern end of the range outside the breeding season and congregate in estuaries in the south of their range in summer.

Reproduction

Belugas are highly gregarious at certain times of year. Outside the breeding season belugas are found in male heads or pods of up to 20 whales or female heads or pods consisting of a mature female and related offspring of varying ages. Mixed sex groups have, however, also been reported. In summer belugas tend to congregate in large numbers on their feeding and calving grounds in shallow estuaries or coastal areas. Females appear to return to the same summer grounds each year.

Belugas calve in the summer but the peak of births may occur at different times between March and September in different locations. The gestation period is somewhere between 13 and 15 months. Mating probably takes place on the wintering grounds or during migration. The calf is about 1.5m long at birth and may be nursed by its mother for up to two years. Many females therefore breed at three-year intervals. Belugas mature at about three to eight years of age. They are relatively long-lived and may survive for over 30 years.

Conservation

Belugas are slow swimmers and are heavily preyed upon by polar bears, killer whales and man. They occasionally become trapped under ice and, without a breathing hole, will die. Their habit of returning inshore or into estuaries has made them extremely vulnerable to over-hunting by commercial whalers. They have also been a traditional prey species, a subsistence resource of the Inuit peoples of the Arctic rim and latterly were subject to local over-exploitation.

Belugas are vulnerable to increasing industrial development in their summering grounds and may be at increasing risk from developments in oil and gas production in the Arctic. Belugas may accumulate pollutants such as PCBs and mercury and other metals to dangerous concentrations; if they were a food item, they would be deemed too dangerous for humans to eat!

Studying belugas

It is likely that belugas are infrequent visitors to Ireland and visits only occur after unusual movements. Belugas are relatively unobtrusive, non-demonstrative and lack a dorsal fin and so are difficult to detect. Sightings of belugas are therefore extremely rare in Irish waters. There are a number of areas abroad where belugas are sufficiently numerous to be readily seen. The best locations for viewing belugas are in Canada (St Lawrence River), Svalbard (Adventdalen River) off the coast of Norway and Greenland (Disko Bay area). Belugas are quite well adapted to shallow waters and this may explain why strandings are so rare. In fact they have often been described as seal-like in many of their habits.

Northern bottlenose whale –
Míol bolgshrónach
Hyperoodon ampullatus, Forster 1770

The northern bottlenose whale is now relatively uncommon but has been recorded all around the Irish coast.

The names

The explorer Forster made the scientific description of this species in 1770, based on a specimen that had been stranded near Maldon in Essex in 1717. The generic name is derived from the Greek *hyperoe* (upper part of the mouth or palate) and *odon* (tooth). This is somewhat confusing since the most obvious teeth are in the lower jaw. It probably refers either to the tiny teeth in the upper jaw or to small projections on the palate, which were mistaken for teeth. The specific name, *ampullatus*, is Latin and derived from *ampulla* (a flask) and – *atus* (provided with). The Irish name means the belly-nosed (*bolgshrónach*) whale (*míol*).

Identification and characteristics

The northern bottlenose whale is the largest of the beaked whales found around Ireland. It has a long cylindrical body with a large bulbous forehead and a short tube-like snout or beak, like a dolphin. Males are larger than females, measuring about 9m and weighing about 7.5 tonnes. Females measure about 8m and weigh about 5.8 tonnes.

The skin colour varies from chocolate-brown to dark greenish brown on the back with lighter flanks and belly. The foreheads of old males are often quite pale or white. Some old females have a white band on the neck.

The dorsal fin is of medium size, usually curved backwards and located about two-thirds of the way along the back. The flippers are short and tapering. The tail flukes are slightly curved without a central notch.

The forehead, which is almost vertical when the whale is mature, contains a deposit of oil which probably affects the buoyancy of the animal, but which may also be used as a lens to focus sounds emitted for echolocation. There is a pair of throat grooves diverging towards the tail.

Older males have a single conical or pear-shaped tooth, at the tip of each side of the lower jaw. These teeth rarely erupt in females. They are about 5cm long in males and shorter in those females in which they do erupt. In some individuals there may be a second, smaller pair of teeth at the apex of the lower jaw. In addition there may be a series (10–20) of minute teeth embedded in the gums of both upper and lower jaws. The tip of the lower jaw extends beyond that of the upper.

The blowhole is relatively wide and is crescent shaped with the horns pointing forwards. It is located in a slight depression behind the prominent forehead. The blow is diffuse and may reach up to about 2m. Bottlenose whales rise fairly high in the water to blow. They generally raise the tail and dive almost vertically. They dive to considerable depths, deeper than 1000m, and may remain submerged for up to two hours, but dives of less than an hour are more usual.

Bottlenose whales may use high-frequency sounds for echolocation and a range of chirps and whistles for communication. Their social calls are not very loud. Their hearing is particularly well developed and their eyesight is good.

Distribution

The northern bottlenose whale is confined to the cold temperate and arctic regions of the North Atlantic. Their world range is shown as the hatched area. They are mainly found in the open sea and deeper waters beyond the edge of the continental shelves. There are two main centres of population, one on each side of the Atlantic.

There is a migratory route off the edge of the continental shelf west of Ireland. They migrate northward in spring and return in autumn. There are occasional strandings of this species along the west coast, mainly in autumn, but strandings have occurred all round the coast. There are no records of this species being landed at the whaling stations that operated on the Mullet peninsula at the beginning of the 20th century. Stranding sites in Ireland are indicated by dark circles.

Diet

Northern bottlenose whales are among the deepest divers. They may submerge to 1000m for over an hour. They eat mainly squid and deep-sea fish such as halibut, ling and skate among others. They also eat starfish and sea cucumbers which they catch on the sea-bed. They obviously have a flexible hunting strategy since they also take herring and other fish found in surface waters.

Social organisation, reproduction and life-cycle

Northern bottlenose whales are normally gregarious. They exhibit caring behaviour and will remain with or come to the assistance of a wounded member of the herd. However, they are generally seen singly or in small groups of four or fewer, although groups of up to 50 may be seen. The basic social unit consists of adult females and their dependent and immature offspring. One or more adult males may also be present, particularly in spring.

The size difference in males and females suggests that dominant males may mate with more than one female. Calves are born mainly between April and May. The gestation period is about 12 months and a single calf measuring about 3.6m long is usually produced at two-year intervals, although some females may breed in consecutive years. The young are suckled for at least a year. Northern bottlenose whales mature at about ten years of age and may survive for more than 35 years.

Conservation

Northern bottlenose whales were hunted extensively in northern Europe from the 1870s, when it was realised that they were a rich source of spermaceti. A number of whaling centres developed to exploit this species in the waters off Norway, off the north of Iceland and in the Greenland Sea. By the 1970s, however, the fishery in northern Europe had become uneconomic. Two factors made bottlenose whales vulnerable to whalers, their curiosity and their reluctance to leave a wounded companion. Their relatively soft social calls are subject to distortion by noise from ships' engines. Although there are no reliable estimates of population sizes, this species may still be in decline in the North Atlantic, since sightings at sea and strandings are reported less frequently than formerly. There has been a decline in strandings and sightings along western European coasts over the last 50 years.

Studying bottlenose whales

Northern bottlenose whales are curious and often approach boats and occasionally leap clear of (breach) the water. They tend to come closer to the shore in late summer. They are occasionally seen in the waters off Cape Clear Island (Co Cork). The northern bottlenose whale is the tenth most frequently stranded whale on Irish coasts, but none have been reported since 1985. The National Museum has a skull and some vertebrae of a bottlenose that was stranded in Co Louth, as well as a 1:12 scale-model on display.

Cuvier's beaked whale – *Míol mór le gob gé*
Ziphius cavirostris, Cuvier 1823

Cuvier's beaked whale, although widespread, is one of the most elusive of the whales and is rarely seen either alive or dead, but most specimens recorded in Europe have been found along the west coast of Ireland.

The names
The great French anatomist Cuvier first described this whale in 1823. His account was based on a skull that had been found at the mouth of the Rhône in France in 1804. It was assumed that the species was extinct and when living specimens began to be recorded they were variously described as belonging to at least eight different species. During the late 19th and early 20th centuries the true identity of these specimens was realised. The generic name is a Latin word, *ziphius*, derived from the Greek *xiphos* (a sword). The specific name means hollow-snout from the Latin *cavus* (hollow) and *rostrum* (a beak). The Irish name means the whale (*míol mór*) with the goose's (*an gé*) beak (*gob*).

Identification and characteristics
Cuvier's beaked whale is one of the most widespread and morphologically variable of the beaked whales. It is a heavily built, cigar-shaped whale with a sloping slightly concave

forehead and a short, poorly defined beak. The lower jaw is slightly protruding. The appearance of the beak gives rise to an alternative name, the goosebeak(ed) whale. The line of the mouth viewed from the side curves downward between the tip of the snout and the corner of the mouth. Females may be slightly larger than males but the average size of sexes is just over 6m. Adults weigh from about 2500 to 3000kg.

The colour is extremely variable. The skin is usually grey or blue-grey. The head is paler, often almost white, in older individuals. There are cream or white spots or blotches on the sides and belly. The basic colour of sub-adults can, however, range from cream through various shades of brown through blue-grey to almost black. The skin also usually has many linear scars on the back and sides and circular scars mainly on the undersides.

The relatively small dorsal fin is variable in size and shape. It ranges from triangular to sickle-shaped and is located about two-thirds of the way along the back. The flippers are small and narrow with a pointed tip and may be tucked into shallow depressions in the flanks. The tail flukes are relatively large, curved and a very slight notch may sometimes be present. The tail flukes may be exposed when the whale dives.

The mouth contains a pair of projecting conical teeth at the tip of the lower jaw only. These do not erupt in females, although they are clearly visible in a cleaned lower jawbone.

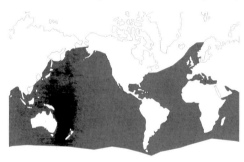

The throat, between the lower jaws, has a pair of shallow grooves. The blowhole is crescent-shaped and is offset slightly to the left. It is situated in front of a slight but obvious depression or hollow which is referred to in the scientific name. The blow is low, relatively gentle and directed slightly forwards and to the left. It occurs at about 20-second intervals before the whale arches its back and rolls gently into the almost vertical dive. Dives may last for 20–40 minutes. Little is known of their communication system. Their hearing is particularly well developed and their eyesight is good.

Distribution

Cuvier's beaked whales are probably found in all oceans and seas worldwide, except the polar seas. The world distribution is shown as the hatched area. Most of our information is derived from stranded specimens. Cuvier's beaked whales are rarely seen at sea and tend to avoid vessels by diving quietly. They are mainly found in open waters and thus are not seen close to the shore, except where the water is deep. They are probably more common in Irish waters than records would suggest. There have been two confirmed sightings of this species at sea in recent years, both off the coast of Cork. Strandings of this species are also rare, but quite frequent for a beaked whale, and most European records come from Ireland. Four were stranded in spring 2000. These Irish specimens were found mainly on the west coast and are indicated by dark circles on the map of Ireland.

Diet

Few stomachs have been examined and so our knowledge of the diet is unsatisfactory. What information exists suggests that Cuvier's beaked whales feed mainly on a variety of species of squid and deep-sea fish. They also eat crabs and starfish.

Reproduction and life-cycle

Cuvier's beaked whales are generally seen singly or in groups containing usually fewer than five individuals. They appear to form mixed-sex groups but there is little information on the social organisation of this species. There is no detailed information on their breeding biology. They may breed throughout the year since there does not appear to be a definite calving season. Newborn calves measure about 2.7m. Cuvier's beaked whales may live for about 35 years.

Conservation

This species has never been systematically hunted, although there were formerly small-scale fisheries in Japan, the Lesser Antilles and the Mediterranean. The current world population of Cuvier's beaked whale is unknown.

Studying Cuvier's beaked whale

A sighting of a deep-water species such as Cuvier's beaked whale is most unlikely. It rarely approaches close to boats and does not often jump clear of (breach) the water. When at the surface, it has been reported to hold its chin slightly out of the water. It has been suggested that one is more likely to see Cuvier's whale from a ship by looking astern. It is capable of remaining submerged for up to 30 minutes. Despite the difficulty in observing Cuvier's beaked whale alive, it is the ninth most common species stranded on Irish coasts. The National Museum has, on exhibit, the skull of a Cuvier's beaked whale that was stranded at Slyne Head (Co Galway).

Gervais' beaked whale –
Miol mór gobach na h-Eorpa
Mesoplodon europaeus, Gervais 1855

Gervais' beaked whale is one of the least known of all the whales. Only two specimens have ever been recorded in Europe and the only complete specimen from Europe was found in Co Sligo.

The names

This whale has rarely been positively identified alive in the wild. It is so rare that the first ten specimens ever found were all given different names and were not identified correctly until 1960. The generic name Mesoplodon is composed of three Greek words, *mesos* (middle), *hopla* (weapons) and *odontos* (tooth). The Latin specific name means European. This part of the name is totally inappropriate. Although the first specimen to be properly described was found in Europe, it happened to be well outside the normal range of the species. This animal had been carried to the English Channel by the Gulf Stream and was found floating near the French coast. It was described by the French palaeontologist from whom it gets its English name. It is sometimes referred to as the Gulf Stream beaked whale. The Irish name means the beaked (*gobach*) whale (*míol mór*) from Europe (*Eorpa*).

Identification

Gervais' beaked whale is small but heavily built, with a slightly bulbous, sloping forehead and a sharp, narrow beak. Unusually for whales, the body is somewhat compressed from side to side. The lower jaw is slightly protruding. It is assumed that females and males are about the same size, although females may be slightly larger. Adults are from 4 to 5m long and weigh about 1200kg.

The skin is uniformly dark grey or blue-grey but paler on the underside with white blotches near the genital opening. The belly of juveniles is white. The overall colour tends to become darker after death. The dorsal fin is small, triangular, shark-like and located about two-thirds of the way along the back. The flippers are small and narrow and are almost on the ventral surface of the body and may be withdrawn into a shallow depression on the body wall. The tail flukes are curved without a notch. The blowhole is located in a shallow depression.

The mouth contains a pair of flat triangular teeth, one in each side of the lower jaw, about one-third of the way along the margin of the mouth from the tip of the jaw. The teeth may not always erupt sufficiently to be visible above the gum in a female. In a skeleton the teeth are located about 15% of the distance along the lower jaw, that is about 7–10cm from the tip. The teeth are deflected outwards like tusks and fit into recesses on the outer edge of the upper

lip. They are visible when the mouth is closed. Like all Mesoplodon whales there are two throat grooves between the lower jaws. Virtually nothing is known of their communication system.

Distribution

This whale has rarely been positively identified at sea since it closely resembles a number of other beaked whales. Gervais' beaked whales are probably usually confined to deep waters of warm temperate and subtropical areas of the Atlantic, mainly north of the equator, between Venezuela and New York. It is unlikely to be a shallow-water species since otherwise it would readily be seen close to coasts.

Of the Mesoplodon whales, it is the most commonly found stranded along the east coast of North and Central America. Nevertheless, there are only about 100 records of this whale from the Atlantic coast of North America. Only two strandings of this species have ever been recorded in Europe and three more from West Africa. It is likely that the two European specimens came northwestwards on the Gulf Stream. The first of these was in found in the 1840s in the English Channel. Unfortunately this specimen was seriously damaged during the bombing of Caen in France during 1944. The second specimen, a male just over 4m long, was found in Ballysodare Bay (Co Sligo) in 1989, indicated by the dark circle on the map of Ireland.

Diet

Beaked whales have quite complicated stomachs that are divided into a number of chambers. It appears that Gervais' beaked whale is a relatively deep diver and, like other beaked whales, feeds mainly on squid, although fish may also be taken. Information on the diet is rather scarce since it is derived from analysis of the stomach contents of the occasional stranded specimens. Unfortunately the stomach of the Sligo specimen was empty.

Reproduction

Almost nothing is known of the social organisation or breeding of Gervais' beaked whales. It is rarely seen, even in the subtropical regions of the North Atlantic, the centre of its range. This suggests that it is not highly social and may be largely solitary, except for pairs of females and dependent young. Scarring on the skin of males may be due to conflict during the breeding season. The teeth that project even while the mouth is closed probably inflict the wounds. The teeth clearly have no role in food capture. It is likely that breeding takes place in winter. Females come into breeding condition when about 4.5m long. The duration of gestation is not known but the young are about 2.1m long at birth. This whale can live for at least 27 years.

Conservation

Gervais' beaked whale has never been subjected to systematic hunting on a wide scale since it is so unobtrusive and dispersed. Almost nothing is known of the current world population and this species will always be an extremely rare visitor to Irish waters.

Studying Gervais' beaked whale

The probability of seeing this whale in the wild even in the centre of its range is fairly remote so a sighting in Ireland is extremely unlikely. Only one specimen has ever been found stranded in Ireland. This specimen provided the only intact skeleton of this species in Europe. This is now in the collection of the Ulster Museum in Belfast.

Sowerby's beaked whale – *Míol mór gobach an tuaisceart*
Mesoplodon bidens, Sowerby 1804

Sowerby's beaked whale is occasionally stranded off Irish coasts.

The names
Sowerby's beaked whale is named after the English naturalist and painter who first described a specimen stranded in the Moray Firth in Scotland in 1800. It is also called the North Sea beaked whale, referring to the assumed centre of its range. The generic name is derived from Greek, *mesos* (middle), *hopla* (weapons) and *odontos* (tooth). The specific name is derived from Latin *bi* (two) and *dens* (tooth). The Irish name means the beaked (*gobach*) whale (*míol mór*) of the north (*tuaisceart*).

Identification and characteristics
Like all Mesoplodon whales, Sowerby's beaked whales are small. Female and male Sowerby's beaked whales are about the same size. They measure about 4–5.5m and weigh about 3 to 4 tonnes. This whale has a long, tapering body with a sloping, slightly bulging forehead and moderately long, well defined beak. The lower jaw is slightly protruding.

The skin is dark grey on the back and flanks and paler on the belly. The head may be sandy grey. There are light spots on the back, sides and belly. The colour becomes darker and less patterned after death.

The dorsal fin is small and triangular and is located about two-thirds of the way along the back. The flippers are small (but relatively long for a beaked whale), about 12% of the body length, and are rounded with a pointed tip. The tail flukes are slightly curved without a central notch.

There is a single flat triangular tooth in the lower jaw, mid-way along each side of the mouth. These teeth may be concealed just below the surface of the gum in adult females and juveniles. In males they are directed outwards and may be evident when the mouth is closed. On a clean skeleton the teeth are located about one-third of the way along the jawbone, about 30cm from the tip. There is a pair of grooves in the throat between the lower jaws.

Sowerby's beaked whales are quite unobtrusive in the wild and appear to be shy of boats. They spend about a minute at the surface and the blow is very gentle, the dive is smooth and the tail does not break the surface. They may remain submerged for up to 15 minutes. They are fast swimmers.

Little is known of their communication system but they use high-frequency ultrasound

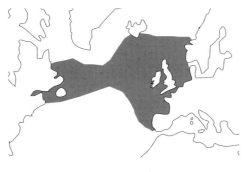

for echolocation. Their hearing is particularly well developed and their eyesight is good.

Distribution

Sowerby's beaked whale has the most northerly distribution of the beaked whales and is confined to the cooler temperate regions of the north Atlantic. The world distribution is shown as the hatched area. Most records of stranded individuals come from northwestern Europe (almost a hundred cases) and the eastern Canadian coast (about ten cases). The centre of the population is probably in the eastern North Atlantic or North Sea. A single specimen has been found in Italy, but it is not yet clear if it is usually present in the Mediterranean. Sowerby's beaked whales are mainly confined to the open sea and deep waters and, although considered to be relatively common, they are rarely seen at sea. No reliable estimates of population sizes are available. They are probably more common in Irish waters than records would suggest. There have been a number of strandings of this species along the west coast. These are indicated by the dark circles on the map of Ireland.

Diet

Information on the diet is derived mainly from the stomach contents of stranded specimens. Little is known of the diet of Sowerby's beaked whales, except that they appear to feed mainly on small squid in offshore waters but will also take fish. They may move southward from the most northerly parts of their range during winter. There may also be a shoreward movement in summer.

Reproduction and life-cycle

Sowerby's beaked whales, although they may be common, are so rarely seen that virtually nothing is known of their social organisation or reproduction. They appear to be largely solitary or to travel in pairs or in small groups, consisting of a female with dependent young. Most strandings have been single animals, rarely pairs.

Males fight for access to females and adult males usually bear scars inflicted by the tusk-like teeth. Births and matings appear to occur in the late winter and the early months of the year. Calves are about 2.4m long at birth. The lifespan of Sowerby's whale is not known for certain but some stranded specimens were about 35 years old when they died.

Conservation

There is no information on the current population size. This species has rarely been subject to a regular and systematic hunt, although they were formerly hunted on a small scale in Newfoundland.

Studying Sowerby's beaked whale

The probability of seeing Sowerby's beaked whale alive in Irish waters is small. Only three strandings have been recorded on Irish coasts during the 20th century. The skull of a specimen stranded in Brandon Bay (Co Kerry) is on display in the Natural History Museum, Dublin and there are also specimens in the Ulster Museum, Belfast.

True's beaked whale –
Míol mór gobach le clár-fiacla
Mesoplodon mirus, True 1913

True's beaked whale was first photographed in the wild as recently as 1993. Most of the European records of this species come from the west coast of Ireland. Little is known of the biology of True's beaked whale. In fact it was first photographed in the wild as recently as 1993. Nevertheless most of the European records of this species come from the west coast of Ireland.

The names

The common name of this whale commemorates the American mammalogist True who first described this species in 1913, from a specimen stranded in North Carolina, USA. The generic name is derived from Greek, *mesos* (middle), *hopla* (weapons) and *odontos* (tooth). True gave it the Latin specific name *mirus* (wonderful) because he was so delighted at having discovered a new species. The Irish name means the beaked (*gobach*) whale (*míol mór*) with the flat teeth (*clár-fiacla*).

Identification and characteristics

True's beaked whale is a heavily built animal with a long, tapering body. It has a sloping, slightly bulging forehead with a long slender beak. The lower jaw is slightly protruding. Females and males are about the same size, from 4.9m to 5.5m long and weigh about 1400kg.

The skin is light grey or blue-grey on the back, lighter on the sides and paler grey on the belly. There is a dark patch around the eyes. There are light spots or mottled patches on the belly and a dark stripe across the back and the dorsal fin is black. Most illustrations of True's beaked whale were based on dead specimens and show the overall colour as darker than in the living animal. This is because the skin colour darkens after death. The skin also usually has linear scars on the back and sides.

The dorsal fin is triangular or slightly sickle-shaped and is located about two-thirds of the way along the back. The head is about one-fifth of the total body length. The mouth contains two flattened teeth projecting forward at the extreme tip of the lower jaw only. These are present but do not erupt in females. The flippers are small and narrow and set fairly low down on the flanks and each may be folded flat into a shallow recess in the body wall. The tail flukes are pointed and curved along the trailing edge and do not have a central notch. Little is known of their communication system.

Distribution

True's beaked whales are probably found in all oceans except the polar seas. The world range is shown as the hatched area. Strandings indicate centres of population along the eastern seaboard of Canada and USA, off the west and south coasts of Ireland, off South Africa and along the south coast of Australia. True's beaked whales appear to be mainly confined to deep

waters and have rarely been positively identified at sea and never in the North Atlantic, although it is believed that the main centre of population is there. Only ten strandings have been recorded in Europe and seven of these were on the west coast of Ireland between Mayo and Kerry. They are probably more common in Irish waters than records would suggest. Sites of strandings are shown as dark circles on the map of Ireland.

Diet

True's beaked whales, in the absence of evidence to the contrary, are presumed to feed in deep offshore waters. Examination of the stomach contents has revealed that they feed mainly on squid and deep-water fish.

Reproduction

Nothing is known of their social organisation or breeding but they are probably largely solitary or associate in small groups. Males presumably fight for access to females, raking one another with their projecting teeth and inflicting the characteristic long linear scars. There is almost no information on their breeding season. A mother with a calf, two metres long, was seen in March, indicating that births occur in spring.

Conservation
True's beaked whale has never been a target for organised whaling because of its dispersed distribution and its size. There is no reliable information on population size.

Studying True's beaked whale
The chance of seeing this species is extremely remote and it is in any case almost impossible to identify it positively at sea. The skull of a specimen of True's beaked whale stranded at Valencia Island (Co Kerry) in 1935 and the tip of the lower jaw of another specimen from Louisburg (Co Mayo) are on display in the Natural History Museum, Dublin.

Common (harbour) porpoise – *Much mhara*
Phocaena phocaena, Linnaeus 1758

The common or harbour porpoise is the smallest and most common cetacean in Irish waters and probably the most abundant cetacean in the northeast Atlantic.

The names

The scientific description of the harbour porpoise is that of Linnaeus, 1758, based on a specimen stranded on the Swedish coast. The scientific name is the Greek word for porpoise (*phocaena*). Many common names refer to a similarity between the porpoise and the pig. This is probably because it builds up substantial amounts of fat in the blubber layer under the skin. In fact the English name 'porpoise' is a corruption of the Roman name *porcus* (pig) *piscis* (fish). The Irish name is the pig (*much*) of the sea (*mhara*).

Identification

The harbour porpoise is a stoutly built, rotund animal with a blunt snout and little or no external evidence of a beak. (A short beak is clearly evident on the skull.) Females are slightly larger than males. Males measure about 1.5m long, females about 1.7m. Weight ranges on average from 45kg to 65kg.

The upper surface of the body is dark grey. The flanks are lighter grey, giving the impression of a large pale patch on the sides. The belly is white. There is a narrow grey line from the flippers to the rear of the mouth. White individuals are occasionally recorded. One was accidentally caught off Dingle (Co Kerry) in 1988.

The dorsal fin is small and triangular and is located halfway along the back. The flippers are short with rounded ends and are located about one quarter of the body length back from the head. The tail flukes are curved with a deep notch and are dark. The blowhole is situated

on top of the head. The mouth contains between 19 and 28 small flattened teeth on both sides of the upper and lower jaw.

They have a moderately complex set of sounds that are used for echolocation and for communication with other porpoises. Their hearing is particularly well developed and their eyesight is good.

Distribution

Common porpoises are found in cool, temperate offshore and coastal waters in the northern hemisphere. The world distribution is shown by the hatched areas. They are found along the north Pacific Rim from California westward to Japan. In the western North Atlantic they range from the Carolinas northwards to Greenland and Iceland. In the eastern Atlantic they are found from Senegal in West Africa as far north as the Arctic coast of Russia. They are typically inshore animals and are usually found within 10km of the shore, often in sea-loughs, bays, harbours, estuaries and large rivers. Several European populations are in serious decline, particularly those in the Baltic, the Mediterranean and the eastern end of the North Sea and the English Channel.

The populations off the west coasts of Ireland and Scotland are now of major significance. They are also widespread in the Irish Sea. Indeed, the earliest record of the porpoise in Ireland comes from a Mesolithic kitchen midden, dating from about 5000–6000 years ago, at Rockmarshall (Co Louth). Its remains are also found in later settlements, including deposits in Wexford town dating from late Viking times (about 900–1000 years ago). Stranding sites are shown as dark circles on the map of Ireland.

Diet

The composition of the diet varies in different parts of the range. Common porpoises feed on a wide variety of fish, including saithe, mackerel, herring, sandeel, whiting and flatfish. They also take cuttlefish, squid and crustaceans when available. Younger animals may eat small planktonic crustaceans (krill). In Irish waters, fish of the cod family, mainly poor cod and whiting, represent between 70% and 90% of the diet, and fish of the herring family, mainly sprat, represent between 10% and 20% of the diet. Porpoises tend to follow sprat and herring as they migrate down to deeper water during the day and come closer to the surface at night. They sometimes hunt the same food as hake and thus are accidentally taken in hake fisheries. Recently, porpoises appear to be taking more of the smaller non-commercial species of fish such as poor-cod and Norway pout. They may eat food totalling 10% of their body weight each day.

It is not known how far individual porpoises wander, but some resident individuals probably have relatively small home ranges. However, they tend to migrate offshore and northwards in winter, returning nearer the coast in summer. There appears to be a general northward migration of porpoises in Irish waters during autumn that is probably related to movements of mackerel and herring. Heavily pregnant females are sometimes accidentally caught in fishing nets in spring.

Reproduction

Common porpoises are generally seen singly or in small groups of up to ten. About three-quarters of sightings consist of fewer than three individuals. Occasionally groups as large as 30 may be seen, often in areas with high food density.

Mating takes place mainly between June and September in Irish waters. The gestation period is about 11 months and a single calf measuring about 70–80 cm is produced, between May and July, usually in inshore waters. There is a major breeding or nursery area off the southwest coast, although very young porpoises may also be seen around Dublin Bay and off the northeast coast. The young are relatively large and may weigh over a quarter of the adult weight at birth. They are suckled for about eight months and grow rapidly. Common porpoises become sexually mature at about three to four years of age and may live for between 15 and 20 years. Female porpoises give birth at about two- to four-year intervals.

Conservation

Common porpoise were probably regularly hunted in Ireland from ancient times and as late as the 18th century porpoise meat from Ireland was exported to England. The present population of porpoises off the Irish coasts is unknown, but it is estimated that there are between 30,000 and 50,000 individuals in the waters between Rosslare and Galway Bay.

Common porpoises have a relatively low reproductive rate and a relatively short lifespan. Their local distribution adds to their vulnerability. It is believed that the decline in parts of their range is due to a combination of coastal pollution, decline in food supply from overfishing and entrapment and accidental drowning in monofilament fishing nets. Between 1000 and 2000 porpoises are accidentally killed annually in the Celtic Sea by entanglement in gill nets set on or near the sea bottom to catch hake. It has been estimated that, in certain areas, up to 5% of the porpoise population may be accidentally captured and killed in fishing nets. Populations of porpoises are unlikely to be able to tolerate such losses in the long term. Porpoises also seem to be susceptible to the morbillivirus that was implicated in mass mortality of common seals in a number of European locations between 1988 and 1990. At least two porpoises infected with the virus were found on the north coast of Ireland in 1988.

Recently it has been noted that most dead porpoises washed ashore show signs of having been attacked by bottlenose dolphins and several attacks have been witnessed. It is still unclear why this occurs. Several suggestions have been made. These include direct competition for food, over-robust play and sexual frustration.

Porpoises, like other cetaceans, because they are at the top of the marine food chain tend to accumulate a variety of pollutants, such as heavy metals and radioactive materials (radionuclides) and chlorinated hyrdocarbons. They are thus important indicators of the state of the oceans. Common porpoises from the Irish Sea have a higher body burden of radionuclides than those from either the west coast of Ireland or the North Sea. Dead porpoises often have various items of rubbish such as plastic bags, bottle tops, fishing line etc in their stomachs.

Studying porpoises

Porpoises are the most common cetacean in Irish waters. They are found around all the coasts and are most likely to be seen between July and October. But observations made on calm days reveal that they may be seen at any time of year. Headlands on the south and west coasts are good viewing areas. Porpoises may be seen from the Old Head of Kinsale, Toe Head and Cape Clear (Co Cork) and Slea Head (Co Kerry). They are regularly seen at Rosslare (Co Wexford) and can often be seen from the ferries sailing to Britain or France, particularly in summer. They may also be seen in Dublin Bay from Howth Head and also from Bray Head and off the coasts of Antrim and Derry. (See page 144 for advice on watching cetaceans.) Dursey Island and Roaringwater Bay (Co. Cork), the Blasket Islands (Co. Kerry) and Galway Bay are other important areas for porpoises.

Watching from a boat may be more rewarding than from land provided the approach does not alarm the porpoises. However, they appear not to be particularly interested in boats and do not approach them or ride the bow wave. Indeed, they may actively avoid close contact with boats. They rarely jump clear of (breach) the water and rest by floating at the surface. They are rather slow swimmers. Porpoises are particularly difficult to detect when the water is choppy, so calm weather offers the best viewing conditions. When mackerel shoals come close to the shore is generally a good time.

The common porpoise is the species most frequently stranded on Irish coasts and represents almost 30% of all individuals recorded. There is a complete skeleton and a life-size cast of a common porpoise on exhibition in the Natural History Museum, Dublin. The skull of a specimen stranded at Sandymount (Co Dublin) is also on display.

Common dolphin – *Deilf/Dorad*
Delphinus delphis, Linnaeus 1758

The common dolphin is one of our most colourful cetaceans and the second most commonly seen around the coasts of Ireland. It is the most abundant dolphin in our waters.

The names

Although this dolphin was well known to the classical authors, the Swedish naturalist Linnaeus did not scientifically describe it until 1758. The scientific name, *delphinus* (dolphin-like) and *delphis* (dolphin), derived from the Greek, emphasises that this is the quintessential dolphin. The Irish name simply means dolphin. A dolphin, probably a common dolphin, appears on the coats of arms of Waterford and Dungarvan.

Identification and characteristics

The common dolphin is a small, slender dolphin with a long, thin, well-defined dark or black beak separated from the forehead by a series of grooves. The tip of the beak is occasionally white. The general appearance of common dolphins varies in different parts of the world. In general, individuals from coastal populations are less brightly coloured and have longer beaks than oceanic individuals. Males are slightly larger than females and measure about 2.4m long; females about 2.1m. Weight ranges from 75kg to over 120kg, depending on sex and location.

The upper surface and upper flanks may range from black to brownish black. The lower flanks are paler. They are cream-coloured or yellowish in front of the dorsal fin and lighter grey behind. The darker pigmentation extends back from above the beak and eyes and broadens in the region of the dorsal fin, rather like a saddle, and then narrows between the dorsal fin and the tail. The overall impression in side view is of a dolphin with a pale hourglass shape on the flanks. There is a black stripe running from the flipper to the middle of the lower jaw under the chin and another from the eye to the base of and along the top of the beak.

The dorsal fin is large, slender and sickle-shaped and is located halfway along the back. It is black but in some individuals has a paler centre. The pectoral fins (flippers) are fairly long, tapering and vary in colour from light grey to black. The tail flukes are curved with a deep notch and are dark grey or black. The stem of the tail does not have a keel on the underside.

The lower jaw projects beyond the upper. The mouth contains between 40 and 60 sharp teeth in each side of the upper and lower jaws. The skull of the common dolphin has a series of deep grooves in the bone that forms the roof of the mouth. The blowhole is situated on top of the head.

Common dolphins are extremely vocal and have a relatively complex set of sounds. The higher frequency (15–150 kHz) clicks and buzzes are used for detection of prey by echolocation and whistles (4–16 kHz) for communication with other dolphins. Each animal may have a characteristic signature whistle. Their hearing is particularly well developed and their eyesight is good.

Distribution

Common dolphins are considered to be an oceanic species and are found worldwide in temperate and tropical offshore waters between about 55°N and 60°S. The world distribution

is indicated by the hatched area. They seem to prefer water temperatures between 10-28°C. This species is widespread around Ireland particularly off the south and west coasts. They are also regularly seen in the Irish Sea. They are so widespread globally that some biologists suspect that what we call the common dolphin may include several species. Sites of strandings on the coast of Ireland are indicated by dark circles.

Diet

Common dolphins have a varied diet but fish is the main component. They particularly like mackerel, whiting, pilchards and pollock but will eat almost any small fish that are available. Recently, common dolphins appear to be taking more of the smaller non-commercial species of fish such as Norway pout and poor-cod. In southern European waters they eat anchovies, sardines and sprats.

Dolphins usually feed on shoals of prey found at about 30m depth, but often hunt at greater depths along mid-oceanic ridges. They also sometimes feed at the surface. Their feeding strategy varies. Sometimes members of a group feed independently of one another; at other times they hunt co-operatively. The composition of the diet of females may depend on their reproductive status. Local movements of dolphins may be influenced by migratory patterns of their prey.

Social organisation and reproduction

Common dolphins are highly social animals and are generally seen in small mixed-sex groups usually of up to 25 but often containing hundreds or even thousands of individuals. They have a relatively complex social life. They appear to cooperate during hunting, birthing and 'baby-sitting'. They sometimes associate with pilot whales and other dolphins.

Common dolphins appear to breed all year round, but births, in the northern hemisphere, may be more likely between June and September. Mating takes place mainly between July and October. The gestation period is about 10 or 11 months and a single calf measuring about 80cm long is produced at about one- to two-year intervals. The young are suckled for about 18 months. Common dolphins mature at about five to seven years of age and may live for up to 30 years.

Conservation

Common dolphins, like other cetaceans, are vulnerable to pollution and tend to accumulate organochlorines and heavy metals in their tissues. They were hunted systematically in a number of areas in Europe such as the Mediterranean and Black seas. They are accidentally caught in drift nets in mackerel and tuna fisheries. The Pacific tuna fishery has seriously depleted some stocks. Common dolphins are the second most frequently reported species taken as a by-catch in Irish waters. It is estimated that about two hundred are killed annually in the tuna fishery off the Irish coasts and a similar number in bottom-set gill-nets set in the Celtic sea by vessels operating from Irish and British ports. The total number killed has not yet been quantified, but it seems unlikely that the populations can sustain such losses in the long-term. It has been estimated that about one-third of the common dolphins stranded on one coast had died in fishing nets.

Studying common dolphins

The common dolphin is found all around the coasts. It is the second most commonly seen cetacean in Irish waters and is also the second most commonly found stranded. Common dolphins are regularly seen off Rosslare (Co Wexford) and from the ferries, particularly in summer. They are also found in Dublin Bay and off the coast of Antrim and Derry. The headlands on the south and west coasts are also good viewing areas. Common dolphins may be seen from the Old Head of Kinsale, Toe Head and Cape Clear (Co Cork), Loop Head (Co Clare) and Slea Head and Ballyheige Bay (Co Kerry). Common dolphins may be seen in the waters off the south-west coast in most months of the year. They may come particularly close to shore when pursuing shoals of mackerel or sprat. (See page 144 for advice on watching cetaceans.)

Watching common dolphins from a boat is usually more rewarding than from land. They are relatively fast swimmers and cruise at 15–25 km per hour. They often approach close to boats or indeed even to larger whales and ride along on the bow wave, often squealing excitedly as they go. They often jump clear of (breach) the water and engage in communal leaping and water slapping.

About 15% of cetaceans stranded on the coasts of Ireland are common dolphins. A skull of a common dolphin, from Dingle Bay (Co Kerry) is on display in the Natural History Museum, Dublin.

Striped dolphin – *Deilf riabach*

Stenella caeruleoalba, Meyen 1833

The striped dolphin is the most strikingly patterned of our dolphins and, although a deep-water species, is regularly seen off the south and west coasts.

The names

Meyen first described the species in 1833 from a specimen captured off the coast of Argentina. The generic name is formed from the Greek *steno* (narrow), with the diminutive ending *-ella* (small). The specific name is Latin from *caerulea* (dark blue) and *alba* (white). The common name 'striped dolphin' aptly describes this animal. The alternative name, euphrosyne dolphin, is that of one of the Graces or Charities of Greek mythology. The Irish name means the striped (*riabach*) dolphin (*deilf*).

Identification and characteristics

The euphrosyne or striped dolphin is a small dolphin with a slender dark beak. Males and females are approximately the same size. Adults measure about 2.5m long and weigh about 100–150kg.

The details of the blue-grey and white skin pattern are striking and allow it to be distinguished from other small dolphins. The colour is somewhat variable. The upper surface may range from brownish grey to bluish grey. The flanks are lighter and the belly is white or pinkish. There are two distinct black stripes originating at the eye. One runs downwards along the flanks to end in a patch round the anus; this stripe gives off a shorter stripe which runs downwards to end just behind the flipper. The second stripe runs downwards from the eye to the flipper. There is also a white or pale blue streak, the shoulder blaze, running from above the eye towards the dorsal fin. This, together with the pale belly, gives the impression of a dark finger running forward from the dorsal fin. The dorsal fin is relatively large, slender and sickle-shaped and is located halfway along the back. The pectoral fins (flippers) are tapering and black. The tail flukes are triangular with a notch and are dark. The stem of the tail may be pale and does not have a dorsal ridge or ventral keel.

The mouth contains between 40 and 50 sharp teeth, which curve slightly inwards, on each side of the upper and lower jaws. The blowhole is situated on top of the head. The blow is noisy but low.

Little is known of their communication system, but they use echolocation clicks for hunting and navigation. They also produce a range of whistles.

Distribution

Striped dolphins are found throughout tropical and warm temperate oceans roughly between 50°N and 40°S. Ireland is thus at the northern end of the range which is indicated by the hatched area on the world map. They are a deep-water oceanic species but may be found close to the coast in waters deeper than 200m. Striped dolphins prefer

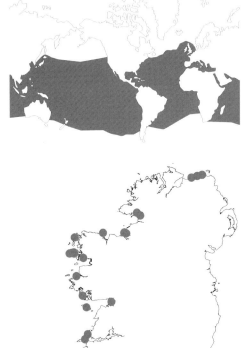

waters where the surface temperature changes greatly throughout the year and where there are upwelling water currents. Their main strongholds in Europe are off the coast of Spain, Portugal and France and in the western Mediterranean, where it is probably the most numerous dolphin. They are, however, also fairly frequently seen off the south and southwest coasts of Ireland and are regularly found washed up on the shore. They are rarely seen in the Irish Sea. Records of striped dolphins from Ireland are becoming more frequent and the species may be extending its range northwards. Sites where striped dolphins have stranded are shown as dark circles on the map of Ireland.

Diet

Striped dolphins seem to prey mainly on fish found in mid-water. They have a varied diet that includes small fish such as hake, herrings, whiting and lanternfish. They also take squid, shrimps, crabs and lobsters.

Recently, striped dolphins are eating more of the smaller non-commercial species of fish. Stomachs of individuals stranded in Ireland contained squid. They probably need 3-4kg of food per day.

Reproduction and life-cycle

Schools containing several thousands of these dolphins have been seen. In Irish waters striped dolphins are generally seen singly or in small groups although on occasion groups of up to 20 may occur. They sometimes associate with common dolphins. Schools of striped dolphins often contain animals of a similar state of maturity. Juveniles tend to associate preferentially with other young dolphins.

The breeding grounds are not known for certain but it seems that breeding occurs throughout their range. The breeding season is variable. Calves are born mainly between July and September but the current information for the northern hemisphere is confusing. In Japanese waters, some females calve in summer, others in winter. Striped dolphins breed for the first time at about 7-9 years of age. The gestation period is between 12 and 13 months and a single calf measuring about 1m long is produced at about two- to four-year intervals. The young are suckled for at least a year but may remain with their mother until they are about three years old. They then join schools of juveniles and do not generally return to an adult group until they are ready to breed. Striped dolphins mature at about eight years of age and may live for about 30 years, but an animal estimated to be over 55 years old has been reported.

Conservation

Striped dolphins were hunted systematically on a large scale by man in areas of the Pacific and to a lesser extent in the Mediterranean. This still continues today and about 20,000 are caught annually in the western Pacific. They are also hunted in a drive-fishery in Japan. Small numbers are also taken accidentally in tuna fisheries in the Pacific and in the north-east Atlantic. In 1990 a serious outbreak of a viral disease, similar to the phocine distemper which affects common seals, occurred in striped dolphins in the Mediterranean. In this area and in others, striped dolphins have been shown to be heavily contaminated by organochlorines and heavy metals.

Studying striped dolphins

Striped dolphins are found in deep waters all round the coasts. The headlands on the south and west coasts are good viewing areas but striped dolphins are not commonly seen, although they appear to be more regular visitors to Irish waters in recent years. (See page 144 for advice on watching cetaceans.)

Watching from a boat may be more rewarding than from land, particularly for a species that rarely approaches the shore. Striped dolphins are generally considered to be easily alarmed but will often approach close to boats and ride along on the bow wave. They are fast swimmers (8-14km/h) and often jump clear of (breach) the water making acrobatic somersaults before re-entry. This is the sixth most commonly stranded species on Irish coasts. A skull of a striped dolphin from Ballycotton Bay (Co Cork) is on display in the Natural History Museum, Dublin.

Bottle-nosed dolphin – *Deilf bolgshrónach*
Tursiops truncatus, Montagu 1821

The bottle-nosed dolphin is probably the second most abundant cetacean in Irish waters. It is the species most often seen in captivity. It also regularly associates with humans. The well-known 'Fungi' off the coast of Kerry is a bottle-nosed dolphin.

The names

The British naturalist Montagu first described the bottle-nosed dolphin in 1821, using a specimen that had been stranded in Devon in 1814. The generic name is derived from the Latin *tursio* (porpoise) and the Greek *ops* (face). The Latin specific name *truncatus* means cut-off. The Irish name means the belly-nosed (*bolgshrónach*) dolphin (*deilf*).

Identification and characteristics

The bottle-nosed dolphin is stoutly built. There are apparently considerable differences in the size of bottle-nosed dolphins from different parts of the world. Males are slightly larger than females. Males measure about 4m long, females about 3.2m. Weight ranges from about 190kg for an adult female up to about 270kg for an adult male. Thus, although males are not much longer than females, they may become substantially heavier.

The upper surface and upper flanks may range from brown to dark grey. The lower flanks are lighter grey and the belly is white. The darker pigmentation extends backward from above the beak and eyes and broadens in the region of the dorsal fin and then narrows between the dorsal fin and the tail. (Newborn calves are paler than adults and have a series of conspicuous white vertical folds in the skin along almost the entire length of the body.)

The bottle-nosed dolphin has a short (c 8cm) but wide, well-defined beak with a rounded tip. The dorsal fin is large, slender and sickle-shaped and is located halfway along the back. The pectoral fins (flippers) are fairly long, pointed and black. The tail flukes are curved with a deep notch and are dark. The stem of the tail has a distinct keel on the underside.

The lower jaw projects beyond the upper. The mouth contains between 18 and 26 sharp teeth in each side of the upper and lower jaws. The mouth is curved upward at the corners, giving this dolphin an apparently mischievous grin.

The blowhole is situated on top of the head. The blow is noisy but low. The bottle-nosed dolphin usually submerges for about a minute but dives as long as ten minutes have been recorded.

The vocal repertoire is impressive and bottle-nosed dolphins are good mimics. They have a relatively complex set of sounds. The higher-frequency clicks (15–130 kHz) are used for detection of prey by echolocation and the lower-frequency calls (0.2–20 kHz) are mainly barks and whistles for communication with other dolphins. The sound beam used for echolocation can be altered, focused and directed by the melon, a deposit of fat and oils which is located on the front of the skull. It may be able to send out two different sound beams in different directions simultaneously. The bottle-nosed dolphin's hearing is particularly well developed to detect a wide range of sounds and echoes and their eyesight is also good. Their ability to discriminate sizes, shapes, textures and composition of objects underwater is amazing.

Distribution

Bottle-nosed dolphins are found worldwide, mainly in temperate and tropical coastal waters. There may also be genetically distinct oceanic populations. In the southern hemisphere they are rarely found further south than 40°. In the northern hemisphere, the eastern Atlantic population extends as far north as the Shetland islands (60°N). This species is common in a number of locations off the coast of southern Europe. It has become less common in the North Sea and the English Channel over the last 20 years, but this decline has not apparently occurred off the south and west coasts of Ireland, where it is regularly recorded.

Although they can dive as deep as 300m, they are typically inshore animals and are usually found within 10km of the coast. They are often found in sea-loughs, estuaries and harbours. In Ireland the main populations are on the west coast: in Clew Bay, Galway Bay, Sligo Bay

and the Shannon estuary. They are also regularly seen in the Irish Sea and may be observed from ferries during the summer months.

They sometimes swim up rivers and may even spend some time in freshwater lakes. Numbers fluctuate in particular areas throughout the year and bottle-nosed dolphins may make seasonal migrations, probably in pursuit of prey. There are six resident populations of dolphins around the coasts of Europe. One of these is found in the Shannon estuary. About 40 individuals live there all year round but during the summer the population may exceed 130 dolphins. Stranding sites in Ireland are shown as dark circles.

Diet

The worldwide success of bottle-nosed dolphins is probably due to their varied diet, of which fish is the main component. They usually hunt bottom-dwelling fish in inshore waters. They particularly like mullet and also eat eels, minnows and shad. They will tackle large dogfish and also take cuttlefish and squid when available. Their feeding strategy varies. Sometimes they feed independently; at other times they hunt co-operatively. They will also follow trawlers to scavenge discarded or injured fish. Lactating females, which have a relatively high food requirement, tend to take a wider variety of prey and hunt closer to the shore. Bottlenose dolphins tend to hunt most actively at times and in locations when the tidal flows are greatest but may hunt by day and night.

Social organisation and reproduction

Bottle-nosed dolphins have a complex social life and incidents of co-operative hunting, defence, assistance at birth and baby-sitting have been reported. They have large brains for their body size, not as relatively large as humans but more developed than those of chimpanzees or gorillas. Long-term studies of populations of bottle-nosed dolphins are beginning to reveal a social life which may be as complex as that of some of the large apes.

Bottle-nosed dolphins are generally seen singly or in small groups of up to about 15. However, if food is superabundant, groups of up to 1000 individuals may form for short periods. Such spectacular groups have occasionally been seen off the west coast of Ireland. They sometimes associate with pilot whales.

Inshore groups often have relatively small home ranges and may be considered resident. Males, however, appear to have somewhat larger home ranges than females. The membership of geographical populations is often quite stable for years, but the membership of sub-groups is extremely variable. Individual dolphins may be considered as temporary members of a particular group. In general, adult dolphins tend to associate with others of the same sex and groups of females often consist of relatives. Adult males often form strong associations with one or two others. These alliances may last for ten years or more and members appear to co-operate during hunting or searching for females. Occasionally two alliances may join together to attack other dolphins or to defend their home ranges.

Bottle-nosed dolphins appear to breed all year round in parts of their range but in the northern hemisphere mating is most likely to occur between May and September. Births may be more likely between March and September. In the Shannon estuary, births take place between June and October, but most take place in June and July. The mating system appears to be promiscuous and a female usually mates with several males during her oestrous period. Courtship is quite protracted.

The gestation period is between 12 and 13 months and a single calf measuring about 1.1m long is produced at about one- to four-year intervals. Females appear to come into breeding condition and become attractive to males within a week or so of losing a calf. Therefore a male could gain a mating opportunity by killing the calf of a female with whom he had not previously mated. This may be why infanticide is as common in the bottle-nosed dolphin as it is in lions. Females, on the other hand, could counteract this behaviour by mating with several males and thus confusing the issue of paternity. The young are suckled for at least a year and perhaps for as long as three. Young adult females often associate with nursing mothers and attempt to interact with the juvenile. It is assumed that the young females learn some parenting skills by this behaviour. Juveniles tend to remain with their mother for about four to six years and then to associate with other young dolphins until they become mature. Bottle-nosed dolphins are fully grown by about ten years of age and may live for up to almost 40 years. Females produce their first calf at about ten years of age.

Conservation

Bottle-nosed dolphins often live in relatively discrete local populations and thus may be severely depleted by a variety of factors. Like other inshore cetaceans, they are vulnerable to coastal pollution and drowning in fishing nets. The catch of dolphins in the purse-seine nets by the fishery for tuna in the Pacific is a cause of concern. They were hunted systematically on a large scale by man in areas of the Pacific and to a lesser extent in the Mediterranean and the Black Sea. There have been reports of dolphins formerly being killed in Irish waters prompted by fear of competition with fishing interests. This, however, is now rare. In some regions in the southern hemisphere bottle-nosed dolphins have been killed by entanglement in gill nets erected as barriers to exclude sharks from tourist beaches.

Bottle-nosed dolphins seem to be susceptible to the morbillivirus that was implicated in mass mortality of common seals in a number of European locations between 1988 and 1990. At least one dead dolphin infected with the virus was found on the north coast of Ireland in 1988. Bottle-nosed dolphins accumulate high concentrations of pollutants in their blubber. This fat is used to make milk by nursing mothers and juveniles are therefore at severe risk from the toxic materials in the milk.

Lone individuals (like 'Fungi') often socialise with humans and may become resident close to centres of human activity and regularly associate with small boats or swimmers. Despite the remarkable tolerance of such individuals, there is a limit to their patience, which must be respected.

There is increasing concern regarding the possible impact of tourist boats on populations of bottle-nosed dolphins (though their cuddly image has been marred by the discovery of their tendency to infanticide and their general intolerance of harbour porpoises). Apart from general disturbance, the noise of engines may interfere with the normal communication between the dolphins. Such populations should be closely monitored in case they become victims of their own appeal. On no account should they be artificially fed, since this may induce a state of dependence and distract them from normal hunting activity. Where dolphin watching occurs on an organised basis, there is a code of conduct which regulates closeness of approach, observation time and boat speed (less than seven knots) and forbids chasing the animals. This code could well be adopted by all who come into contact with dolphins.

Studying bottle-nosed dolphins

Bottle-nosed dolphins are extremely intelligent and tractable and this is the usual species exhibited in aquaria.

The coasts of Ireland are among the best places in Europe from which to see bottle-nosed dolphins. Scattered populations are found all around the coasts, but they are less common in the east. There is a resident population of bottle-nosed dolphins in the Shannon estuary, which is one of the best locations in Ireland for viewing them. Numbers are highest in May, June and July. The home range of the Shannon population is part of a Special Area of Conservation and dolphin watching is regulated by a code of conduct to control the impact on the dolphins. There are other populations in Clew Bay and Killary Harbour (Co Mayo), Bantry Bay (Co Cork) and Dingle Bay (Co Kerry). They are also found in Galway Bay and off the coasts of Sligo and Donegal.

Bottle-nosed dolphins may be seen from many of the headlands on the south-west coast such as the Old Head of Kinsale, Slea Head, Clogher Head, Sybil Head and Cape Clear Island. Watching from a boat, particularly in areas with resident populations, is usually more rewarding than from land. Bottle-nosed dolphins are relatively slow swimmers but often approach close to boats or indeed larger whales and ride along on the bow wave. Wave riding reduces the cost of swimming by up to 30%. They often jump clear of (breach) the water. Sometimes they hang vertically holding their heads above water.

Local activity and distribution of bottle-nosed dolphins seems to be affected by the state of the tide. Bottle-nosed dolphins may be seen all year round but most sightings are reported between July and October. Sighting rates of bottle-nosed dolphins vary from one sighting per hour to one per 5 hours. Individual dolphins may be recognised, using binoculars, from features such as tears, nicks or scars on the fins or skin. Many of these may have been inflicted during fights. The overall shape of the dorsal fin or of patches of diseased skin may also be used. Long-term students of dolphins assemble a library of photographs that assist in photo-identification and keeping track of individuals.

Although bottle-nosed dolphins are common in Irish waters, records of strandings are quite rare. It ranks eleventh in order of frequency of stranding during the 20th century. The skull of a bottle-nosed dolphin from Ringsend, Dublin, is on display in the Natural History Museum.

White-sided dolphin – *Deilf le cliathán bán*
Lagenorhynchus acutus, Gray 1828

Atlantic white-sided dolphins are common in the offshore waters off the west coast of Ireland and represent between 5% and 10% of all cetaceans stranded annually.

The names
Gray originally named this species in 1828 in London, based on a skull which had been found in the Faroe islands. In 1841 the same skull, now in the Netherlands, was described again and given a different name, but the confusion was resolved in 1846. The generic name derives from the Greek *lagenos* (flask) and *rhynchus* (snout or beak). The specific name is Latin, *acutus* (sharp). The Irish name is a direct translation of the English: (*cliathán*) side, (*bán*) white.

Identification and characteristics
The white-sided dolphin is a large, stoutly built dolphin with a short, well-defined beak. Males are slightly larger than females. Adult males are about 2.5m long; females are 2.25m. Adult males weigh about 230kg, females about 180–190kg.

They are strikingly patterned. The beak is usually black on top and white below. The back is black and the flanks are dark. There is a white band on the flanks extending from approximately just below the front of the dorsal fin to an area above the anus. This is partly overlapped on the upper side by a yellow band that continues towards the tail. The underside of the head and the belly are white. A dark line runs from the beak to a dark spot that encircles the eye. There is also a narrow dark line running from the flipper to the corner of the mouth.

The dorsal fin is large, slender and sickle-shaped and is located halfway along the back. The mouth contains between 29 and 40 small sharp teeth on each side of the upper and lower jaws. The flippers are black, pointed and sickle-shaped. The tail flukes are curved with a slight notch and are dark. The stem of the tail is relatively thick as far back as the flukes and then narrows abruptly. It has a strong keel above and below. The blowhole is situated on top of the head.

They have a relatively complex set of sounds. The higher frequencies in the form of pulses are used for detection of prey by echolocation and the lower-frequency calls, barks and whistles for communication with other dolphins. Their hearing is particularly well developed and their eyesight is good.

Distribution

White-sided dolphins are largely confined to cool waters (7-12°C) in offshore areas of the North Atlantic from Cape Cod in the west along the southern coasts of Greenland, Iceland and Scandinavia as well as the North and Baltic Seas and the coastal waters of the British Isles. The range is shown as the hatched area on the world map. It seems likely that all the white-sided dolphins in the North Atlantic are members of the same population, although

genetic studies have not been carried out. Although they are considered relatively common over their range the main concentrations are found off the west coast of Scotland. They are also common off the west and north west coasts of Ireland, but are scarce in the Irish Sea. They are typically found further from the shore than the white-beaked dolphin along the edge of the continental shelf, but can regularly be found less than 10km offshore. They are sometimes seen in the presence of pilot whales. Mass strandings of white-sided dolphins occasionally occur, the most recent being in Killala Bay (Co Mayo) in September 1994, when 19 individuals died. Sites of strandings in Ireland are shown as dark circles.

Diet

White-sided dolphins are fast swimmers and feed on a variety of schooling fish such as mackerel, herrings, cod and whiting as well as squid and gammarid crustaceans. Stomachs of individuals stranded contained mackerel, herring and pout. They sometimes feed in association with larger whales. They may undertake small-scale migrations in pursuit of prey.

Social organisation, reproduction and life-cycle

White-sided dolphins are generally seen singly or in groups of fewer than ten, but larger herds containing several hundred individuals have often been sighted. Significantly more males than females have been stranded in Ireland. This suggests that they may form single-sex groups. However, they also appear to form mixed-sex groups because the group stranded in Killala Bay in 1994 included adult males, adult females and juveniles. There is little information on the social organisation of this species. There is, however, some evidence for social bonds. When the 19 individuals stranded in 1994 were examined all were healthy except for the largest male in the group who appeared to have suffered heart failure. This presumably caused him to be beached on the shore, where he was followed by the other healthy group members, who then became stranded and died.

White-sided dolphins apparently breed in Irish waters, because lactating and pregnant females have been stranded on Irish coasts. They give birth mainly between May and July, probably in offshore waters. Mating probably takes place mainly between June and September. The gestation period is between ten and 12 months and a single calf measuring about 1.1m long is produced at two- to three-year intervals. The young are suckled for about 18 months. White-sided dolphins mature at about five years of age and may live for about 25 years.

Conservation

This species has been traditionally hunted on a small scale in northern Europe and Canada. They still are hunted or trapped along parts of the Scandinavian coasts. Individuals are occasionally killed accidentally in fishing nets. White-sided dolphins are considered to be abundant in the Atlantic particularly in western parts of its range. There are, however, no reliable estimates of population sizes available.

Studying white-sided dolphins

White-sided dolphins are found all around the coasts but are more common off the south and west. They appear to be found closer inshore in summer and migrate to deeper waters in winter. The headlands on the south and west coasts are good viewing areas for dolphins but white-sided dolphins are rarely sufficiently close to the shore to be seen. (See page 144 for advice on watching cetaceans.)

Watching from a boat, particularly for a species such as this which rarely approaches the shore, is usually more rewarding than from land. They occur at low densities along the edge of the continental shelf off the south-west and west coasts. White-sided dolphins are relatively fast swimmers and sometimes approach close to boats but rarely ride along on the bow wave. They often jump clear of (breach) the water and do so much more frequently than white-beaked dolphins. Strandings of white-sided dolphins in Ireland have been increasing since the 1980s and it is now the fourth most frequently stranded species. Thirty cases were recorded between 1990 and 1995. Most of the strandings occur in spring and summer. The skull of a white-sided dolphin from Arranmore (Co Donegal) is on display in the Natural History Museum, Dublin.

White-beaked dolphin –
Deilf na ngoba bána
Lagenorhynchus albirostris, Gray 1846

The white-beaked dolphin is a large, stoutly built dolphin.

The names
The English zoologist Gray first described this species in 1846 from a specimen washed ashore in Yorkshire. The scientific name is derived from the Greek words *lagenos* (a flask) and *rhynchos* (a snout) and the Latin words *albus* (white) and *rostrum* (a beak). The Irish name *deilf* (dolphin) *na ngoba* (of the beak) *bána* (white) is a direct translation of the English and the specific names.

Identification and characteristics
The white-beaked dolphin has a short, thick, well-defined beak that is usually, but not always, white or light grey. There is usually a well-defined groove between the base of the beak and the melon. Males are slightly larger than females. Adult white-beaked dolphins measure about 2.5–2.7m and weigh about 180kg.

The most characteristic features are two white or pale grey patches on the flanks, one in front of the dorsal fin and the other running from below the fin upwards across the back in front of the tail. These patches fade soon after death and the colour of stranded white-beaked dolphins can be deceptive. The upper surface and flanks as far as the rear edge of the dorsal fin range from dark grey to black. There is a grey to white band extending from near the eye over the edge of the flipper, towards the anus. The flanks behind the dorsal fin are pale grey. The undersides of the head and the belly are white.

The dorsal fin is large, slender and sickle-shaped and is located halfway along the back. The flippers are broad at the base, pointed and dark. The tail flukes are curved with a slight notch and are dark. The stem of the tail is relatively thick and has a strong keel above and below.

The lower jaw projects beyond the upper. The mouth has fewer teeth than other dolphins and contains between 22 and 28 small sharp teeth on each side of both upper and lower jaws. The blowhole is situated on top of the head and is surrounded by a dark grey patch.

Little is known of their communication system but they emit a series of clicks and whistles. Their hearing and eyesight are well developed.

Distribution

White-beaked dolphins extend further northwards than other dolphins and are confined to the colder waters of coastal areas of the North Atlantic from Cape Cod in the west along the southern coast of Greenland, Iceland, the North and Baltic Seas and the coastal waters of Scandinavia and the British Isles. The world range is shown as the hatched area. Although they are considered common over their range, the main concentrations are found off the west coasts of Ireland and Scotland. They are also occasionally seen off the south coast but are scarce in the Irish Sea. They are typically more inshore animals than the white-sided dolphin. There are no reliable estimates of population sizes. Stranding sites are shown on the map of Ireland as dark circles.

Diet

White-beaked dolphins feed on a variety of fish such as mackerel, herrings, cod and whiting, as well as squid and crustaceans. They are often found in the presence of herring shoals. They also apparently feed on the sea-bottom. They have a variety of hunting techniques and often hunt fish cooperatively. During winter they are found more towards the northern end of their range and migrate southwards in spring. Nevertheless, they appear to be present in Irish waters all year round.

Reproduction

White-beaked dolphins are generally seen singly or in groups of fewer than ten, but larger groups have often been sighted. They appear to be found closer inshore in summer and migrate to deeper waters in winter. There is little information on the social organisation of this species.

They probably breed in Irish waters, since a late-pregnant female and a young calf have been stranded on Irish coasts. They appear to give birth mainly between May and August, probably offshore. Mating probably takes place mainly between July and October. The gestation period is about ten months. The single calf measures about 1.2–1.5m at birth. Neither the intervals between births nor the lactation period are known, and there is no information on lifespan.

Conservation

Like other inshore cetaceans, white-beaked dolphins are vulnerable to coastal pollution and drowning in fishing nets. They are hunted off Newfoundland and Labrador and were formerly hunted off Greenland, Iceland and in Scandinavian waters. The white-beaked dolphin may be one of the most vulnerable cetaceans in the north-east Atlantic.

Studying white-beaked dolphins

White-beaked dolphins are found around our southern, western and northern coasts. The highest densities are off the north-west coast. The headlands of the south, west and north coasts are good areas for watching whales and dolphins but white-beaked dolphins are rarely close enough to be positively identified. The probability of seeing white-beaked dolphins is somewhat greater from aboard a ship.

Although white-beaked dolphins are relatively fast swimmers, they often approach close to boats and ride along on the bow wave. They often jump clear of (breach) the water. About 5% of stranded cetaceans recorded around Ireland were white-beaked dolphins and they are the thirteenth most frequently stranded. The skull of a white-beaked dolphin from Donaghadee (Co Down) is on display in the Natural History Museum, Dublin.

False killer whale – *Cráin dubh bréagach*
Pseudorca crassidens, Owen 1846

The false killer whale is extremely rare in Irish waters. It has only been recorded on three occasions.

The names

Owen first described the false killer whale in 1846 from a skeleton found inland in Lincolnshire, England, on an area formerly covered by the sea. The first intact specimen was not recorded until 1862, on the German coast. The generic name is a combination of Greek *pseudos* (false) and Latin *orcus* (underworld, but previously used to name the killer whale). The specific name is formed from two Latin terms, *crassus* (thick) and *dens* (tooth). The Irish name means the false (*bréagach*) killer whale (*cráin dubh*) - literally black (*dubh*) sow (*cráin*).

Identification and characteristics

The false killer is a slender whale with no beak. It superficially resembles a large dolphin. It is the third largest of the dolphin-like cetaceans. Males are larger than females. Adult males measure about 5.5m long, females about 4.5m. Adult male false killer whales weigh from 1200 to 2000kg, females about 1100kg. The body is almost totally black or dark grey. The throat and neck may be slightly paler.

The dorsal fin is of medium size, about 6–10% of the body length, but much smaller than that of the killer whale. It is curved with a rounded tip and is located about halfway along the back. The flippers are narrow and black and about one-tenth of the body length. They curve sharply backward from about mid-way along the flipper so that the front edge is noticeably S-shaped. This is sometimes described as a bump or a shoulder on the front edge of the flipper. The tail flukes are black and triangular with a notch. The head is relatively small, the forehead somewhat rounded and tapered and the jaw is underslung. The mouth usually contains between seven and 13 pairs of large conical teeth in the upper and lower jaws. The blowhole is situated on top of the head. They blow at about 15–20 second intervals and ride relatively high in the water.

They have a relatively complex set of sounds. The higher frequencies are used for detection of prey by echolocation and the lower-frequency calls and whistles, which are sometimes audible above water, for communication with other whales. Their eyesight and hearing are particularly well developed.

Distribution

False killer whales are probably common throughout the world in tropical and warm temperate oceans (above 20°C), usually in deeper offshore waters but sometimes inshore. Ireland is close to the northern limits of their range. The world range is shown as a hatched area. It has been suggested that they may move along the paths of ocean currents. Because they are largely oceanic they are not commonly observed although strandings are regularly reported from around the world. They have rarely, if ever, been positively identified alive in Irish waters. The only candidates from Ireland are two specimens from the west coast. The stranding sites are indicated by circles on the map.

Diet

False killer whales can take relatively large prey, since they have a wide gape and their teeth are quite strong. They mainly eat squid, tuna and cod and occasionally smaller dolphins.

Reproduction

False killer whales are generally seen in small groups of fewer than 30 individuals, although they may form larger associations – a number of mass strandings, one involving about 800 animals, have been recorded. Herds consist of mixed sexes, but little is known of their social organisation.

Breeding seems to occur throughout the year. The breeding grounds are not known for certain but it seems that births occur throughout their range. The gestation period is somewhere between 11 and 15 months while lactation lasts for at least 18 months. False killer whales mature at about ten years of age and are long-lived; males may survive for up to 40 years.

Conservation

Small numbers of false killer whales are taken in net and long-line fisheries throughout the world. Substantial numbers are taken locally in drive-fisheries in Japan apparently in retaliation for a decline in fish stocks which, however, is more likely to be due to overfishing by man. There is little information on which to base an assessment of the current world population.

Studying false killer whales

False killer whales are very fast swimmers and may approach boats and ride on the bow wave. They are, however, extremely rare in Irish waters and there are only three reports of this species from Ireland. Two skulls were found on Achill Island. These have been provisionally identified as those of false killer whales but this has yet to be confirmed. There is a skull and an earbone from a false killer whale stranded at Dornoch in Scotland on exhibition in the Natural History Museum, Dublin.

Killer whale (Orca) – *Cráin dubh/Orc*
Orcinus orca, Linnaeus 1758

The orca or killer whale has undergone a remarkable change of image in recent years. Far from being seen as a vicious killer (though it does prey on other cetaceans), it is now perceived to be a highly intelligent social whale. This has led to its capture for display in aquaria, a practice that now seems to be in decline.

The names
The scientific description was written by the Swedish biologist Linnaeus in 1758. The scientific name implies that the killer whale is a sea-monster: *orcinus* is Latin for demon-like and *orcus* is the underworld. The common name is based on the numerous observations of killer whales attacking other, larger whales. The Irish name means the black (*dubh*) sow (*cráin*).

Identification and characteristics
This is the largest of the dolphin-like cetaceans. Males are larger than females. Adult males measure from about 7 to 9.5m long, females from about 5.5 to 8.5m. Male killer whales weigh about 5000 to 9000kg, females about 3500 to 5000kg.

The killer whale has a striking black and white patterned body. The details of the pattern are quite variable and it is possible to recognise individual whales. The upper surface and most of the flanks are black. There is a white oval patch behind the eye and a white to grey saddle behind the dorsal fin. The chin and underside are white and a curved white stripe extends upwards and backwards from the belly onto the flanks behind the dorsal fin. Calves have similar patterns to adults but the white patches are often light-brown to reddish-yellow.

The dorsal fin is large and conspicuous, and is located halfway along the back. It may be up to 2m tall in adult males; in females it rarely exceeds 1m. The dorsal fin is triangular and usually upright in adult males but is curved backwards in females and immature whales. The pectoral fins (flippers) are large and rounded. The tail flukes are triangular with a shallow notch and the underside of the tail is white. The head, viewed from the side, appears to have a slight beak. The mouth contains between ten and 13 pairs of large, slightly curved, conical teeth in the upper and lower jaws. The blowhole is situated on top of the head.

The blow is noisy but low. Killer whales make a series of short dives lasting about 20 seconds and then a longer submersion of from one to four minutes. Killer whales are generally rather energetic and inquisitive. They often rest vertically in the water, scanning their surroundings (spyhopping). They occasionally leap clear of the water (breaching) and often wave the flukes in the air.

They have a relatively complex set of sounds used for social interaction and hunting. The higher frequencies (up to 20 kHz) are emitted in pulses of up to 300 per second and are

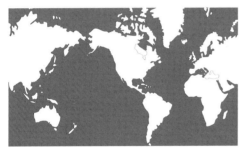

probably used for detection of prey by echolocation. Other lower-frequency pulsed calls and whistles are mainly used for communication with other whales. Their hearing is particularly well developed and their eyesight is good.

Distribution

Killer whales are one of the most widespread cetaceans and are found throughout the oceans from the tropics to the polar regions, but are more common in colder waters. The world distribution is shown as a hatched area. They may be found in deep waters, usually within 500km of the coast. But they may also be found in estuaries and shallow bays. They apparently do not undergo extensive migrations other than those required by the movements of their prey. Groups (pods) of killer whales may occupy large home ranges, up to about 1000 km². Killer whales are numerous around the Faroe islands and parts of the coast of Norway. They are regularly seen in small numbers off the Irish coasts. Stranding sites are shown as dark circles.

Diet

Killer whales are opportunistic predators and have a varied diet that includes fish, squid, other marine mammals and birds. They take herrings, mackerel, cod and salmon. They prey on minke, humpback and pilot whales, porpoises and seals.

They employ a wide range of hunting techniques and have been seen hunting co-operatively at sea. Pods of killer whales will herd fish such as herrings into tight shoals at the surface. They use visual signals, sounds and bubbles to keep them there, before stunning them with tail-slaps. They usually take turns to feed on the fish. They will also drive prey into shallows before attack. They have been observed attacking prey such as seals which were resting above the waterline. They have even been reported to co-operate with Australian whalers in pursuit of humpback whales.

Social organisation and reproduction

Populations of killer whales appear to contain individuals that have a relatively stable home range. These are termed residents by contrast with transients, who wander more widely. Killer whales are generally seen singly or in small groups of up to 30 individuals although, on feeding or breeding grounds, groups of over 50 may be seen. The average size of a group is about five. The small groups, called pods, usually contain related females and calves, under the leadership of a matriarch. Males, however, may also be present. Many pods may be resident and there are usually strong bonds between members of the pod. The home ranges or territories of the pods may be quite large and they may travel up to 200km in their daily foraging. There are differences in the patterns of vocalisations between pods. These dialects probably aid social cohesion.

The size difference in males and females suggests that dominant males may mate with more than one female. The breeding grounds are not known for certain but it seems that breeding may occur throughout their range. Calves are born mainly between October and January in the North Atlantic. The gestation period is relatively long, somewhere between 12 and 16 months, and a single calf measuring about 2.1m long is produced at about three- to five-year intervals. The young are suckled for at least a year. Females probably do not produce their first calf until at least 12 years of age. Males, although mature at about 15 years of age, probably do not breed until at least 20. Killer whales are long-lived and males may survive for more than 50 years, females for over 80.

Conservation

Man has never hunted killer whales systematically on a large scale although they are occasionally taken in Greenland by conventional methods and in the Faroe islands by driving onshore. There was a small commercial fishery for killer whales in Norway and occasional live captures off Iceland. They are still threatened in parts of the Indian and Pacific Oceans. They are considered to be common overall but under local threat because of perceived competition with fishing interests. In some areas they are subject to illegal shooting. Some also fall victim to fishing nets.

Studying killer whales

The coasts of Ireland are probably the best places in Europe from which to see cetaceans. In Irish waters killer whales are probably the third or fourth most frequently sighted whale. Most sightings occur off the west coast, but they are sometimes seen in the Irish Sea. For example in recent years they have been seen off the coasts of Wexford, Cork, Galway and Antrim.

They are widely distributed in small numbers all along the west and south coasts but despite their abundance they are rarely found stranded. This is probably because they are well able to cope with shallow water. They appear to move closer to the shore in summer and headlands on the south and west coasts are good viewing areas. (See page 144 for advice on watching whales.) They occasionally enter fresh water. In early November 1977, a killer whale hunted salmon in the River Foyle on five consecutive days.

Watching from a boat is usually more rewarding than from land and killer whales often approach boats closely. They are extremely fast swimmers. They appear to be sensitive to ship traffic and noise and excessive disturbance by whale watchers.

There are fewer than 20 records of stranded killers from the 20th century and these have been recorded from 14 different coastal counties. The National Museum has, on exhibit, the skull of a killer whale stranded at Killala Bay in 1871 and a tooth from a specimen from Kilkee. There is also a 1:12 scale-model on display.

Long-finned pilot whale – *Míol phíolótach*
Globiocephala melaena, Traill 1809

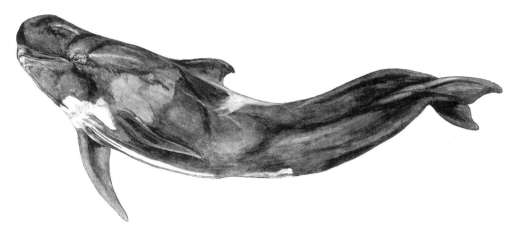

This animal, though called a whale, is one of the most highly social dolphins.

The names

Traill, a medical professor from Edinburgh, first scientifically described this whale in 1809. The generic name is composed of the Latin *globus* (round) and the Greek *kephalos* (head). The specific name *melaena* is Latin for black. Pilot whales are so-called because of their habit of swimming in an apparent formation following a leader. (They are highly gregarious.) The Irish name is a translation of pilot (*píolótach*) whale (*míol*).

Identification and characteristics

The long-finned pilot whale, also known as the blackfish, is really a medium-sized dolphin and is the second largest of the dolphin-like creatures after the killer whale. Males are slightly larger than females. Adult males are about 5.7m long, females about 4.5m. Adult males weigh about 2500kg, females 1300kg.

The long-finned pilot whale is a stoutly built dolphin with a square, bulging head and a slightly protruding upper lip. The beak is very small and, in side view, the line of the mouth slopes upwards. The back and flanks are black or dark grey. There is an anchor- or W-shaped white or grey mark under the chin. There may also be a narrow greyish area on the belly and a greyish saddle behind the dorsal fin.

The dorsal fin has a long base and thus appears lower than it really is. It is sickle-shaped and is located slightly forward of halfway along the back. The flippers are black and sickle-shaped, they sweep strongly backward giving the impression of an 'elbow' and are about 15–20% of the body length. The stem of the tail has a strong keel above and below. The tail is concave and is deeply notched.

The mouth contains between eight and 12 small peglike teeth on each side of the upper and lower jaw. The blowhole is situated on top of the head but slightly to the left of the midline. Long-finned pilot whales blow about once every one or two minutes and the blow rises about 1.5m. They usually swim slowly just below the surface. They apparently can sink to 30–60m without actively swimming, merely by controlling their buoyancy. They usually remain submerged for about five minutes, but they can perform longer dives and reach as deep as 1000m.

They have an extraordinarily complex set of sounds, probably due in part to their extreme sociability. The lower-frequency sounds include squeaks, whistles, buzzes, chirps and rattles and are probably used to communicate with other whales. The higher frequencies are probably used for detection of prey by echolocation. Their hearing is particularly well developed and their eyesight is good.

Distribution

Pilot whales are widespread in cold temperate oceans. The world distribution is shown by the hatched areas. There are two geographically separate populations, one in the North Atlantic and the other stretching around the globe roughly between latitude 50°S and the

edge of the Antarctic Ocean. It is relatively abundant in the North Atlantic and is one of the most commonly observed cetaceans in the waters around Ireland, particularly in late summer and autumn. It is found mainly in offshore waters along the edge of the continental shelves. It is typically found further from the shore than the white-beaked dolphin, but can regularly be found within 10km of the coast.

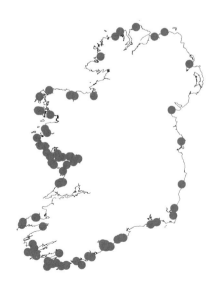

Although they are considered relatively common over their range, the main concentrations are found off the west coast of Ireland. They are occasionally seen in the Irish Sea. Mass strandings of pilot whales frequently occur throughout their range. For example, evidence that a pod of whales was stranded many years ago near Killala (Co Mayo) was discovered in the late 1970s. In some areas strandings of up to several hundred individuals have occurred. Stranding sites are shown as dark circles on the map of Ireland.

234

Diet

In the Atlantic, long-finned pilot whales feed on up to nine different species of squid at depths of between 100 and 500m. They also feed at the surface and take a variety of shoaling fish such as mackerel, cod, pollock, pout, hake and whiting. There may be some local movement, tracking the migration of prey.

Social organisation and life-cycle

Pilot whales are highly social and gregarious. Herds or pods of 20–40 are regularly seen. On occasion, groups over one thousand have been reported. They appear to form mixed-sex groups, consisting of a few mature males and larger numbers of adult females with their dependent young and immature animals. The pods are matrilineal groups, that is to say, groups united by kinship through the female line. The males in the pod are also usually related to the females and apparently do not disperse from their natal group.

The size difference between male and females suggests that males probably compete for reproductive access to the females. Resident males, however, rarely father calves within the pod. It may be that while the female and immature males are permanent members, the adult males may occasionally wander between pods. Most of the calves are the offspring of males which briefly visit the pod and are temporarily resident and which may mate with more than one of the resident females.

Most of the matings occur in the early summer, although they may occur at any time. Births occur mainly between July and September, but can take place throughout the year. For example, pregnant females, which died in a mass stranding of 63 individuals in Kerry in November 1965, contained foetuses of markedly different sizes, who would have been born at different times of the year. The gestation period is between 14 and 16 months and a single calf measuring about 1.8m long is produced at about three- to four-year intervals. The young are suckled for almost two years. Male pilot whales mature at about ten years of age while females may be old enough to breed at six years of age. Pilot whales may live for up to 60 years. The average life expectancy of males is less than that of females and there are usually about twice as many adult females as males in the population.

Conservation

The strong social bonds between pilot whales has often proved their undoing. This whale is so highly social that it has traditionally been captured in drive-fisheries throughout its range. For example, they have been harvested by herding onto beaches in the Hebrides off Scotland since medieval times. They still are hunted by this method in the Faroe islands where boats are used to stampede and drive the whales onto the shore. Over 1500 individuals are killed annually in this hunt. The social bonds are so strong that individuals that could escape the slaughter refuse to leave the scene. They may swim onshore to join the remainder of the pod in the shallows, even as the killing goes on. It is difficult to justify such exploitation. Pilot whales are often observed carrying the remains of dead whales or other marine mammals.

Drive hunts have also taken place, from time to time, in the west of Ireland up to the early part of the 20th century. In fact, a school that entered the head of Brandon Bay (Co Kerry) as late as 1965 was captured and used to feed captive mink. Pilot whales are also taken accidentally in a number of net fisheries. There were estimated to be about 780,000 pilot whales in the central and eastern North Atlantic in 1989.

Pilot whales accumulate organochlorines and PCBs in blubber and liver. Burdens of pollutants increase with age in males but seem to be periodically unloaded by females as they produce milk and transfer the pollutants to their calves. There is evidence that pilot whales change their vocal activity in response to underwater sonar and thus may be sensitive to underwater noise.

Studying long-finned pilot whales

Long-finned pilot whales are found all around the coasts, usually offshore, but they enter inshore waters in late summer and autumn. They are more likely to be seen off the northwest and southwest coasts from about April to June and closer to the shore from September to December. (See page 144 for advice on watching whales.) Watching from a boat is usually more rewarding than from land, particularly for species such as long-finned pilot whales that do not usually approach the shore. Pilot whales are relatively slow swimmers and often allow close approach by boats but rarely ride along on the bow wave. They rarely jump clear of (breach) the water and often rest motionless in the water, either horizontally or vertically with the head and chest out of the water (spyhopping). They are sometimes seen in the presence of other cetaceans such as Risso's, bottle-nosed and white-sided dolphins. Pilot whales are the third most frequently stranded whale in Ireland. The National Museum has, on exhibit, the skull of an adult long-finned pilot whale stranded at Rosslare (Co Wexford) and that of a calf from Killala Bay. There is also a 1:12 scale-model on display.

Risso's dolphin – *Deilf liath*
Grampus griseus, Cuvier 1812

This is about the fifth most commonly seen cetacean in Irish waters and represents 2–5% of animals stranded annually.

The names

This species was first described by the French palaeontologist Cuvier in 1811 from a specimen that had been found near Nice, in France, by a naturalist called Risso. The generic name is apparently a corruption of the French, either *gras poisson* (fat fish) or *grand poisson* (big fish). The specific name *griseus* is Latin for grey. The Irish name means the grey (*liath*) dolphin (*deilf*).

Unusually for cetaceans, there are a number of place names in Ireland which refer to Risso's dolphin. There are several Grampus Rocks off the south coast and a place known as Grampus Field (*Páirc na nGrampuisí*) at Ardmore, Co Waterford.

Identification and characteristics

Risso's dolphin is a large stoutly built dolphin, rather slender posteriorly, between the dorsal fin and tail. It has a blunt rounded head. Males are slightly larger than females. Adult Risso's dolphins are about 3.5m long and weigh from 350–400kg.

The overall colour ranges from dark to light grey and animals become paler with age. Newborn calves are grey with seven paler vertical stipes. They soon lose this juvenile colour and become somewhat darker. There is a whitish anchor-shaped patch on the chest and the underside of the belly is also white. There are usually many parallel pale scars on the skin of the head and flanks. There may also be pale, roughly circular scars on the body.

It has no beak and the melon is quite small. The forehead has a deep V-shaped vertical groove running from the snout to the blowhole. The dorsal fin is large, slender and sickle-shaped and is located halfway along the back. It is more triangular and erect in males. The flippers are long (about one-sixth the length of the body), dark and sickle-shaped. The tail flukes are curved with a slight notch and are dark. The body behind the dorsal fin is relatively slender and narrow. This gives the animal an appearance of being disproportionately front-loaded. The stem of the tail is relatively thin.

The mouth contains between two and seven, usually three or four, peglike teeth at the tip of each lower jaw. There are usually no teeth in the upper jaw but occasionally one or two tiny teeth may be hidden in the gum. The line of the mouth is tilted upwards towards the eye.

The blowhole is situated on top of the head. The blows occur at about 15–20 second intervals for about three or four minutes and then the dolphin dives for about one or two minutes. They have a relatively complex set of sounds. The higher frequency clicks are used for detection of prey by echolocation and the lower frequency calls, barks, grunts, whistles and buzzes for communication with other dolphins. Their hearing is particularly keen and their eyesight is good.

Distribution

Risso's dolphins are found worldwide in deep tropical and temperate oceans around the world. The world distribution is shown as a hatched area. The northern limit of their range is about the Orkney Islands, Newfoundland and the Kamchatka peninsula. They are widely distributed along the west coast of Europe but are nowhere very abundant. They are relatively common off the west coast of Ireland, but apparently less so in the Irish Sea. They are more often sighted during the summer. They are regularly found within 10km of the coasts of Ireland although in other parts of their range they are considered typical of edges of the continental shelves. Stranding sites are indicated as dark circles on the map of Ireland.

Diet

Risso's dolphins feed almost exclusively on squid, cuttlefish and octopus. The circular suckers on the squid's arms presumably cause most of the circular wounds seen on the skin of Risso's dolphin. Risso's dolphins also eat small quantities of fish. They hunt in deep and shallow waters and often forage cooperatively.

Social organisation and reproduction

Risso's dolphins are generally seen singly or in groups of fewer than ten, but larger groups are not uncommon. They appear to be found closer inshore in summer and migrate to deeper waters in winter. Risso's dolphins may form stable groups and occupy the same home range for several years at least. They appear to form mixed-sex groups consisting of a mature male and four to six adult females with their dependent young. Males apparently fight for control of these female groups. Although males and females are approximately the same size there appears to be substantial aggression between males. This is apparently the reason for the linear scars that are more common in males than females and are particularly evident in older males. Risso's dolphins first breed at three or four years of age.

In the North Atlantic calves are born mainly between March and June, probably in deeper water offshore. Mating probably takes place mainly between June and September. The gestation period is not known and the single calf measures about 1.5m long at birth. Risso's dolphins breed off the Irish coast. For example, one was born in Blacksod Bay (Co Mayo) in the 1930s and a small individual with seven light grey vertical stripes, the typical coloration of a new-born Risso's dolphin, was stranded in July 1990 at Rosbrin Cove (Co Cork).

Conservation

Risso's dolphin is hunted on a small scale throughout its range but particularly so in Sri Lanka. It is also occasionally killed in fishing nets. There are no reliable estimates of population sizes available.

There have been occasional reports of hybridisation between Risso's dolphin and the bottle-nosed dolphin both in captivity and in the wild. Three suspected hybrids were detected in Blacksod Bay (Co Mayo) in the late 1930s. This suggests that these species may be more closely related than their taxonomy would suggest.

Studying Risso's dolphins

Risso's dolphins are widely distributed all along the west and south coasts. They are also regularly seen in the eastern Irish Sea. They appear to move closer to the shore in summer. The headlands on the south and west coasts, such as Courtmacsherry Bay and the Old Head of Kinsale (Co Cork) and Benwee head (Co Mayo), are good viewing areas. They may occasionally be seen near the Saltee Islands and at Rosslare (Co Wexford), the Skelligs and the Blasket Islands (Co Kerry). (See page 144 for advice on watching dolphins.)

Risso's dolphins are relatively slow swimmers and although they often approach close to boats, rarely ride along on the bow wave. They often jump clear of (breach) the water but not as often as white-beaked dolphins. Interactions between Risso's dolphins are often quite boisterous. They are sometimes seen in the presence of pilot whales and other dolphins. Risso's dolphin is the eighth most frequently stranded species on the Irish coasts. There is a 1:12 scale-model of Risso's dolphin, together with a skull from a specimen stranded in Blacksod Bay (Co Mayo), in the Natural History Museum, Dublin.

Hedgehog – *Grainneóg*
size : approx. 26 cm

Pygmy shrew – *Luch féir/Dallóg fhraoigh*
size : approx. 50 mm

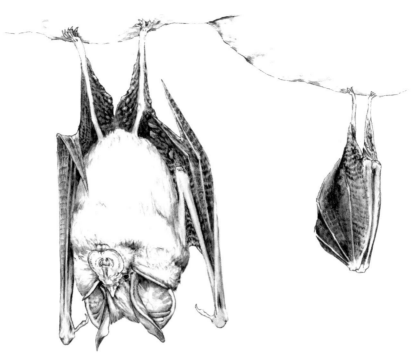

Lesser horseshoe bat – *Ialtóg crúshrónach/Crú-ialtóg beag*
size : approx. 37 mm

Whiskered bat – *Ialtóg ghiobach*
size : approx. 41 mm

Natterer's bat – *Ialtóg Nattereir*
size : approx. 45 mm

Daubenton's bat – *Ialtóg uisce*
size : approx. 47 mm

Leisler's bat – *Ialtóg Leisler*
size : approx. 59 mm

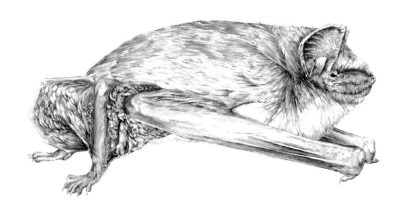

Common pipistrelle – *Ialtóg fheascrach*
size : approx. 42 mm

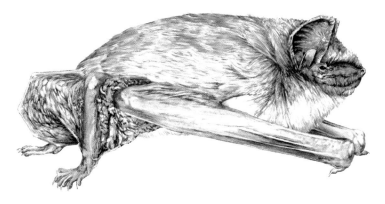

Soprano pipistrelle – *Ialtóg fheascrach sopránach*
size : approx. 41 mm

Nathusius' pipistrelle – *Ialtóg Nathusius*
size : approx. 42 mm

Brown long-eared bat – *Ialtóg fhad-chluasach*
size : approx. 42 mm

Rabbit – *Coinín*
size : approx. 50 cm

Brown hare – *Giorria gallda*
size : approx. 65 cm

Mountain (Irish) hare – *Giorria*
size : approx. 61 cm

Red squirrel – *Iora rua*
size : approx. 48 cm

Grey squirrel – *Iora glas*
size : approx. 40 cm

Bank vole – *Luch Rua/Vól bruaigh*
size : approx. 15 cm

Wood mouse – *Luch (luchóg) fhéir*
size : approx. 17 cm

House mouse – *Luch thí*
size : approx. 17 cm

Brown rat – *Francach donn*
size : approx. 26 cm

Black rat – *Francach dubh*
size : approx. 22 cm

The northern right whale – *Fíormhíol mór na Bioscáine*
size : approx. 15 m

Humpback whale – *Míol mór dronnach*
size : approx. 15 m

Fin whale – *Míol mór eiteach*
size : approx. 20 m

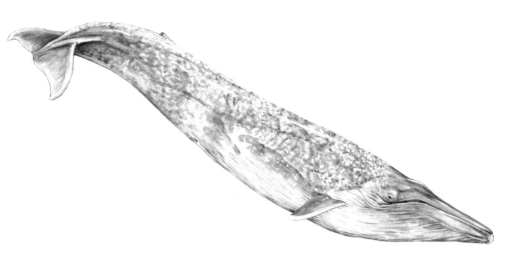

Blue whale – *Míol mór gorm*
size : approx. 25 m

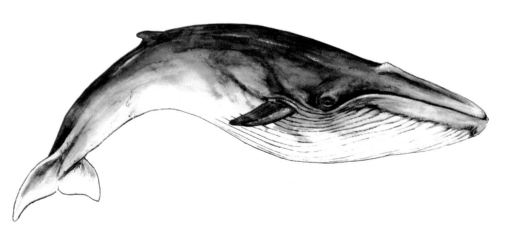

Sei whale – *Míol mór an tuaisceart*
size : approx. 15 m

Minke whale – *Droimeiteach beag/Míol mór mince*
size : approx. 8 m

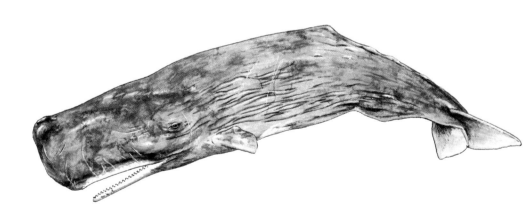

Sperm whale – *Caisealóid*
size : approx. 14 m

Pygmy sperm whale – *Caisealóid beag*
size : approx. 3 m

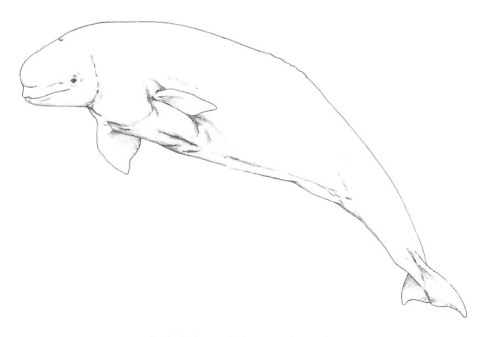

Beluga/White whale – *Míol mór bán*
size : approx. 4 m

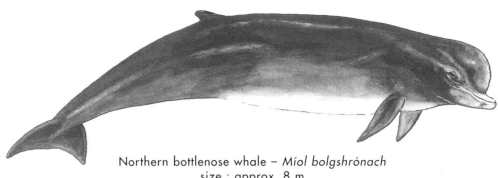

Northern bottlenose whale – *Míol bolgshrónach*
size : approx. 8 m

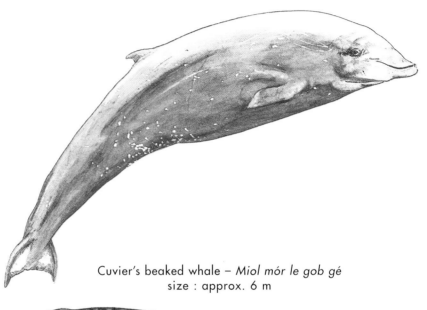

Cuvier's beaked whale – *Miol mór le gob gé*
size : approx. 6 m

Gervais' beaked whale – *Miol mór gobach na h-Eorpa*
size : approx. 4 m

Sowerby's beaked whale −*Miol Mór gobach an tuaisceart*
size : approx. 5 m

True's beaked whale − *Miol mór gobach le clár-fiacla*
size : approx. 5 m

Common (harbour) porpoise – *Much mhara*
size : approx. 1.5 m

Common dolphin – *Deilf/Dorad*
size : approx. 2 m

Striped dolphin – *Deilf riabach*
size : approx. 2.5 m

Bottle-nosed dolphin – *Deilf bolgshrónach*
size : approx. 3.5 m

White-sided dolphin – *Deilf le cliathán bán*
size : approx. 2.5 m

White-beaked dolphin – *Deilf na ngoba bána*
size : approx. 2.5 m

False killer whale – *Cráin dubh bréagach*
size : approx. 5 m

Killer whale (Orca) – *Cráin dubh/Orc*
size : approx. 7.5 m

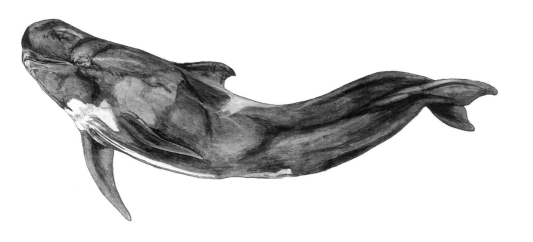

Long-finned pilot whale –*Miol phíolótach*
size : approx. 5 m

Risso's dolphin – *Deilf liath*
size : approx. 3.5 m

Red fox – *Sionnach/Madra rua*
size : approx. 100 cm

Pine marten – *Cat crainn*
size : approx. 65 cm

Irish stoat – *Easóg*
size : approx. 35 cm

American mink – *Minc mhericeánach*
size : approx. 55 cm

Badger – *Broc*
size : approx. 90 cm

Eurasian otter – *Dobharchú/Madra uisce*
size : approx. 115 cm

Common (harbour) seal – *Rón breacach (beag)*
size : approx. 1.5 m

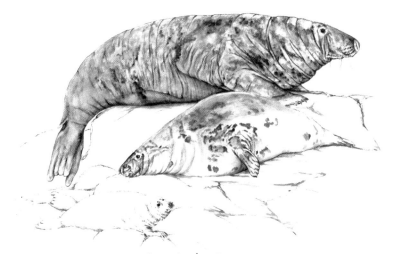

Grey seal – *Rón mór*
size : approx. 2 m

Walrus – *Rosualt*
size : approx. 3 m

Red deer – *Fia rua*
size : approx. 115 cm tall

Sika deer – *Fia Seapánach*
size : approx. 70 cm tall

Fallow deer – *Fia buí*
size : approx.90 cm tall

Wild (feral) goat – *Gabhar fiáin*
size : approx. 60 cm tall (varies widely)

CHAPTER 8

Order Carnivora – Cat-like and Dog-like Mammals

The lion glares
A hungered; and, behind, as meaner beasts
that wait the lions onset for their share
Outlaw'd and reprobate of many a land,
The ravening crew.
S. Ferguson (1810-1886)

The Carnivora first arose about 60 million years ago, soon after the disappearance of the dinosaurs. Although a number of types evolved, only one line survived to act as the ancestor of all modern Carnivora. This ancestral group gave rise to two main lines, the Canoidea (dog-like carnivores) and the Feloidea (cat-like carnivores). Most of the Canoidea, including the racoons (Procyonidae), the bears (Ursidae) and the weasels (Mustelidae), appeared between 30 and 40 million years ago. The dog family itself (Canidae) did not appear until about 20 million years ago. The Feloidea, including the hyenas (Hyaenidae) and the mongooses (Viverridae), first appeared between 30 and 40 million years ago. The cat family itself (Felidae), like its counterpart the dogs (Canidae), was a relatively late arrival, about 20 million years ago.

The classification of seals causes some debate among zoologists. The seals date from about 20–25 million years ago and have evolved certain characteristics, associated with their aquatic lifestyle, which distinguish them from other carnivores. For this reason they are sometimes considered as a separate order, the Pinnipedia (and that is how they are treated in this book).

Characteristics

Carnivora range in size from the least weasel which weighs as little as 35g, to the brown bear, which may weigh up to 750kg. Modern Carnivora are, in general, carnivores or meat-eaters. They range, however, from species which live on a diet consisting exclusively of meat or fish (such as the lion and the polar bear) to those such as the aardwolf which is almost exclusively insectivorous. On the other hand, the giant and red pandas are mainly vegetarian, although they may supplement their diet with meat and invertebrates. Many of the Carnivora are omnivorous.

The teeth are their most characteristic features. Their incisors are shaped like gouges and strip meat from bones. The canines are long and sharp for stabbing, slashing and grasping their prey. The cheek teeth have a particular innovation that involves the last upper premolar and the first lower molar on each side of the jaws. These are enlarged and particularly sharp and shear past one another with a powerful scissors-like action. This allows the Carnivora to slice through flesh, hide and tendons and, in certain cases, to splinter bones to extract the marrow.

Carnivora have adapted to almost all habitats and have mastered almost all modes of progression except flight. Some live above ground, some in burrows, some in trees and yet others are aquatic. Most can run, climb and swim.

The limbs vary in length and the faster runners usually have relatively long, slender limbs. There are five digits (fingers/toes) on each foot in many species. However, in some species these are reduced to four.

The digestive system varies in different dietary specialists. In general the gut is rather simple, but because of the difficulties in digesting plant material the digestive system in vegetarians is relatively longer and more complex.

Diversity

The modern Carnivora contains seven families. The superfamily Canoidea contains 126 species in four families: the Canidae (dogs etc), Mustelidae (weasels etc), Ursidae (bears) and Procyonidae (racoons). The superfamily Feloidea includes 58 species in three families: the Viverridae (mongooses), Hyaenidae (hyenas) and Felidae (cats).

Worldwide distribution

The living Carnivora are widely distributed across the globe and are native to most land areas except Antarctica, Australia and New Zealand. They are also absent from most oceanic islands. Accidental transport or deliberate introduction by man has extended the current distribution of many species to regions well outside their natural range. For example, dogs, cats, foxes, stoats, ferrets and mongooses are now living wild in either Australia or New Zealand.

Distribution in Ireland

There are members of seven families of Carnivora in Europe, and two of these, the Mustelidae and Canidae, are currently represented in Ireland. (Domestic cats are not counted, and so we do not say we have the Felidae in Ireland.) The five mustelids found in Ireland are the badger, the otter, the stoat, the pine marten and the mink. The sole canid in Ireland, excluding the domestic dog, is the red fox. However, in former times the wolf (Canidae), the brown bear (Ursidae), the wild cat (Felidae) and the spotted hyena (Hyaenidae) were present. There have been recent reports of ferrets living in the wild in some northern counties, but whether this species will become established remains to be seen.

Studying carnivores

The local rangers of Dúchas The Heritage Service of the Department of Arts, Heritage, Gaeltacht and The Islands (RoI) or of the Environment Service of the Department of the Environment (NI) will be able to provide information on carnivores locally. The local game clubs and hunts will have information on areas where foxes may be seen; members of the local angling club know where otters may be seen; local foresters will be able to provide information on pine martens.

Red fox – *Sionnach/Madra rua*
Vulpes vulpes, Linnaeus 1758

The red fox is common and widespread in Ireland, and public attitudes to it are often ambivalent.

The names

The scientific description of the fox is that of Linnaeus, written in 1758 and based on specimens from Sweden. The scientific name uses the Latin for fox (*vulpes*) for both parts, so the name may be translated as the foxy fox. The derivation of the Irish name *sionnach* is not clear, but *madra rua* means red dog. There are many place names in Ireland which refer to the fox, eg Pollnashinnagh, the hole (*poll*) of the fox (Co Galway), Monashinnagh, the bog (*móin*) of the fox (Co Limerick), Derrintinny, the wood (*doire*) of the fox (*an tsionnaigh*) (Co Cavan), Craigmaddyroe, the rock or crag (*carraig*) of the fox (*mada* or *madra rua*) (Co Donegal), which might be translated as 'Foxrock'. A male fox is called a dog; a female is a vixen; and the young are cubs.

Identification and characteristics

The fox is one of our most handsome mammals. It is our only wild member of the dog family, and is easily recognised by its general dog-like appearance. The red fox is about as large as a big domestic cat, and males are slightly larger than females. Male foxes (dogs) may weigh up to 9kg but are more usually about 6-7kg; large females (vixens) may weigh up to 8kg, although 5-6kg is more usual. The total length of an adult dog fox is about 100cm, including 41cm of tail. Vixens are about 5% smaller (96cm). It is difficult to tell the dog from the vixen unless she is feeding cubs. Then her enlarged mammary glands will be more obvious.

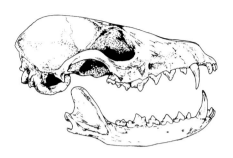

The fox's overall coat colour is due to the longer guard hairs, which usually range from yellowish brown to reddish brown, but individuals that are almost black or grey are sometimes encountered. The shorter underfur is greyish. The erect ears have black tips and backs. There are also black markings on the face but the muzzle is white. The underside of the throat is usually white also but it may be greyish. The feet are generally black. The black socks extend for variable extents up the legs. The coat is moulted and replaced beginning in spring. There is a secondary phase of hair growth in autumn that thickens the coat before winter. In summer foxes may appear rather thin and scruffy when their coat is partly moulted and the tail is less bushy. The long, bushy tail is usually held horizontally out behind the animal. It is nearly the same length as the body and has a white tip.

Foxes normally travel through their territory at a leisurely walk or a slow trot or canter. There are five toes on the fore-feet although only four touch the ground. The hind-feet have four toes. The general design of the teeth of a fox is quite similar to that of the domestic dog. Foxes have 20 teeth in the upper and 22 in the lower jaws.

The fox's eyesight is particularly suited to conditions of low light but is otherwise not particularly good. Foxes have relatively long sensory whiskers on the face that extend outwards over 10cm on either side. They have an extremely well-developed sense of smell and scents play an important role in communicating information about potential enemies, prey or other foxes. Foxes have a number of scent glands, around the anus and on the upper side of the tail, which are used to mark their home ranges. The caudal scent gland lies under a patch of slightly darker fur 6–7cm from the base of the tail. Urine is also an important signalling system and foxes frequently urinate at particular locations within their territory. This conveys information about the identity of the owner, his or her status and breeding condition. Faeces (droppings or scats) are also often deposited in conspicuous locations on trails or grass tussocks.

The sense of hearing of foxes is particularly acute and is important for hunting and communication. Some prey such as earthworms on the soil surface or insects and mice in grass may be detected by sound. Foxes are also highly vocal and have a wide range of sounds, the most characteristic of which are a triple bark and a high-pitched chilling scream. Vixens usually emit this latter sound during the breeding season in winter. Visual signals are also important and much information is transferred between foxes by body postures and facial expressions.

Distribution

Foxes of the genus *Vulpes* first evolved in Eurasia about 4–5 million years ago. The earliest record of the red fox dates from Europe 400,000 years ago. It is indigenous to northern Eurasia but is now one of the most widespread mammals in the world. It is widespread in Europe but absent from Iceland. It was introduced from Europe to North America in the 18th century and is now found across most of the northern hemisphere. The current distribution in the northern hemisphere is shown. It was also introduced to Australia.

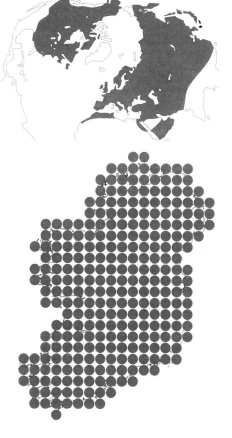

Foxes are quite adept at crossing land or ice-bridges and so it might have been an early postglacial colonist in Ireland. Nevertheless, bones of the red fox have only been found in archaeological sites from neolithic times onwards, dating from about 5000 years ago. The fox has been continually present here in varying numbers during historic times. For example, exports of fox skins from Ireland were quite variable during the 18th century, but had declined to a trickle by the beginning of the 19th. Indeed, foxes were translocated within the country and imported from Wales and released to augment wild stocks in the late 19th and early 20th centuries. It is now common and found all over the country. The size of the present population is unknown but comparisons with data from Britain suggest that there are probably between 150,000 and 200,000 foxes in Ireland. Up to 35,000 fox pelts were exported from Ireland each year during the 1970s and 1980s without any apparent effect on the population size. There is almost no 1km square of dry land in the country that is not visited by a fox, but they are absent from most offshore islands. The distribution map shows the 20 km squares in which foxes occur in Ireland.

Habitats, social organisation and habits

The fox is so successful because it is an adept opportunist and not over-specialised for any particular lifestyle. It thrives in a variety of locations and has no particular habitat requirements. If food and shelter are available, then the fox will prosper particularly in areas of habitat diversity. Foxes are found in farmland, woodland, coastal areas, sand dunes, uplands and in suburban areas; they have been seen in Dublin since at least the 1930s, and also in

Belfast. There appears to have been a major expansion in Dublin during the 1970s and 1980s, as the suburbs expanded; for example, in parts of Dublin there may be up to five family groups per square kilometre. The fox is mainly nocturnal and active at dawn and dusk but may be seen by day if disturbance and persecution are minimal. Vixens nursing cubs are likely to be active by day.

There has been little or no study of the social organisation of foxes in Ireland, and most studies in Britain have been carried out on high-density populations in suburban and urban-edge habitats. In general foxes are territorial and live in family groups. The composition of the group varies. In high-density populations it usually contains one adult male, a breeding vixen and a number, usually one or two, of adult, non-breeding females. These females are usually young relatives of the most dominant female, and act as helpers and playmates for the cubs. It is generally assumed that the non-breeding females temporarily sacrifice the chance to disperse and perhaps breed in favour of staying with their mother and helping to rear their younger relatives. In due course they might themselves become the dominant vixen and inherit the territory. In lower-density populations breeding pairs are more usual. The area of a fox's territory varies with the abundance of food. Territories may be as small as 20 hectares in suburbs or larger than 1000 hectares on upland areas. The territories are marked with urine and faeces, which are often deposited at conspicuous locations. Foxes use definite paths or trails that traverse their territories. Hair can often be found on brambles or on wire, which are close to pathways.

Foxes excavate underground dens, termed earths, in a variety of locations. They may be found in banks, enlarged rabbit burrows, disused (or even currently used) badger setts, rock crevices, drains, disused buildings, under sheds and so forth. There are usually a number of earths in each territory. Earths tend to be used by foxes in bad weather or by breeding females with cubs. Otherwise foxes prefer to lie up in secluded areas or under cover above ground. Earths occupied by cubs are detectable by debris of fresh food strewn around the entrance and by a strong smell of fox and often of rotting food.

Diet

Although the fox is primarily a carnivore, it is a non-specialist and its diet is extremely varied. It displays a range of hunting and foraging techniques depending on the particular prey. If the fox has a specialised skill, it is that of a pouncing vole- or mouse-killer.

In Ireland the composition of the diet depends greatly on the location and time of year. The principal items are rabbits, young hares, brown rats and wood mice. Foxes tend to switch to brown rats when rabbit populations are reduced by myxomatosis. Irish foxes take proportionately more rats than do foxes in Britain even where rabbits are present. This is probably because the field vole *(Microtus agrestis)*, an important prey of the fox in other parts of Europe, is absent from Ireland. Small birds, pigeons, game birds and eggs and nestlings of ground-nesting birds are also eaten, as are a wide variety of invertebrates, particularly beetles and earthworms. Foxes also eat a range of fruit, particularly blackberries and apples.

Foxes living on or near the coast will eat crabs and fish. In most areas, foxes scavenge carcasses of, for example, sheep and deer. They will occasionally kill larger prey such as newborn lambs or deer, but this is probably unusual and of little significance in their overall diet. Foxes will bury food in caches for future use. They appear to be adapting to life in towns, particularly suburban areas with large gardens, where they forage on lawns and in parks, scavenge around dumps and raid dustbins. Many are being fed by householders, which further improves their condition.

Reproduction and life-cycle

In Ireland the breeding season occurs from late December to early February. Foxes are largely monogamous and although they are mature at about ten months of age, usually breed for the first time during their second year. Social constraints usually ensure that only one vixen in each group bears cubs, but in exceptionally rich territories two may breed.

During the breeding season foxes become particularly vocal. They use a characteristic triple bark to find one another. Courtship is complex and may be protracted. It involves a range of characteristic scents, vocal signals and body posturing. While the vixen is in heat (oestrous) the dog remains in constant attendance. Females are fertile for about three days during their three-week oestrous period. A male may spend all his time close to the female during this period to defend her against other males. Females usually emit blood-curdling wails or screams during the breeding season. Males sometimes also do so. The screaming often attracts rival males and fighting is common. These fights are highly ritualised and the males barge and wrestle one another but do not usually bite. The territorial male usually wins.

The gestation period is about 53 days and the cubs are born between late February and the end of April. Foxes produce one litter a year. The normal litter size is four or five. The cubs weigh about 100g each and are blind and deaf at birth. Their coats range from chocolate-brown to black and they have blue eyes. The vixen stays with the cubs for the first three weeks and food is brought to her by the dog fox. She may move the cubs from one earth to another during this period. She carries them in her mouth, holding them by the scruff of the neck. By four weeks of age, the cubs are developing their adult coat colour, their eyes begin to change to the amber colour of adults and they are beginning to venture above ground. If they now change earths the vixen makes them follow her on foot.

Cubs are almost fully grown by seven months of age. They begin to disperse about November. Young males usually leave and attempt to establish territories of their own; while some young females disperse, one or two remain with their mothers as helpers. Mortality of cubs is high; at least half (and perhaps as many as 80%) die before their first birthday. Foxes rarely live beyond four years in the wild although, exceptionally, an animal may survive for ten years. Foxes may become infected with sarcoptic mange. This is caused by a parasitic mite that burrows into the skin, creating severe irritation and weeping ulcers. Infected foxes may lose large patches of fur and they become thin and debilitated. Many foxes in infected populations die from this disease.

Watching foxes

The presence of foxes is generally revealed by their scats (droppings), which they deposit in conspicuous locations throughout their territory. The scats resemble those of dogs but have a characteristic foxy smell. This is mainly due to urine, which is often sprayed in the vicinity. Secretions from glands just inside the anus, which are released as the faeces are produced, also add to the cocktail of scents. The scats are more structured than those of dogs and contain traces of undigested prey, fragments of beetles, bone fragments, seeds and hair. Hair from ingested prey often gives a characteristic twisted tail to the trailing end of the scat. Foxes also use urine to mark key locations within their territory and the characteristic strong musky smell is a sure sign that a fox has recently been in the vicinity. The footprints are about 3–4cm across and about 5cm long and usually show four toe marks with slight claw impressions. It is sometimes difficult to distinguish between the prints of a fox and a dog, but the fox keeps its toes closer together, whereas those of a dog are wider relative to their length. Fox hair is often found entangled on wire or brambles where the fox uses a gap to cross a hedge or fence-line. The general impression of fox hair is fluffy but the long guard hairs are red at the base, darker in the middle and reddish at the tip.

Feathers of birds eaten by foxes are usually chewed through. Larger prey items such as lambs often have puncture marks made by the upper canine teeth, which are about 3cm apart, and the lower pair, which are about 2.5cm apart. If there is bruising around the bite marks then the wounds were inflicted while the prey was alive. If there is no bruising then the prey was scavenged after death.

Suburban foxes are perhaps easiest to observe, as they are relatively accustomed to man's activities and are not systematically persecuted. Foxes will quickly learn if scraps of food are left out for them and will incorporate a nightly visit to the feeding site during their hunting trips. The best place to watch foxes is at an earth which contains cubs, usually in May or June. An occupied earth will usually have remains of food items strewn around and will smell of fox. Fox cubs may be seen playing around the earth and one or both of the parents will be near by and will visit the cubs from time to time. When viewing foxes at an earth, care must be taken to remain concealed and sufficiently far away that the animals are relaxed and behaving in a normal manner. It is of course important to remain downwind of the earth.

Conservation and management

Man and fox have traditionally had an uneasy relationship and foxes are generally considered to be vermin. There is little data from Ireland on the extent of predation by foxes on domestic birds and mammals but they may have a significant effect locally. It is, however, difficult to substantiate the claim that the fox is a major predator of lambs.

Foxes occasionally indulge in surplus killing, particularly if they gain access to hen houses, pheasant rearing-pens or colonies of ground-nesting birds. Some of this is probably influenced by the general state of confusion and panic among the birds. Foxes may also kill substantial numbers of newly released pen-reared gamebirds, which seem ill-equipped to deal with life in the wild. Reduction of fox numbers locally appears to increase the number of gamebirds shot in the autumn, but since most birds shot in any one season are usually birds that were released earlier in the year, it is not clear if the resident breeding population of gamebirds is increased when foxes are culled.

In other countries the fox is a major carrier of rabies, but at present Ireland is rabies-free. Killing foxes as a means of controlling the spread of rabies in continental Europe has now largely been abandoned in favour of vaccination. Foxes readily accept an oral vaccine added to offal and this approach is now a major factor in controlling rabies in western Europe. Rabies was quite common in Ireland until the early 20th century. The main reservoir of the disease was the domestic dog. There has only been one documented case in Ireland of rabies having been contracted from a fox, a tame individual, in 1887.

Foxes in Ireland have been trapped or shot for their pelts but this practice decreased during the 1980s. There are indications that fox numbers have increased since then, despite a renewal of vermin control by regional game councils, farmers and hunters, killing an estimated 30,000 foxes annually. Accurate statistics on the population dynamics of foxes in Ireland are not available but the total population is probably between 150,000 and 200,000 foxes before the breeding season each year. This would have increased at the end of the year by a further 40,000–50,000 due to cubs surviving to their first winter.

There are no reliable objective data on the relative importance of the various mortality factors normally acting on fox populations that are not subjected to artificial control. It is even less clear what proportion of additional annual mortality of foxes is due to man's activities, such as vermin control or hunting. It is clear, however, that where vermin control is carried out, it is the major mortality factor affecting adult foxes but whether it actually reduces fox density is not clear. The effect of foxhunting with hounds on fox populations is particularly unquantified. Foxes have traditionally been hunted by packs of foxhounds or harriers. At present there are about 250 packs of foxhounds or harriers, of which about 70 are followed on horseback. It is not clear how many foxes are killed by hunting with hounds in this country. Figures from Britain indicate that each hunt kills fewer than 50 foxes a year. If the situation in Ireland is similar then the impact of hunting must be less than 10,000 foxes per annum, although this is almost certainly an overestimate. Thus the estimated mortality of culling and foxhunting combined scarcely keeps pace with the annual increase in population. Fox-hunting alone certainly does not seem capable of stabilising fox numbers, although it cannot be excluded that it has a localised effect. It seems likely that, with the ongoing increase in afforestation and their continuing movement into urban areas, the population of foxes will increase further. This additional element exploiting new and improved habitats will probably prove extremely difficult to manage.

Pine marten – *Cat crainn*
Martes martes, Linnaeus 1758

The pine marten was extremely localised and quite rare until recently. It is now recovering and extending its range to most parts of the country.

The names

The pine marten was first described from Swedish specimens by Linnaeus in 1758. The scientific name uses the Latin for marten (*martes*) for both parts. The Irish name is cat (*cat*) of the tree (*crainn*). It was well known to our forefathers and there are many placenames, particularly in the west of Ireland, which refer to a cat. Most of these, given their location, almost certainly refer to the tree cat (the pine marten). Some examples are Carrickacat (Co Mayo) and Carrigacat (Co Cork), both meaning the rock of the cat or cats, Craignagat (crag of the cats, Co Antrim), Glennagat (glen of the cats, Co Tipperary), Knockaunacat (hill of the cat, Cos Mayo, Galway and Waterford).

Identification and characteristics

The pine marten is one of our most beautiful and distinctive animals. It belongs to the family Mustelidae, which also includes the otter, mink, stoat and badger. The pine marten is a medium-sized mustelid: males usually weigh from 1.5 to 1.9kg. Females are smaller, 1.1–1.5kg. The pine marten has a long, slender body. Males measure 66–73cm from nose to the tip of the tail, females 61–66cm.

The pine marten is somewhat cat-like but with a longer, flatter and more pointed head. It has quite long legs and its tail is long and fluffy. The tail is much bushier than that of a red squirrel. The ears are large and rounded and are pale on the insides. There are 18 teeth in the upper set and 20 in the lower. The coat is a rich dark brown and may be almost black. The underfur is reddish. It has a creamy-white throat patch. The nose is black.

Its feet are relatively large and the soles are hairy. There are five digits, equipped with sharp claws, on the fore- and hind-legs. The claws may be partially retracted. In this the pine marten falls somewhere between the dog, whose claws are permanently extended, and the cat whose claws may be totally withdrawn. It has a rather erect stance and a characteristic loping gait. It is well adapted for life in trees and is an athletic climber. It can jump between branches and uses its long tail for balance. This is probably where it gets its Irish name of tree-cat.

Pine martens are not particularly vocal, but they have a variety of calls including coughs, growls, purrs and meows. Their sense of smell is excellent and their hearing and eyesight are also well developed. They are quite inquisitive and will regularly visit artificial feeding sites once their trust has been gained.

Distribution and population density

The pine marten is widespread in forests throughout Europe except in Spain and Greece. It extends into western Russia. The pine marten is often assumed to have colonised Ireland about 8000–9000 years ago, just after the last ice age. However, it has not yet been found in prehistoric sites and is not common in archaeological sites until the early Christian era. The earliest dated specimen is from 2780 years ago.

It was formerly widespread in Britain and Ireland but suffered serious decline in the 17th century with the deforestation of the country, which destroyed its habitat. Pine martens further suffered in the 19th century, due to persecution by gamekeepers and trappers. The former considered it vermin while the latter sought their pelts. Nevertheless, up to the 1940s pine marten were still recorded throughout most of the country. However, it then declined and until recently it was considered one of our rarest mammals. It was largely confined to the mid-west of Ireland in suitable sites from Limerick to Sligo and particularly in the Burren (Co Clare). There was also a population in the Slieve Bloom mountains and two smaller ones at Portlaw (Co Waterford) and in the Boyne Valley (Co Meath).

In recent years its numbers have been increasing, its range is expanding, and there is good evidence that this mammal is recovering from its former decline. There are now verified reports of its further occurrence in Wicklow, Kildare, Laois, Carlow, Dublin, Fermanagh, Tyrone, Antrim and Down. There is also a small population in and around the Killarney National Park (Co Kerry), which has been reinforced with animals from Clare. It is probably now to be found in about half the counties of Ireland, but recovery of the pine marten will probably be slow east of the Shannon.

The national population of pine martens is unknown. The population density may range from one pine marten per square kilometre to one per 10km². The higher densities are associated with more mature woodland on good soils. The distribution map shows the 20 km squares where pine martens may occur in suitable habitats.

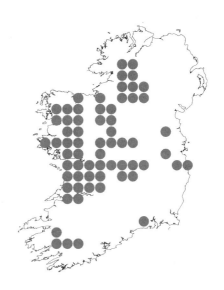

Habitats and habits

The pine marten may be found in a variety of habitats across Europe, but it mainly occurs in coniferous or deciduous woodland or scrub. It is an extremely adaptable and opportunistic animal and may also be found in pasture areas, moorland or on the coast. In Ireland, its main strongholds are deciduous woodland or scrub with good ground cover. It is also relatively common in the extensive areas of hazel scrub on the limestone pavement of the Burren. Recently it has begun to colonise mixed woodland and coniferous thickets. It apparently also likes to hunt in areas where conifer forest has been clear-felled, particularly where herb and scrub species have begun to re-colonise the ground.

Pine martens are territorial and solitary. Males and females defend territories independently of one another. They mark the boundaries with faeces and urine. They have a number of scent glands on their bodies that they use to deposit scents at strategic locations in their territory. They use their anal gland throughout the year but their abdominal gland appears to be most active and used most frequently during the breeding season. The anal glands produce a yellowish fluid used to mark on prominent objects in the territory. Territories of males and females may overlap but animals are quite intolerant of others of the same sex. The territories defended by males tend to be larger than those of females. In the mixed woodlands of Dromore in the west of Ireland, territories of males range from 50 to 80ha, while those of females vary from 14 to 25ha. It is likely that larger territories are defended in poorer habitats. Pine martens may have a number of dens in their home range. Nest sites or dens may be found in a variety of locations such as hollow trees, clefts in rocks, abandoned squirrel nests or outbuildings. Although of nervous disposition, they are not particularly shy of humans and may even take up residence in the roofs of occupied buildings.

Diet

The pine marten is primarily a carnivore that preys on a wide variety of small animals and birds. It supplements its diet with fruit and invertebrates. Although it is a very skilled climber, it hunts mainly on the ground. It preys on rodents such as wood mice and rats but also hunts rabbits, young hares, frogs and roosting birds. It occasionally eats squirrels. In coastal areas it will eat shore crabs and fish. It also eats invertebrates such as earthworms, cockchafers and other beetles. In autumn, it eats a range of berries, including blackberries and ivy berries. It will also eat other fruits such as sloes and it eats mushrooms in winter. In parts of Ireland fruits and berries may form a major component of the diet for about six months.

The fact that pine martens readily eat carrion makes them susceptible to poisoned bait laid to control foxes. Pine martens are mainly nocturnal but may be seen by day, particularly in summer, when females are feeding young. They are particularly active at dawn and dusk. They may carry out more hunting trips each night in winter when food is more difficult to find.

Reproduction and life-cycle

Reproduction in pine martens is not well understood. They breed once a year. The mating season is from August to September, when food is abundant. At this time the normally solitary male and female pine martens are more tolerant of each other. Courtship is quite frantic and borders on the violent. Females may mate several times during the fertile period. It seems likely that a female may mate with more than one male, depending on local population density.

Gestation does not begin immediately. Implantation of the fertilised eggs in the womb may be delayed, by environmental factors such as food supply or weather conditions, for up to six months. This mechanism allows birth to occur during more suitable conditions. When development of the foetuses begins, it is quite rapid and the young (kits) are born about 30 days later, usually in late March or April. Normally litters contain three kits, but litter size may range from one to five. The kits weigh about 30g at birth and are blind, deaf and covered with short greyish fur, which is gradually replaced by red–brown hair.

The kits grow rapidly and begin to venture from their den at about six to eight weeks of age. Weaning begins when the kits are about eight or nine weeks of age. They will stay with their mother until August or September. By then they will be almost fully grown and will disperse to find territories of their own. Pine marten may enter breeding condition when they are about 17 months of age but it is unusual for animals to breed successfully before their third year. Pine martens may live for over ten years in captivity but most do not survive past five or six years.

Watching pine martens

This is one of the most elusive of our mammals. But paradoxically if they take up residence near human habitations, they may become quite tame and habituated to humans if they are not harassed. Its low density and territoriality makes it still somewhat difficult to find, but the effort is well repaid by the reward of observing such a fine animal. Chance observation is the most likely means of seeing them. However, a good strategy is to make contact with someone like the local conservation ranger who may have an interest in and information on pine martens in the vicinity. Pine martens may sometimes be found in the vicinity of outbuildings in rural areas and may become quite tame.

The most common field signs of pine martens are their droppings, which they tend to deposit in conspicuous locations. The droppings are variable in appearance and their shape and persistence depends to some extent on the diet. Fresh droppings often have a purple tinge. If the pine marten has been feeding on small mammals then the droppings range from about 7 to 15mm in diameter and have a general twisted or braided appearance and are usually folded back on themselves. Unlike the droppings of foxes or mink, they do not have a strong odour when fresh. When the main element of the diet is berries, then the droppings are rather more moist and shapeless and disintegrate within a day or so. The droppings can often be found at intervals along linear features of the habitat such as forest tracks and roads or on prominent features such as mounds, rocks or trees. The best way to check a forest for the presence of pine martens is to walk the forest roads and trails in search of the droppings. This will then indicate areas where sightings might be most likely. Dromore Wood (Co Clare) and Muckross Peninsula (Co Kerry) are good sites for observing pine martens.

Conservation and management

The fur of the pine marten has been highly prized, and they have certainly been trapped for their fur throughout historical times and, on a small scale, into the 20th century in Ireland. It is still an important fur-bearing species in parts of Europe and Asia. It has never been successfully recruited by the fur-farming industry, however, because, unlike the mink, it matures relatively late, produces small litters and is more particular regarding the conditions of its captivity. It has, however, been bred successfully in captivity for reintroduction programmes in this country.

The former classification of the pine marten as vermin contributed to its persecution, but the major cause of its recent decline seems to have been the use, in sheep-farming areas, of strychnine-loaded carrion to control foxes, which were believed to be a major predator of lambs. Pine martens survived in areas of less intensive sheep-farming such as Co Clare, where presumably the use of poisons was less widespread. The ban on the use of strychnine for vermin control lessens the probability of inadvertent poisoning, and the pine marten now appears to be recovering from its very restricted status in Ireland. Its future range expansion seems likely as afforestation increases.

Since the pine marten now exists in a number of isolated populations, translocation of individuals to found new populations may not now be so necessary as was formerly thought. Its apparent tolerance of man and increased sightings may enhance public awareness and concern for its future. Despite recently changing attitudes to the pine marten, it is well to remember that it is primarily a predator and individual pine martens may cause considerable damage if they gain access to poultry or gamebird pens. Wherever there are large numbers of vulnerable animals, such as in gamebird rearing-pens or poultry pens, then protection must be provided by appropriate fencing and extreme vigilance.

The pine marten is listed in Annexes II and IV of the Habitats Directive as a species of European interest, which requires both strict protection and the designation of special conservation areas. It is also listed in Appendix III of the Bern Convention as a species requiring protection. It is totally protected in the Republic of Ireland and Northern Ireland.

Irish stoat – *Easóg*
Mustela erminea, Linnaeus 1758

The stoat is the smallest and most elusive of Ireland's carnivores. It differs somewhat from stoats elsewhere and is considered to be a separate subspecies.

The names

The scientific account of the stoat is based on Swedish specimens described by Linnaeus in 1758. The generic name *mustela* is Latin for a weasel. *Mustela* itself is a combination of *mus* (mouse) and *telum* (a spear), a reference to the slender body of the stoat. The specific name is derived from the Old French for stoat (*hermine*). The white winter pelts, known as ermine, were used to trim ceremonial robes. The Irish name *easóg* refers to the eel-like shape of the stoat (*eas* means eel). Although the stoat is one of our most long-established mammals it has given its name to relatively few placenames. An examples is Drumaness (*Drom an easa*, ridge of the stoat, Co Down). In many parts of Ireland, the stoat is confusingly known as the weasel. The true weasel, *Mustela nivalis*, which is smaller than the stoat does not, however, occur in Ireland.

Identification and characteristics

The stoat belongs to the family Mustelidae. This family also includes the otter, mink, pine marten and badger. Like the first three, the stoat has a long slender body.

The stoat is our smallest mustelid and males are larger than females. It is difficult to summarise the information on the size of Irish stoats, since there is an apparent gradual

281

decrease in size as one moves from the south to the north of the island. Adult males in the south usually weigh from 300 to 400g; females are smaller, 110–200g, less than half the weight of the males. Males measure 34–39 cm from nose to the tip of the tail. In the north males weigh between 200 and 300g, while females range from 100 to 160g, and total body length ranges from 31 to 39cm for males and from 24 to 29cm for females.

The stoat's coat is reddish-brown and the throat and underside is creamy-white. In Ireland the white area on the underside is quite narrow. The boundary between the brown fur and the pale fur in most (90%) stoats in Ireland is an irregular wavy line and in this they resemble weasels, which, however, are much smaller and do not occur in Ireland. The irregular boundary between the brown and white fur distinguishes the Irish population from populations of stoats in Britain and continental Europe and Asia. In these latter areas the boundary between the brown and the white fur is a more or less straight line. The size and shape of the white areas on Irish stoats are extremely variable. Stoats moult their coat in spring and autumn. In other countries, particularly in the north of Europe and America, stoats replace their brown summer coat with a white one in winter, and the winter coat is in turn moulted in spring. Stoats in Ireland only very occasionally turn white in winter.

The tail of the stoat is short but relatively long for a mustelid. It ends in a conspicuous tuft of black hairs. This is the most reliable feature to distinguish stoats from weasels. The ears are small and rounded. The head is pointed and rather flat. Their teeth are extremely sharp; there are 16 in the skull and 18 in the lower jaws. The legs are relatively short and the feet are furry. Stoats are often only glimpsed fleetingly, but their loping bounding gallop is quite characteristic. They are extremely agile and give every appearance of being high-spirited and playful. They are very curious animals and often sit upright to investigate their surroundings.

Vision in stoats is good. They hunt largely by sight and visual signals are also important

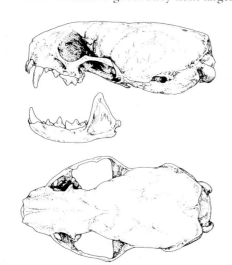

in communication between individuals. The sense of smell is important for interpreting scent signals from other stoats and particularly when hunting underground. Their hearing is also quite keen and is used to detect prey above ground. Stoats are not particularly vocal but they have a wide variety of sounds and calls ranging from twittering calls used by mothers with her young (kits) to hisses when alarmed and chattering threats.

Distribution

The stoat evolved in central Europe about one million years ago and then spread across the northern hemisphere, evolving into a number of different types in the process. It is now found throughout Europe, Asia and North America roughly north of latitude 42°N. It has also been introduced to New Zealand.

It is not known when the stoat arrived in Ireland. Its remains have been found in Castlepook cave (Co Cork) and so it may have been present here 35,000 years ago, before the last glacial maximum. The earliest dated specimens, 10,680 and 9980 years ago, are just before and after the cold Nahanagan stadial. It is unclear if it survived through this last ice age around 10,500 years ago. It is well capable of surviving arctic conditions and may have done so. If not, it was clearly one of the earliest colonists and has probably been here continuously since then. It has not, however, been recorded from neolithic sites and the next postglacial remains were found in early Christian sites.

Stoats in Ireland are different in a number of respects, particularly coat pattern, from others throughout their range and are classified as a subspecies endemic to this country and the Isle of Man. Thus the full scientific name is *Mustela erminea hibernica* (*hibernica* meaning Irish) to record this fact. The stoat is widespread in Ireland and is locally limited only by the availability of suitable cover and sufficient food. There has not been a systematic survey of stoats in Ireland, but information on distribution is available from local and regional studies, from records of road casualties and opportunistic sightings. The distribution map shows the 20km squares in which stoats have been recorded since 1990.

Habitats and habits

The stoat is an extremely adaptable and opportunistic animal. It is successful in a variety of habitats and appears to avoid only open, exposed locations. It may be found in woodland, farmland, moorland, mountain, marshes, hedgerows, dry-stone walls, heather or scree. However, in Ireland they are particularly associated with open woodland and rocky scrub-covered areas. Stoats' nests or dens may be found in a number of locations: in rabbit burrows, in hollow trees, in rock crevices, or occasionally in unoccupied buildings. Stoats may have a number of dens in their home range.

They are solitary and territorial. Territories of males and females overlap, but stoats are quite intolerant of others of the same sex, though males become less territorial during the breeding season in spring and range widely in search of females. Stoats mark their territories by depositing scent from anal glands on faeces that they leave at distinct landmarks. They appear to be quite familiar with their territories and they use the same paths regularly as they hunt for food. The home ranges of stoats, depending on food supply, may be as large as 100ha but on a good site may be as small as 20ha. Stoats appear to search through their territory systematically, taking several days to cover it all. During these tours they may use most of their dens to rest between hunting trips. Stoats are active in bouts, with rest periods in between, throughout the day and night. However, they are mainly nocturnal during autumn and winter, and are active for longer periods by day in spring and summer.

Diet

The stoat is primarily a carnivore. It is quite efficient and, uniquely for carnivores found in Ireland, may kill prey more than five times its own weight. It needs to be an efficient predator because it has a high rate of energy consumption. This is for two reasons. Firstly it is quite a small animal. Small animals require more food in relation to their body weight than larger ones. Secondly the stoat has an unusual shape for a mammal. It comes as close as any mammal to the shape of a snake. This means that it has a relatively large surface area from which heat may be lost. It may be estimated that the cost of being shaped like a stoat is between two and three times greater than if it were shaped more like a guinea pig, for example. Stoats eat food equal to about 20% of their body weight per day.

The stoat does not specialise in any particular prey items but will eat whatever is available. This generalist strategy accounts in large part for its success. It will hunt in burrows or on the ground surface and it also climbs well. For this reason the composition of the diet may differ in different locations. Stoats are active hunters and detect their prey mainly by sight and sound. They capture prey from ambush, by stalking, by chasing or by mesmerising them by apparently bizarre behaviour. In general, small mammals comprise over 90% of the diet. Rabbits may at times comprise almost half of the diet, though this varies as rabbit populations fluctuate due to recurrent outbreaks of myxomatosis. Rats and mice are also eaten, as are shrews, but less frequently. Stoats also prey on birds such as pigeons and a number of species of songbirds, some of which are taken as nestlings. They also eat insects and other invertebrates, often in large quantities. Although in general stoats will eat almost any prey, there are some differences in the hunting strategies of males and females. Females concentrate on smaller prey such as mice, shrews, young rats and birds. Males are quite prepared to tackle adult rabbits and rats.

Reproduction and life-cycle

Stoats are normally solitary animals and breed once a year. The mating season is May to July, and aggression between males is intense at this time. Males adopt a number of breeding strategies. Some expand their ranges to increase potential contact with females and may mate with more than one. Other males may restrict their wanderings and attempt to remain close to a resident female in her territory. Females ovulate in response to mating. Pregnant females become fiercely intolerant of males who, although much larger, are chased from the territory of the female. This ensures monopoly of the local food resources by the female.

Development of the foetuses inside the mother takes about 30 days but pregnancy may appear to be as long as ten months. This is because the fertilised eggs may develop slightly to form small balls of cells known as blastocysts which are not implanted in the lining of the womb to begin development immediately. Implantation may be delayed by environmental factors, such as food supply or weather conditions. Active development of the foetuses usually begins when the blastocysts implant in March. This event is triggered by the increasing day length. This strategy allows birth to occur at a time when conditions are more likely to be suitable.

The young (kits) are born in April or May. The litter size varies but usually ranges from three to ten kits. The kits are born in a very immature state. They weigh about 3–4g and are blind and deaf and covered with a pale fluffy fur. They are unable to regulate their temperature very well. If the nest becomes very cold, when the mother is away, they may enter a torpid state, rather like that of bats. They grow a temporary brown mane by which the mother carries them when necessary. The females develop a voracious appetite when lactating to cope with the demands of the kits. The kits grow rapidly and can eat solid food within five weeks of birth. They are weaned when about 12 weeks of age, by which time they can hunt efficiently. It is not unusual, in summer, to see a group of stoats which consists of a mother and her litter. Observations of such family parties, particularly if they include almost fully grown kits, have inspired a number of country traditions that stoats have a most complicated social organisation.

Adult females return to breeding condition soon after the birth of their litter. The reproductive system of female kits matures rapidly. Female stoats may attain breeding condition as juveniles, often when they are only about three weeks old. They often mate before their mothers have weaned them. Because of delayed implantation they will not, however, deliver this litter until they are about one year old. Females do not disperse far from their mother's territory. The young males, on the other hand, may disperse considerable distances to find territories of their own. By this time they are almost fully grown and will breed the following spring.

The population density of stoats in Ireland is very variable and depends largely on the availability of food. If weather conditions in spring are poor, very few of the potential young may survive the delayed implantation and litter sizes will be small. Although the potential reproductive rate is high, winter and spring mortality is particularly severe in dispersing juveniles. Lifespan is not known in Ireland but a stoat is unlikely to survive more than four years.

Watching stoats

Chance observation is probably the most likely means by which stoats are seen initially. However, regular observations are possible in good habitats, such as areas of rocky scrub with a sunny aspect and a good population of rabbits. The behaviour of stoats is somewhat predictable, particularly in areas where prey is abundant. Although stoats are nervous they are quite curious and this sometimes provides an opportunity to obtain good views. If you see a stoat briefly, it is advisable to remain still, because it will often return to observe the observer. There are few more entertaining mammals in Ireland, particularly when stoats are seen in a family party.

The droppings are about 6cm long and about 5mm in diameter and have a twisted appearance with at least one tapering end. The droppings usually contain fur, feathers and pieces of bone. They are often found in a pile close to the den but also at stones along trails regularly used by stoats, or on stone walls.

Conservation and management

There was a short-lived decline in stoat numbers in Ireland after reduction of rabbit populations by myxomatosis. However, as rabbits develop resistance to this disease and population density increases, stoats are becoming more common. The stoat was traditionally considered to be vermin and indeed individual stoats may cause considerable damage if they gain access to poultry or gamebirds' pens. Wherever there are large numbers of vulnerable animals such as in gamebird or poultry pens or colonies of ground-nesting birds, protection must be provided by appropriate fencing and extreme vigilance.

The stoat is listed in Appendix III of the Bern Convention as a species requiring protection and it is now totally protected in the Republic of Ireland and Northern Ireland.

American mink – *Minc Mhericeánach*
Mustela vison, Schreber 1777

The American mink first escaped from fur farms and began to establish itself in the wild in Ireland during the 1950s. It caused great alarm when it became clear that it could not be eradicated, but its spread, although undesirable, has not been the total catastrophe that was originally feared.

The names
The scientific account of the American mink is based on Canadian specimens described by Schreber in 1777. The generic name *mustela* is Latin for a weasel. *Mustela* itself is a combination of *mus* (mouse) and *telum* (a spear), a reference to the slender body of the mink. The specific name is the French for mink (*vison*). The Irish name is a direct translation of American (*Meireacáineach*) mink (*minc*).

Identification and characteristics
The mink is a medium-sized mustelid or member of the family Mustelidae, which also includes the otter, pine marten, stoat and badger. Male pine martens measure from 50 to 60cm from the nose to the tip of the tail. Males usually weigh from 0.9 to 1.3kg; they are almost twice as heavy as females, which weight 0.5–0.8kg.

The mink's tail is long and bushy but less so than that of the pine marten or fox. Although on farms mink are bred for a variety of coat colours, ranging from white through a number of pastel blues and greys, populations in the wild usually revert to a more uniform dark colour, similar to the original colour of wild mink. Wild mink are usually black or dark brown with a white patch under the chin extending onto the throat and underside. The size and shape of these white areas are extremely variable and can be used to identify individual mink.

The legs are relatively short. Mink are semi-aquatic and are good swimmers and the feet are partially webbed. The footprints, often clearly visible along the water's edge, are star-shaped. There are 16 teeth in the skull and 18 in the lower jaw.

The senses of the mink are well developed and it can see well under water. It also uses its long sensitive whiskers to detect fish when the water is muddy or murky. It swims underwater using all four limbs and rarely submerges for more than 20 seconds. In fact, most dives last little over 10 seconds. When fishing it tends to attack slower fish in shallow water. The eyesight of mink on land is also very good and they have a wide repertoire of visual signals, such as body postures and facial expressions, which are used in interactions with other mink. They are usually vocal only when close to other mink or when they feel threatened. They have a range of squeals, squeaks and chuckles.

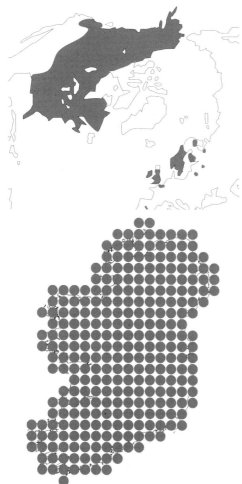

Distribution and population density

In its natural range, the American mink is found throughout most of Canada and northern USA. It is related to the Eurasian mink, *Mustela lutreola*, which, however, has never been recorded in Ireland. The Eurasian mink is now largely extinct in western Europe, but is found eastward from Finland, Russia and the Balkan states, although it is in decline there.

The American mink was first introduced to fur farms in Europe in the 1920s for commercial pelt production. It has become established in the wild in most countries where it was farmed. These include Britain, France, Spain, Germany, Scandinavia, Iceland, Poland and Russia. These feral populations were founded by individuals that escaped or, in some cases, were deliberately released. It is not yet clearly established whether the American mink contributed to the final extinction of the European mink over part of its range or alternatively if it has occupied the habitats formerly used by the European mink prior to its local extinction and to which it is preventing recolonisation.

The mink was first farmed in Ireland in 1951. By 1961 reports of escapees were increasing and mink are now widespread in Ireland and are found in at least 95% of the country. They originally spread through Leinster, south and west Munster and Donegal. They have recently colonised Connacht. By 2000 they had colonised almost all available habitat throughout the whole country. The map shows the 20km squares in which mink have been recorded since 1990.

Population density of mink in Ireland is very variable throughout the country and depends largely on habitat quality. In poor habitats, such as upland rivers in the northwest of the country, there may be only two or three mink per 10km of river. In good quality habitats, along the shores of the lakes in the midlands, there may be from seven to 13 mink per 10km of shoreline. Populations often explode and reach high densities in recently colonised areas. These may then acquire a lower relatively stable density related to food supply. This is because mink populations have a self-regulating mechanism related to their territorial behaviour.

Habitats and habits

The mink is successful in a variety of habitats. It is an extremely adaptable and opportunistic animal but is not usually found far from water. Mink may be found along rivers, streams, lakes, canals and the coast. They prefer slow-flowing shallow rivers or lakes with thick vegetation along the banks. Mink rarely burrow, but nevertheless live in dens that are usually close to a river. Dens may be in rabbit burrows, in hollow trees or occasionally in unoccupied buildings. Mink may excavate their own burrows in areas of soft peaty soil. They may have a number of dens in their home range.

Mink are solitary and territorial, both males and females defending stretches of watercourse. Territories of males and females overlap and animals are quite intolerant of others of the same sex. There may also be vagrant mink, usually younger animals, which do not have a territory. These animals wander throughout the territories of other permanent residents until they find somewhere they can settle.

Diet

The mink is primarily an aquatic carnivore. It does not specialise in any particular prey items and will eat whatever prey is available. This generalist strategy accounts in large part for its success. It will hunt in burrows, on the ground surface, in trees or under water. For this reason the composition of the diet may differ in different locations. The diet of mink may be determined by identifying remains of fur, feathers and bones in the scats.

In some locations in the midlands, as much as two-thirds of the diet is freshwater crayfish. It usually hunts by diving from the bank or overhanging branches. During dives it may remain underwater for between five and 20 seconds. In general crayfish, slow-swimming fish and birds comprise over 90% of the diet. Coot and moorhens are the main birds eaten, with lesser numbers of duck. Pheasants or domestic fowl are not, overall, a major element in the diet.

Perch and eels are the usual fish eaten, with lesser amounts of trout or young salmon. Rabbits may at times comprise over half of the diet. Rats, mice, shrews, frogs and insects are also eaten. In parts of Russia, bank voles are the main component of the diet of the Eurasian mink, and the American mink in Ireland may eventually include this rodent when it has spread further throughout the country.

Reproduction and life-cycle

Mink breed once a year. The mating season takes place from February to April, but mainly in late February. They are solitary animals and a female may mate with more than one male if they visit her territory during her oestrous period. This may last for about a month. Aggression between males is intense at this time. Fights may be severe and involve screaming and hissing, release of overpoweringly pungent odours, posturing with teeth, body and tail and finally wrestling and biting. Males do not apparently attempt to guard their mates but resume their solitary habits after mating.

The females do not shed their eggs spontaneously like most mammals but instead, ovulation takes place after mating. Development of the foetuses inside the mother takes about 30 days, but pregnancy may appear to be as long as 76 days. This is because implantation of the fertilised eggs in the womb and the beginning of development may be delayed by environmental factors such as food supply or weather conditions. This allows the births to occur at a time when conditions are more likely to be suitable. The young (kits) are born in April or May. The litter size varies but usually ranges from three to five kits. The kits are quite immature at birth. They weigh about 5g and are deaf, blind and hairless. They develop a covering of dark grey fur between one and four weeks of age, by which time their eyes are open. They grow rapidly and are weaned at about eight weeks of age. By this time they are beginning to hunt for themselves and are usually heavier than their mother, who has lost condition during lactation. They will stay with their mother until August or September and will then disperse to find territories of their own. By this time they are almost fully grown and will breed the following spring.

Although reproductive rate is high, winter and spring mortality is particularly severe in dispersing juveniles and non-territorial individuals. Therefore a mink is unlikely to survive and breed unless it can obtain and successfully defend a territory of its own. However, although populations may be stable, turnover of individuals is quite high. A mink in captivity may live for ten years, but an individual in the wild is most unlikely to survive for more than four years.

Watching mink

The best opportunities for observing mink are in slow-flowing rivers or lakes in the more long-established parts of their range. Mink favour waterways with lush bank-side vegetation. They are shy animals and may be quite difficult to observe on river systems, less so on lakes.

It is first necessary to find an area used by mink and then it is a matter of waiting for the animal to appear as it travels along its linear territory. A suitable location will have signs of mink activity such as scats and trails. Mink use sites such as large boulders or fallen logs in the stream, the foundations of bridges or the confluence of streamlets with the main river to deposit their scats. The scats are smaller than those of otters (spraints) and usually have a most unpleasant smell, particularly if they have been smeared with a gelatinous secretion from the scent glands around the anus. On calm waters, the wake made by a swimming mink may be seen. When swimming, the mink rides relatively high in the water with most of its body-length visible. By contrast only the top of the head and part of the tail of a swimming otter is usually visible above water. On the surface, a mink swims using a dog paddle propelled by its front limbs.

It is important to continue to track the spread of the mink into the few areas so far free of the animal, and so sightings of animals should be reported to the wildlife authorities.

Management

Mink farming may only be carried out under licence from the government Department of Agriculture, Food and Rural Development (RoI) or the Department of Agriculture (NI). There are requirements on the farmer to take precautions to minimise the probability of escapes. However, it is now unrealistic to expect that feral mink could ever be eradicated from this country and we must accept it as another resident member of our wild fauna.

The overall impact of mink in Ireland has not been as catastrophic as was at first feared. Although it may take some food items also taken by the otter, there is no evidence that the mink has a negative impact on the otter in most habitats. The situation regarding water birds is less clear. There are many reports of declining populations in areas recently colonised by mink. Wherever there are large numbers of vulnerable animals, such as fish farms, gamebird rearing-pens, poultry pens or isolated colonies of ground-nesting birds then fencing and trapping must be employed to provide protection. Trapping along perimeter fences or in areas proposed for release of gamebirds may be considered as part of the protective measures. If it is to be carried out, then cage traps, baited with fresh fish, are recommended and the mink should be despatched humanely.

Control on a wider scale is possible but involves considerable effort and a large number of traps deployed over a number of months, preferably in the spring. Trapping, unless it is particularly intense, will have little effect on the density of the breeding population. This is because it will probably remove non-territorial vagrant mink that were not breeding anyway. Even if trapping removes a resident animal its territory will quickly be occupied by a vagrant which will then breed.

Badger – *Broc*
Meles meles, Linnaeus 1758

The badger is one of our most beautiful and fascinating animals, but, being strictly nocturnal, it is rarely seen alive by most people. The relationship between badgers infected with bovine tuberculosis and similarly infected cattle is currently a major wildlife issue.

The names
When Linnaeus wrote the first scientific description of a Swedish specimen of a badger in 1758 he thought that it was a species of small bear. The scientific name uses the Latin for badger (*meles*) for both parts. There are a number of explanations of the modern English name, the more plausible of which are that badger is a reference to the striped face or 'badge' of the animal or that badger is derived from the French for digger (*becheur*). Male badgers are called boars; females, sows; and the young, cubs. The Irish name is *broc* and this or *brocach*, a badger sett, are found in many placenames in Ireland, such as Clonbrock (Co Galway), the meadow (*cluan*) of the badger; Brockaghbeg (Co Offaly), the little (*beag*) sett (brocach); and Brocklagh (Co Longford), a sett. It may be noted that the old English name for the badger is also brock.

Identification and characteristics
The badger belongs to the family Mustelidae, which also includes the otter, pine marten, mink and stoat. Unlike these, the badger is stockily built, with relatively short and powerful legs and a short bushy tail.

Males are larger than females. Boars may weigh up to 17kg but are more usually about 10 or 11kg; females may weigh up to 12kg although 9 to 10kg is more usual. The total length of an adult male is about 90cm, including 15cm of tail. Sows are about 5% smaller. It is difficult to tell the boar from the sow unless she is feeding cubs when her enlarged mammary glands will be more obvious.

Badgers have a white head with a black nose and two broad black stripes running from just behind the muzzle to behind the ears and including the eyes. The overall colour appears grey because the long guard hairs on the back

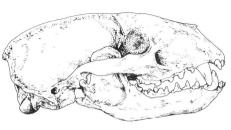

and flanks have a white base and tip with a dark band in the middle. The legs and under-surface are dark. The underfur is pale and may be relatively sparse on the underside.

The head is rather small and broad with an extremely mobile and slightly cocked nose. The ears and eyes are small. The overall impression of the skull is broad, usually with a conspicuous bony ridge or crest along the upper surface. This is for attachment of the very powerful jaw muscles. Badgers have a powerful bite. They have 16 teeth in the upper jaws and usually 18 (sometimes 20) in the lower. The last molar in the skull of the badger is quite characteristic. It is much larger than all the others, is almost square and is adapted for crushing food items.

The body is held low to the ground and the limbs have five toes equipped with large, strong claws, particularly on the front feet. The footprints of badgers are broad, about 5–6cm across, with all the claws relatively close together. Badgers usually travel their territory in a slow, ambling trot, reminiscent of that of a rhinoceros. When relaxed they are quite noisy. In the open they pause frequently to sniff the air and if alarmed they gallop for cover quite quickly. Their climbing ability is limited, but they can swim quite well.

The hearing of badgers is acute. They are also highly vocal and have a wide range of sounds ranging from whickering by cubs, which sounds like magpies, through purring, growling and screaming. The badger's eyesight is poor but its eyes are adapted to work well in low light, since these are nocturnal animals. Visual signals are not as important as scent and sound. They have an extremely well-developed sense of smell and scents play an important role in communication. They have a number of scent glands, around the anus and just below the base of the tail, which are used to mark other members of the social group and important sites in their home ranges. Urine is also an important vehicle for signal scents.

Distribution

Fossil badgers indistinguishable from modern animals first appeared in the fossil record of central Asia about 500,000 years ago. By 250,000 years ago they had reached Britain. The badger is now widespread across Europe and Asia from Ireland in the west through sub-Arctic Europe and central Asia to China and Japan in the east. It is absent from Iceland, northern Scandinavia and the islands of the Mediterranean.

The first arrival of the badger in Ireland was some time between 5000 and 10,000 years ago. The badger has not been found in contexts earlier than the neolithic period, and no specimens

have been dated. The earliest example of a badger from Ireland comes from a neolithic wedge grave at Lough Gur (Co Limerick).

The badger is common and widespread in Ireland today. From a survey of badger setts, it has been estimated that there may be about 200,000 to 250,000 badgers in Ireland, organised into 40,000 to 50,000 social groups. The distribution map shows the 20km squares in which occupied badger setts have been found. It is based mainly on the badger and habitat survey of Ireland published in 1995.

Habitats and habits

Badgers are generally considered to be animals of woodland/farmland mosaics. In Ireland, however, badgers have adapted well to the relative lack of woodlands and are found in all habitats below about 500m altitude where the soil is dry and not subject to flooding. They may be found on mountains, but tend to be more solitary in these habitats.

Badgers are social animals and live in complex underground tunnel systems called setts. Each territory contains one main sett, together with a number of smaller setts. Main setts typically have four to seven entrances but may exceptionally have more than 30. Badgers are compulsive and powerful diggers and spend considerable time maintaining and modifying their setts. They are extremely fastidious animals and regularly renew the bedding in the nest chambers. The entrances to setts may be marked by conspicuous spoil heaps which contain excavated soil, discarded bedding, dried grass, leaves, straw and so on. The internal structure of the sett may be extremely complex and contain a number of bed chambers and a long network of tunnels. One exceptionally large sett excavated near Dublin contained 25 chambers and over 260 metres of tunnels and passages. Badgers are creatures of habit and the same setts, latrines and traditional pathways may be used over many generations. This is why badgers are killed by cars at certain locations on roads over many years.

Setts are more likely to be excavated in hedgerows than in scrub or woodlands. For example, over half of the setts in Ireland are found in hedgerows that occupy only about 5% of the available land area. Sett sites are an important resource for badgers and may continue in use long after hedgerows have been removed and the setts exposed in open fields. Setts may continue in use even in built-up areas, provided cover and access to foraging areas are maintained and disturbance is minimal. The availability of suitable sites for the excavation of setts may be an important factor in determining the distribution of badgers and their population density.

Badgers are nocturnal. They generally emerge from their setts about dusk and may remain above ground until dawn. In summer, from about May to September, they usually emerge before dark. At other times they delay their active period until darkness has fallen. They are rather less active in mid-winter and may become slightly torpid, meaning that they may drop their body temperature by a few degrees and thus save energy. They do not become as torpid as bats, for example, and they certainly do not hibernate. The nocturnal activity of badgers is somewhat dependent on the weather. They are less active in cold weather and dislike strong winds and heavy rain.

Diet

The badger is omnivorous. It may be classified as a generalist or opportunistic feeder, that is, it takes a wide variety of foods as available. Although they live in social groups, badgers usually forage independently. They will gorge themselves on whatever item of food is locally abundant. They will forage in all habitats from sea-shore to mountain-top.

It is sometimes considered that the distribution of earthworms is the primary determinant of badger abundance, and indeed the most common item in the diet is earthworm. Over 90% of badger droppings contain earthworm chaetae (you can feel this if you gently stroke the underside of an earthworm). A badger may eat up to 200 earthworms in a single night. This is more likely to occur during mild, moist nights in late spring and summer, when earthworms are more likely to be at the soil surface. However, earthworms do not always represent the bulk of the diet. Badgers also eat beetles, slugs, snails, leatherjackets, cockchafers, frogs, frogspawn, and small mammals such as rats, young rabbits, mice and hedgehogs. They also take a wide range of plant and vegetable foods such as cereals, apples, blackberries, elderberries, acorns, beech-mast, fungi, clover and grass. Badgers particularly like cereal before it is fully ripe; they remove the grain by pulling the stalks through their mouths. Although badgers change their diet with the seasons, it is rare for any single component to represent over 50% of the diet in any season.

Despite the variety of foods eaten, badgers must cope with periods of food shortage. Hot dry summers are often difficult times for badgers, because earthworms move deeper into the soil and the autumn cereals and fruits are not yet available. Adult badgers are at their lightest in mid-summer. They accumulate substantial amounts of fat in late summer and autumn and are at their heaviest in November and December.

Social organisation

Unlike its near relatives, the badger is an extremely social animal. Badgers live in groups occupying a communal area, which they defend against neighbouring groups by a system of boundary latrines, at which various scents are deposited. Conspicuous paths often interconnect these latrines with the main sett. Badgers regularly patrol these boundary paths, visiting latrines and renewing scent deposits. Territorial activity is most intense in spring and autumn. Males are somewhat more active than females in territorial marking. Badgers also deposit scent on one another and on pathways and other objects in their territory. Most of these scents are produced by glands inside the anus and under the tail. Urine is also used in scent marking and is deposited near setts, at latrines and on pathways, particularly where they pass through hedges or fences.

Badger territories in Ireland vary in size from about 60 to 200 hectares and may contain a group of from two to 23 badgers. The usual group size, however, is five or six individuals. Badger groups contain males and females but the proportion of males and females is variable. There is usually one dominant male in each group. The relationships between the other members are less clear, although the females may operate a dominance hierarchy. Young females tend to remain in their home area; young males tend to disperse and attempt to establish themselves in another territory. Dispersal usually takes place in spring and this partly explains the abundance of badgers killed in traffic accidents during this period. Badgers living in poor habitats at higher altitudes tend to have very large home ranges, and to be rather solitary outside the breeding season.

Reproduction and life-cycle

Territorial activity and aggression by males increases in February and March. Mating may take place between March and November but most adult females, some of whom may be nursing their current litter, mate in April and May. Female badgers come into heat spontaneously but ovulate in response to mating. A female may mate several times during her oestrous period, which may last for five or six days. The resident males probably father most of the cubs but males may move between groups in search of receptive females at this time, so foreign males may father some litters.

Complete development of the fertilised egg does not take place immediately. It develops to form a hollow ball of cells, called a blastocyst. There is then a period of delayed implantation, for up to nine months, before the blastocyst implants in the wall of the womb. This usually occurs in late December. Yearling females tend to mate in October and November and their period of delayed implantation is correspondingly shorter. Therefore true pregnancy is about seven to eight weeks. A major unexplained feature of badger reproduction is the fact that although most females in the population become pregnant, only about one-third of them apparently rear a litter. Indeed, although all adult females in a social group may become pregnant, it is unusual to find more than one female in the group rearing cubs.

When females enter their proper gestation, they begin to prepare a birth chamber, usually but not always within the main sett. It is, however, usually in a secure location where disturbance will be minimal. Old bedding is taken to the surface and aired or discarded and replaced by fresh material. Bedding material outside a sett entrance is usually a sign of an imminent birth. Badger cubs are born in February and March. Litter size ranges from one to five but usually two or three cubs are born. Cubs weigh about 100g at birth and are covered in fine grey hair with their facial stripes already visible. They are born blind and their eyes remain closed until about five weeks of age. They begin to venture above ground at about six to eight weeks of age. The mothers feed them for about 12 weeks but lactation may sometimes extend for about five months. Cubs are usually independent of their mothers by the end of the year but some may not disperse until the following spring.

Conservation and management

The badger is totally protected in the Republic of Ireland and Northern Ireland. It is listed in Appendix III of the Bern Convention as a species to be protected and whose exploitation must be regulated. The badger does not appear to be under any threat to its continued existence in Ireland. Current changes in agricultural practices and increased afforestation are likely to make habitats even more suitable for badgers.

Bovine tuberculosis is endemic in badgers. About 20–25% of badgers in Ireland may be infected. Most social groups contain an infected badger, but it is extremely unusual for all the members of a group to be affected. It is not clear how the disease is maintained in badgers and cattle, but it is suspected that an unknown proportion, probably between 10% and 20%, of outbreaks of TB in cattle might be due to cross-infection from badgers. For this reason, badgers have been removed under licence in efforts to understand how this disease is maintained. It is unlikely that widespread removal of badgers could or should be incorporated into the strategy of control of bovine TB. The possibility of developing a vaccination programme as is being used in Europe for control of rabies in foxes is probably the most appropriate strategy.

A major local threat to badgers is the practice of badger baiting. This is cruel and illegal. In a nationwide survey of badger setts, between 15% and 22% of main setts showed evidence of either digging or blocked entrances.

Watching badgers

The presence of badgers is generally revealed by paths that are usually quite conspicuous and may be followed back to a sett. Badger hair is often found entangled on barbed wire or brambles where a badger path crosses a hedge or fence-line. The long guard hairs are whitish at the base, have a black band in the middle and are pale at the tip. The underfur is grey.

Badgers deposit their faeces in conspicuous shallow dung pits. These are often found along paths, although they are concentrated at latrine sites, mainly at the boundaries of their territory. The faeces are rather loose and less structured than those of dogs and contain traces of undigested prey, fragments of beetles, seeds or grain; they may be covered with secretions. The footprints are about 2–3cm across and about 6cm long and usually show five toe marks with distinct long impressions of the claws. The claws, uniquely for Irish mammals, lie in parallel, almost like a rake. This makes the prints quite characteristic.

Badgers are best seen close to setts because a range of activities may be carried out nearby. These include social interactions, removal and renewal of bedding, particularly if cubs are in the sett, and cubs at play. Indeed, badgers can be encouraged to linger near the sett if peanuts are scattered about in the vicinity before they emerge. It is important to arrive and be in position before the badgers emerge. This depends to some extent on the particular location and how tolerant the badgers are of humans, but the observer will soon learn the habits of the particular group. To begin with, the observer should be in position before dark. A reconnaissance visit is advisable to select a suitable viewing point and to make any adjustments necessary. It is important to avoid startling the badgers, so a number of obvious precautions should be taken. Dark, warm, non-noisy clothes should be worn and a comfortable position should be taken close to but downwind of the sett, so that the observer's scent silhouette is not obvious. It may be possible to select a viewing point in a nearby tree. Take a cushion, as such perches become very uncomfortable. The best viewing opportunities occur soon after the badgers first emerge for the night and while they are busy grooming and interacting in the vicinity of the sett. When the badgers move off to visit the boundary latrines or to their favoured foraging areas it is as well to move away home quietly (and write up one's observations).

It is also possible to entice badgers to visit artificial feeding sites in gardens by providing food for them. They are particularly partial to fresh peanuts, dried fruit, fruit or dog pellets. Badgerwatch is an organisation composed of a number of groups interested in the conservation, welfare and study of the badger and organises activities for those interested in badgers. A newsletter is produced regularly. The badger groups can be contacted at (01) 626 8479.

Eurasian otter – *Dobharchú/Madra uisce*
Lutra lutra, Linnaeus 1758

The otter is almost extinct in several countries in Europe, which makes the Irish population of otters particularly important.

The names

The scientific description of the Eurasian otter is that written by Linnaeus in 1758, based on Swedish specimens. The Latin word *lutra*, meaning otter, is used for its scientific name. Both Irish names mean the hound (*cú*) or dog (*madra*) of the (flowing) water (*dobhar, uisce*). Although the otter has presumably been common and widespread in Ireland for centuries, its name is not very common in Irish placenames, but two otter-related placenames are Pouladorane (near Cork city) and Pollnamadraeesky (near the Shannon in Co Longford), which means the den or holt (*poll*) of the dog (*madra*) of the water (*uisce*), ie otter-holt.

Identification and characteristics

The otter belongs to the family Mustelidae. This family also includes the pine marten, mink, stoat and badger. The otter is our largest mustelid, and is in fact our fourth largest land mammal – only the three deer species are larger. Adult males usually weigh about 11kg but range from 7 to 16kg; females are smaller, about 7kg, but may range from 5 to 9kg. Males measure about 120cm from the nose to the tip of the tail, while females are about 110cm.

The body is long, muscular and streamlined. The tail, thick at the base, is long and flattened and tapers to a point. The head is broad and rather flat and the ears are small, rounded and

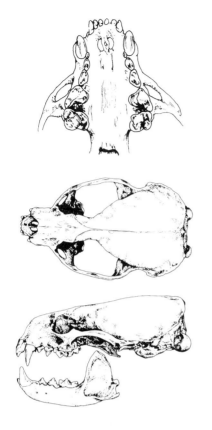

almost buried in the fur. The eyes are directed forwards and are situated towards the top of the head. The nostrils lie towards the top of the snout, which is well equipped with long stiff whiskers. These are important sense organs for foraging under water. The front legs of otters are relatively short and the feet are webbed. There are 18 teeth in the skull and either 18 or 20 in the lower jaws.

The dense coat is usually dark brown on the back and grey–brown on the underside. The lips and throat are paler and may be creamy-white. The guard hairs are long and oily. There is a dense layer of fawn underfur that traps air so that the skin never gets wet. Maintenance of the condition of the fur is extremely important to insulate the animal, since otters, unlike seals, do not have a thick layer of blubber. When in the water the oily guard hairs fold over the underfur and, by trapping a layer of air and repelling the water, keep the fur and the skin dry. The trapped air makes the otter glisten underwater. It reduces heat loss and prevents hypothermia, which is a perpetual risk for otters, since they may spend up to eight hours a day in the water. On land, a wet otter appears to be covered in short spines because the guard hairs, repelled by the water, tend to stick together until the water is shed.

Their senses are well developed. Smell is most important for detecting potential threats on land and scents convey important social information between otters. Their hearing is particularly acute, although their eyesight on land is rather poor. However, in clear water, otters hunt by sight. In murky water or in poor light, otters detect the movements of their prey using their sensory vibrissae (whiskers). Otters are not particularly vocal, but they emit a contact whistle to inform other otters of their whereabouts and they have a variety of chatters and chuckles used in social interactions. Otters are most vocal during courtship.

Otters swim at the surface by paddling. They may rest in the water with only the nose and eyes breaking the surface. When swimming, an otter usually shows only the top of its head and part of its tail, in contrast to the mink, which rides relatively high in the water with most of its body-length visible. They swim underwater by flexing the back and tail up and down. The hind limbs move in parallel with the body and tail while the forelimbs are held tucked close to the body. They dive quietly, arching the back and tail out of the water as they submerge. When hunting underwater they may remain submerged for up to 40 seconds, although dives of eight to ten seconds are more usual. When actively searching for food, otters come to the surface for two to three seconds between dives.

Otters are generally extremely shy and retiring, but nevertheless are curious animals and carefully investigate their surroundings. On land, otters hold their heads low because of their relatively short forelegs. They are quite agile and can clamber up riverbanks and over tree stumps and smaller obstacles. The otter normally progresses in a slow walk but can move surprisingly rapidly using a bounding gait.

Distribution and population density

The range of the Eurasian otter extends throughout Europe, sub-arctic Asia, China, Japan and the Far East. It is absent from Iceland and the Mediterranean islands. In many parts of its range, however, this otter is in serious decline or extinct. The Eurasian otter, together with other species of otter, is classified as vulnerable on a world-wide scale.

Otters are present on many of the more remote offshore islands of the British Isles and the opening of the gap between Ireland and Britain at the end of the ice age should have posed no problem to the otter. It has probably been a member of Ireland's fauna since at

least the end of the last glaciation, about 10,500 years ago. Despite this, no remains of otters have yet been recovered from mesolithic settlements, and the earliest archaeological record is from 3000–4000 years ago in a Bronze Age site at Ballinderry (Co Offaly).

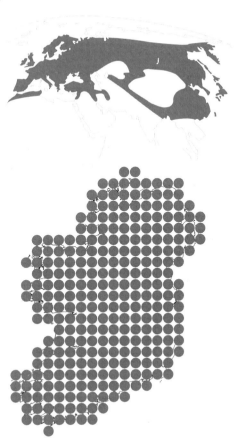

The otter is now found throughout Ireland and has apparently avoided the population declines that have occurred in many other countries. This country now holds the densest population of otters in western Europe. The distribution of otters is usually monitored by surveying appropriate habitats for sites where otters are likely to deposit their droppings or spraints. This gives a general indication if otters are using a particular area. It is, however, difficult to estimate the population density of otters. The number of spraints per unit length of riverbank or shoreline gives only an approximate figure for the number of otters actually present. This is because production of spraints depends on how active the otters are. In good habitats along lakeside there may be one otter per 4km of shore. On the coast there may be one otter per kilometre. The distribution map shows the 20km squares that contain otters.

Habitats and habits

The otter may be found in a variety of aquatic habitats such as rivers, streams, lakes, marshes, estuaries and on the coast. Coastal otters, however, require access to a supply of fresh water to wash salt deposits from their fur. If such water is not available, the fur loses its insulating properties and the animals may become hypothermic. Otters may even be found in urban areas and have been detected close to the centres of Dublin, Cork, Limerick, Waterford and Galway. Otters are rarely found far from water and tend to occupy linear home ranges. They require suitable bank-side vegetation as cover for their burrows or rest sites, termed 'holts'. Otters are largely solitary and territorial. If a group of otters is seen, it is almost certainly a mother and her current litter, although adult females often associate with one another.

Home range and territory

The area of the home range depends to some extent on food supply. The home ranges of males are much larger than those of females. Thus ranges of males and females overlap. Otters are usually quite intolerant of others of the same sex and exclude them from their territories. Males become less territorial and thus wander more widely than normal in spring and summer during the breeding season as they search for females. They are extremely mutually antagonistic at this time. Scents play an important role in transferring information between otters. They indicate age, sex and ownership of a territory. Otters mark their home ranges by depositing their droppings, termed 'spraints', at distinct landmarks such as grassy mounds, large rocks or ledges under bridges. These favoured sites are known as 'seats' and are usually found at important locations. These include access points to the water, preferred fishing areas, grooming areas and rest sites and near key locations such as holts or boundaries.

Otters may have a number of burrows or holts in their home range. These are usually based in natural recesses under the edge of the riverbank, usually among root systems of trees. The trees most favoured are ash, sycamore and horse chestnut. Holts often have a number of entrances, as many as six, some of which open under water. Otters do not apparently carry out extensive excavations but will sometimes use rabbit burrows or vacant fox earths if they are in a suitable location. Occasionally maternity holts may be some considerable distance from the water. Otters may also uses resting places (couches) above ground. These couches are often found on islands or in dense cover. Otters spend some time arranging the vegetation to build a comfortable platform-like structure with a resting site in the middle. Otters repeatedly use the same slides, which are chutes in mud, down which they slip into the water. Otters are generally considered to be nocturnal, and are mainly active after dusk and just before dawn. They may be seen early in the morning and late in the evening, particularly on the coasts. They are more diurnal during cold weather.

Diet

The otter is primarily a fish-eater and preys particularly on a number of species of slow-swimming, bottom-dwelling fish. Its diet, however, differs in different parts of the country, depending on what food is available. In most cases, information on the diet of otters is obtained by identification of remains of their prey in the spraints. In the Killarney lakes over 75% of otter spraints contain remains of eel. Salmon or trout and shad are next in importance. In the large lakes and their associated streams and rivers in the west of Ireland eels are also the main prey but the diet includes substantial numbers of perch. Frogs are also eaten, particularly in marshy areas. In the Blackwater system in the south, eels are again the main prey, with the locally abundant dace, young trout or salmon and stone loach also taken. In smaller streams that are nursery areas for trout and salmon, otters concentrate on these fish. In limestone lakes in the midlands and elsewhere, freshwater crayfish may be a major component of the diet. Otters living on the coast eat a wide variety of small fish such as rocklings and wrasse. They also eat crabs. Otters occasionally prey on water birds such as duck, coot and moorhens and may eat small mammals and carrion.

Otters will switch from one prey to another as their relative abundance changes. For example, in rivers where roach are recently spreading, otters have begun to concentrate on this species. Otters usually catch their prey in their mouths and, if it is too large to eat at the water surface, will take it ashore to eat it.

Reproduction and life-cycle

Reproduction of otters in Ireland has been little studied. It appears that otters may breed at any time during the year but are more likely to do so in spring and summer. Females coming on heat appear to signal this fact by scents. Male and female otters become more vocal at this time and whistle at one another. Several males may be attracted to a female in heat and usually fight for access to her. A male may attempt to remain close to an oestrous female for up to a week before mating. Courtship is a vigorous affair and mating may take place on land or in water. A successful male may remain with the female for up to two weeks after mating before he departs.

Unlike several other species in this family, implantation is not delayed in the otter, and pregnancy lasts for about 62 days. Although the cubs may be born at any time of year, those born in summer are most likely to survive. The litter size is usually two or three, but may be as large as five. Newborn cubs are fully furred but their eyes do not open for about four or five weeks. The mothers nurse their cubs for about 15 weeks, although cubs begin to venture out of their den at about eight weeks of age. Apparently, otter cubs may be somewhat reluctant to take to the water naturally and need to be encouraged by their mother. They have usually begun to swim at about 12 weeks of age. They do not disperse to find a separate home range for at least six months and are sometimes with their mother for as long as a year. It is therefore not unusual to see a group of otters consisting of a mother and her litter.

Adult females usually breed only once a year unless they lose their litter soon after birth. Otters become mature during their second year but may not breed for the first time until their third year.

Winter and spring mortality may be particularly severe in otter populations. Lifespan is not known in Ireland, but an otter is unlikely to survive over five years in the wild, although captive otters may live to over ten years.

Watching otters

Otters are extremely elusive and are quite difficult to observe in river systems and lakes, but less so at the coast. It is first necessary to find an area used by otters and then it's a matter of waiting for an animal to appear. This may take some time, since an otter's linear territory may be quite long from end to end.

Small lakes are often worth inspecting for signs of otters. A suitable location will have signs of otter activity such as spraints and trails where the otters may have worn a smooth trackway in the vegetation. These trails are quite distinctive and often cut across a headland at the coast or a bend in a river. They sometimes lead to a holt or to a muddy slide leading to the water. On calm waters the wake made by a swimming otter may be seen. Fresh spraints are slimy and black or brown with a fishy smell. They become paler with age and often bone fragments may be visible. Sometimes a jelly-like substance, which is produced by the anal glands, is deposited at the sprainting sites. This imparts a musky, almond-like scent to the spraints.

Otters are most easily seen while foraging among seaweed and in rock pools on the seashore. Otters that live on the coast appear to be more active by day than those found along inland waterways. However, in all locations otters may be active by day during cold weather. Although otters are shy, they are also quite curious and often allow quite prolonged views if not unduly alarmed. A good view of a wild otter is well worth the effort but, to begin with, a visit to Dublin Zoo to see a captive otter is worth while. The spraints of this specimen are easily seen from the viewing areas and are a useful introduction to the field signs of otters.

Conservation

There are records of otters having been killed for their pelts from the 15th century until the implementation of the Wildlife Act in 1976. On average, almost 350 skins a year were exported from this country during the second half of the 18th century. However, the otter is now fully protected by law in the Republic of Ireland and Northern Ireland.

Individual otters may cause considerable damage if they gain access to fish ponds in hatcheries, so protection must be provided by fencing. There were formerly a number of packs of otter hounds operating during the first half of the 20th century, but this practice has now apparently ceased.

Most of the known causes of mortality may be due directly or indirectly to man. These include road accidents, drowning in fish traps, pollution of waterways by toxic chemicals such as PCBs, illegal hunting and disturbance and destruction of habitat.

Drainage schemes, introduced to 'improve' rivers by canalising the riverbed, have a serious impact on otters by destroying holt sites and removal of bank-side vegetation. It is now being realised that these arterial drainage schemes have also degraded habitats for fish and a number of rehabilitation schemes to reverse the 'improvements' are in progress. These involve alteration of the flow characteristics of the river bed, restoration of pools and replanting of bank-side trees. It is likely that otters will, eventually, benefit from these initiatives.

Eurasian otters are considered to be vulnerable on a world-wide scale. The population of otters in Ireland is of international importance. They are strictly protected throughout Ireland. Conservation and restoration of suitable habitats and preservation of clean water are the main priorities for maintaining our internationally important population of this beautiful animal. The otter is listed in Annexes II and IV of the Habitats Directive as a species which is of European interest and which requires strict protection and the designation of special conservation areas. It is also listed as requiring strict protection in Appendix II of the Berne Convention.

CHAPTER 9

Order Pinnipedia – Seals

Fegaid úaib fo-thuaid
In muir múaid mílach
Adba rón, rebac rán
Ro gab lán lined.

See in the fish-flecked ocean
Away to the far north east
Where the happy seals are frolicking
Amid the full-tide's feast.
(Anon 7th-8th century, trans. T.J. Hayden)

The Pinnipedia (flipper-feet) are so called because their feet are modified for swimming. While it is quite easy to recognise a seal or sea lion for what it is, zoologists are in some disagreement as to whether they should be grouped together into a separate order or be included within the Carnivora. Pinnipeds have a generally uniform appearance because they have evolved as aquatic predators. This similarity may almost conceal evidence that they may be descended from two separate types of ancestor. The true seals (the Phocidae) are descended from an otter-like creature. The sea lions (the Otariidae) and the walrus (the Odobenidae), on the other hand, may be descended from an ancestral bear-like carnivore. Disregarding how this uncertainty may be resolved, it is clear that pinnipeds appeared relatively late in the mammalian story. The earliest fossils date from about 20–25 million years ago.

Diversity

The Pinnipedia are divided into three families, containing thirty four species in all. The Phocidae contains the nineteen species of true seals. The Otariidae comprises the sea lions (five species) and the fur seals (nine species). There is only one living species in the family Odobenidae, the walruses.

Characteristics

The life history of pinnipeds is constrained by two main considerations, feeding at sea and breeding on land. All pinnipeds are specialised for swimming in cool waters. Their relatively large bodies are streamlined with as few projections as possible. Even the reproductive organs and mammary glands do not mar the smooth outline. The external ears are either extremely small, as in the Otariidae (sometimes known as the eared seals) or absent, as from the Phocidae (true seals).

Their skin is an effective organ for control of heat exchange and has beneath it a thick layer of blubber for insulation. It may also have a thick growth of underfur. The underfur is coated by a thin layer of an oily secretion from the skin glands. This repels water and keeps the underlying skin dry. There is also an array of bypasses and shunts incorporated into the blood vessels in the skin that control heat flowing from or into the body. The feet are webbed between the elongated fingers and toes to produce flippers. The remainder of the limb is relatively short and much of it is hidden underneath the general body contour, so much so that the armpit of a true seal is located at its wrist! In the sea lions it is close to the elbow. This contrast is due to a fundamental difference in the manner in which they generate propulsion in water.

True seals (Phocidae) have their 'engine mounted aft'. Their flexible back and associated muscles and hind-flippers generate most of the propulsion. The hind-limbs are directed backwards and are incapable of rotation under the body, while the fore-limbs are mainly kept tucked close to conserve streamlining. This is why true seals are so ungainly on land: they must drag themselves forward using their fore-limbs only.

The Otariidae, by contrast, generate power at the front end and have well-developed neck and shoulder muscles. Flapping the front flippers generates propulsion and they fly through the water like penguins. The hind-limbs are mainly used for steering. Sea lions are quite mobile on land, due to the greater range of movements of the more exposed fore-limb and the forward rotation of the hind-limb so that it can be used to push the animal forward. The swimming style of the walrus is somewhat intermediate.

Distribution

The Phocidae arose in the southern reaches of the North Atlantic, from which they colonised mainly polar and temperate waters, but they are also found in a number of tropical or subtropical areas.

The Otariidae, on the other hand, evolved on the northern Pacific seaboard and then spread southward. They are now found along the North Pacific rim and in parts of the Arctic ocean, in coastal regions of south America, southern Australia and New Zealand and South Africa. They have never colonised the North Atlantic and thus there are no sea lions or fur seals native to Europe. Walruses also evolved from ancestral fur seals in the North Pacific and at one time there were several species present there. Some of these colonised the North Atlantic where they also became quite common. All the original species of walruses in the Pacific are now extinct and the sole remaining species is derived from the Atlantic stock. It is now largely confined to the parts of the Arctic ocean, from where it has, however, recolonised parts of the North Pacific.

There are eight species of pinnipeds found in Europe. Of the seven species of European seal, two, the grey seal and the common seal, breed in Ireland. Two or perhaps three other species may occasionally visit Irish waters. The walrus now appears to be a regular visitor to waters off the northwest coast.

How you can help

The rangers of Dúchas The Heritage Service of the Department of Arts, Heritage, Gaeltacht and The Islands (RoI) or of the Environment Service of the Department of the Environment (NI) will be able to provide information on the status of seals locally and of sightings of walruses. If you see a walrus, you should report it to either of these groups or to Dr Don Cotton at the Sligo Institute of Technology (e-mail: cotton.don@itsligo.ie).

Occasionally, orphaned or abandoned common seal pups are encountered in mid- and late summer. If an apparently abandoned pup is found, it is recommended to wait until high water to allow for the return of the mother. If the pup is clearly abandoned, injured, ailing or in distress then intervention may be considered. Pups have sharp teeth and may be quite vicious and must be handled carefully. They should be sheltered in a clean, airy place on a continuous surface such as a rubber mat, carpet or chipboard. If hypothermia is suspected, a fan heater may be used. More direct heat sources may cause hyperthermia (the opposite of hypothermia – overheating). Common seal cubs require special food such as liquidised fish that will probably have to be delivered by stomach tube. They should never be given cow's milk or human milk formula, as their composition is quite unsuitable. Hand-rearing a seal pup is a major undertaking. It is recommended to seek professional advice or veterinary assistance or more appropriately to transfer it to a seal sanctuary if possible. If you need help with an abandoned or sick seal, contact the Irish Seal Sanctuary, An Clochán, Tobergregan, Garristown, Co Dublin (01-8354370) or Marinewatch (01-2697865 or 01-8492015) or the ISPCA (01-4977874).

Common (harbour) seal – *Rón breacach (beag)*
Phoca vitulina, Linnaeus 1758

The common seal is the rarer of the two species found in Ireland.

The names

The original description by Linnaeus in 1758 is based on a specimen that originated in the Baltic Sea. The generic name uses the Greek word for seal (*phoca*). The specific name derives from the Latin for 'calf-like' (*vitulus*). The common seal is also known as the harbour seal in English. Males are bulls and females are cows. In Irish the common seal is known as the spotted (*breacach*) seal (*rón*) or the small (*beag*) seal.

Identification and characteristics

The common or harbour seal is the smaller of the two seals resident in Irish waters and, despite its name, is now the less common of the two. However, this is the seal usually seen in estuaries or basking on sandbanks. When on land, common seals often adopt a head-up tail-up posture rather reminiscent of a banana. This keeps their heads and hind flippers clear of wet sand. Bulls are slightly larger than cows, measuring about 1.5m (1.3–1.6m) from nose to tail and weighing about 90kg (60–105), whereas cows are 1.4m (1.2–1.5m) long and weigh about 75kg (50–90kg).

The background colour is extremely variable and may range from dark grey to beige. The surface is covered by numerous small black spots that tend to be more closely spaced on the dorsal surface. Bulls are usually darker overall than cows. Adults moult their coats in late August and September. Pups are born with a coat resembling that of adults, but it is darker and the spots are less obvious. The spots may also be poorly defined in yearlings.

The head is well defined relative to the body. It is rounded and has a short snout and the profile in side view is noticeably concave. This gives the impression that the nose is turned up. The nostrils are arranged in a V-shape and almost make contact at their lower ends.

The claws on the fore-limbs are short and extend slightly beyond the tips of the digits. There are nine teeth on each side of the upper jaw and eight on each side below. The milk teeth are usually lost before birth and the adult teeth are in place relatively early in life. The cheek teeth are flattened from side to side and all except the first consist of three obvious points (cusps). They are inserted obliquely in the jaws.

Common seals are not particularly vocal. Their repertoire includes snorts and growls. Their hearing is, however, well developed and their eyesight is quite sensitive, particularly in bright light.

Distribution and population

Common seals are mainly found in coastal waters between latitudes 30°N and 80°N. Their range extends from eastern Siberia along the coast of Alaska and as far south as California. They are also found on the northeast coast of Canada, southern Greenland and Iceland. The eastern North Atlantic population includes common seals from the coastal waters of Sweden, the Baltic Sea, the North Sea and the coastal waters of Britain and Ireland.

At the beginning of the 19th century the common seal was relatively common and was the most abundant seal in Ireland. By the middle of the 19th century, numbers had declined considerably and eventually it became the less abundant of our two seals. It is found all round the Irish coast but is more common in shallow, sheltered waters, particularly in sea-loughs and estuaries, on the western seaboard and northeast coasts. The largest populations in Ireland are in Strangford Lough and Dundrum Bay (Co Down). They are also common in Galway Bay, Kilkieran Bay and Slyne Head (Co Galway), Bantry Bay and Kenmare Bay (Co Kerry), Clew Bay and Blacksod Bay (Co Mayo), Drumcliffe and Ballysadare (Co Sligo), Mountcharles, Gweebane, Dunloe Bay and Donegal Bay (Co Donegal), Bantry Bay and Glengarriff (Co Cork).

The last survey of the common seal was carried out in 1989. The distribution map indicates the locations of breeding colonies. There is no recent information on the population of common seals in Irish waters. The minimum estimate for the current population of Britain and Ireland is about 100,000 seals and in 1989, after the arrival of the distemper epidemic, there were at least 3000 common seals in Irish waters. Although most common seals do not disperse very far from their birth area, there is sufficient exchange between locations to prevent substantial genetic differences emerging between populations in the northeast Atlantic.

Habitats and habits

Common seals are the typical seals of sandbanks, estuaries, sea-loughs and shallow sheltered waters. They appear to be rather solitary when in the water, but are quite gregarious when on land. Common seals often have rest areas (hauling-out sites) on sandbanks and mudflats with ready access to deep water. Large groups may sometimes be seen in haul-out areas and seals may have a number of sites that they use, depending on tidal and weather conditions. Individual seals usually have a number of favourite resting areas and the same animal can regularly be found hauled out at the same site.

It is not clear if common seals are migratory, but some young seals may disperse over 100km from their birth area. However, this is unusual and most remain in the general vicinity of their birth site. They may travel up to 50km to feeding grounds but they usually feed within about 30km of their base.

Common seals usually rest at low tide but this may not be so in all cases. They swim by lateral movements of the hind flippers and steer with the forelegs. They usually fish in water up to 50m deep. Active dives usually last up to six minutes with rests of a minute or two at the surface. They may rest vertically in the water, often submerging for over five minutes before bobbing up again. They sometimes travel relatively long distances up the larger rivers and have been known to spend extended periods in lakes along such river systems.

Diet

Common seals require about 2–3kg of food a day. Their diet in Irish waters is not well understood. To find out what a seal has been hunting it is necessary to examine the faeces for the presence of distinctive hard parts of their prey, which pass undigested through the gut. They appear to be opportunistic hunters, taking whatever species are locally available and catchable near the seabed. For this reason it is difficult, even if the composition of the diet for one year is known, to predict what will be eaten in the next. They take sandeels, herrings, whiting, flatfish and saithe among others. The composition of the diet is related to the nature of the sea bottom over which they fish. Where fish are scarce they will eat octopus, squid and crustaceans. They also eat molluscs such as whelks. Newly weaned pups feed almost exclusively on shrimps, crabs and other crustaceans for the first few months of independent life.

Reproduction and life-cycle

The breeding strategy of common seals in Ireland has not been much studied, nor is their social organisation at mating time well understood. It is not clear if the males defend territories or harems of females. However, it appears that individual males may pursue different strategies to maximise their chance of acquiring a mate. While an increase in the incidence of fresh wounds to the neck and hind-flippers of males can be seen from late July onwards, there appears to be less fighting than in grey seals. Most of the fighting takes place in the water and it is thought that mating takes place in the shallows.

The fertilised egg does not implant in the uterus for about two to three months. When daylight reduces to 12 hours, this switches on the reproductive system of the female. It appears that a day with 12 hours of light is the signal for the little ball of cells, the blastocyst, to implant and for gestation proper to begin. Thus, although mating takes place some time between mid-August and early October (about 320–330 days before birth occurs), development of the foetus does not usually begin until October and continues for 36–39 weeks. At the latitudes 50–65°N, pups are born in June and July. At lower latitudes, between 45° and 30°N, the pupping season is advanced by about four days for each degree of latitude nearer the equator.

Female common seals give birth to their single pup on the mainland coast or offshore islands close to the coast. Birth takes place in shallow water or on land. As is typical of seals, the pups are large. In fact, common seal pups are particularly advanced at birth and, at 10kg, are about 13% of the mother's weight. They can swim and dive from birth and are good swimmers by the time they are weaned. They grow rapidly and double their weight in about three or four weeks. Weaning is quite an abrupt process and most pups are weaned by late July. At weaning they weigh about 25kg, of which 30% is fat. However, it takes about two weeks before the pups are feeding themselves and they lose weight during this fasting period.

Mating takes place again as soon as the pups are weaned. Females mature at three or four years of age, males not until they are about six. Females may survive to 30 years of age; males rarely exceed 20.

There is little information on the mortality factors that affect common seals in northwestern Europe. Apart from the juvenile mortality, the main causes of death are disease and predation by man, sharks and killer whales. The major diseases are parasitic infections of the respiratory system. In the late 1980s there was an epidemic of a disease, related to canine distemper, caused by phocine distemper virus, which affected European seals. The virus responsible was first identified from common seals in Northern Ireland. Common seals are particularly susceptible to this virus and some sections of the North Sea population suffered 70% mortality. The mortality overall was about 30%. The most seriously affected area in Ireland was Strangford Lough. In other areas only occasional deaths were recorded. It is suspected that reproduction in seals is sensitive to pollutants such as polychlorinated biphenyls (PCB). This is particularly so for common seals that inhabit shallow waters in estuaries, where pollutants may be more concentrated.

Watching common seals

Ireland's largest population is in Strangford Lough (Co Down), which contains about a thousand individuals. There is a population of about two hundred at Glengarriff (Co Cork).

Other good sites are the east end of Galway Bay, inner Donegal Bay, Lissadel (Co Sligo), Achill Sound and Clew Bay (Co Mayo), Bertaghboy and Kilkieran (Co Galway), Ballyvaughan (Co Clare), the Kenmare river (Co Kerry) and Bantry Bay (Co Cork).

Common seals may become tolerant of small boats and visitors. However, it is important not to disturb seals, particularly during lactation. At worst, pups may be abandoned and will certainly die. Even modest disturbance may interrupt nursing. This can have profound effects on the pups, since they must grow rapidly and lay down a substantial deposit of fat off which to live after they are weaned and while they are learning to hunt.

Conservation and management

Common seals are protected under the provisions of the Wildlife Act since 1976 and may only be culled under licence. Before that a bounty system was used in an attempt to reduce their impact on fish stocks. Common seals may be pests of inshore fisheries. They steal fish caught in nets or on long-lines. They also damage fish in nets. They may also be a nuisance at fish farms or fish cages particularly, since these tend to be located in the sheltered bays favoured by the common seal. It appears that the damage caused by common seals may be due to the habits of particular rogue individuals. A number of deterrent systems are under investigation. Common seals are generally considered to have a lesser impact on fisheries than grey seals.

Grey seal – *Rón mór*
Halichoerus grypus, Fabricius 1791

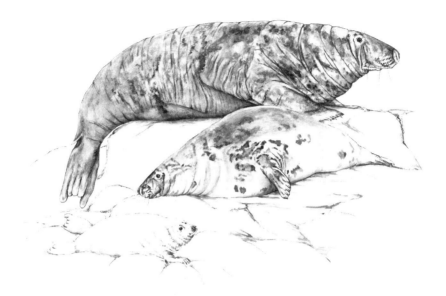

The grey seal is the larger and more abundant of the two seals resident in Irish waters.

The names

The original description by Fabricius is based on a specimen that originated from Greenland. The generic name uses the Greek words for sea (*halios*) and little pig (*khoiros*). The specific name is the Latin for hook-nosed (*grypus*). In Irish it is known as the big (*mór*) seal (*rón*) or the grey (*glas*) seal. Male grey seals are bulls and females are cows.

Identification and characteristics

Grey seals are larger than common seals and bull grey seals are substantially larger than cows. Bulls have a bulky neck and shoulders; they measure from 1.95 to 2.3m from nose to tail and weigh about 240kg (but may range between 170 and 310kg), while cows are 1.65–1.95m long and weigh about 155kg (ranging 105–186kg).

The colour is extremely variable. The bulls are usually dark grey or brown with a slight pale mottling. The underside is a paler grey. The cows are light grey on the back and creamy-grey on the belly with scattered dark blotches. These dark blotches or spots are clearly larger than the spots on the common seal. The apparent colour depends on whether the fur is wet or dry and during the moult large brown patches appear. The pups are white at birth but begin to lose their birth coat after about two weeks and become fawn coloured.

The head of the grey seal is large and has a long snout and the profile in side view is noticeably convex in males, less so in females. The side view of the head is usually described as having a roman profile as opposed to the turned-up nose of the common seal. Young grey seals are sometimes difficult to distinguish from common seals because their heads are more rounded and have not yet attained the adult shape. The nostrils of grey seals are almost parallel slits and do not make contact at their lower ends. There are nine or ten teeth on each side of the upper jaw and eight on each side of the lower jaw. The cheek teeth are large and conical. The claws on the front flippers are long and thin and extend about 2–3cm beyond the ends of the digits.

Grey seals are quite vocal when hauled out in a group on land and they have a variety of growls, hisses, snarls, hoots and rumbles which are used in social interactions. They also use a range of sounds under water. These include a variety of grunts, growls, knocks, clicks and roars. Some may be used for echolocation, particularly when swimming under ice. Facial expressions and gestures with flippers are also important in seal communication.

Distribution

There are three main populations of grey seals in the world with probably some exchange of individuals between them. The western North Atlantic population is concentrated around the Gulf of St Lawrence and Nova Scotia in Canada. There is a small population in the Baltic Sea. The eastern North Atlantic population includes grey seals in Russia, Norway, Sweden, Denmark, Iceland, Britain and Ireland and small numbers in France.

This seal was first positively identified as present in Irish waters in 1836 from a specimen obtained in Cork, but had clearly been here for far longer than that. For example, remains of a grey seal found in a mesolithic kitchen midden on Dalkey island at the southern edge of Dublin Bay was shown by radiocarbon dating to be about 6400 years old.

In the second half of the 19th century the grey seal was relatively rare and the common seal was the more abundant. Since then the grey seal has increased in numbers and the population of the common has declined or remained relatively static. By the middle of the

1960s there were over 50 breeding sites (each containing at least ten adults) known. This does not include sites used by smaller groups or breeding pairs.

There is no recent information on the population of grey seals in Irish waters. The minimum population estimate for Britain and Ireland is about 110,000 seals. It was estimated that in 1989 there were at least 2000 breeding grey seals in Ireland and that the population had increased over the previous five years. To this must be added an unknown but certainly larger number of non-breeding seals. The seals found in Irish waters are not a discrete population but are part of the wider population that occupies the eastern North Atlantic. Grey seals are found all round our coast wherever habitats are suitable and they are most abundant along the south, southwest and west coasts. The two major breeding sites are Inishkea (Co Mayo) and the Blasket islands, each containing 500–700 individuals, with smaller groups at Lambay and Dalkey islands (Co Dublin) and the Saltee Islands (Co Wexford). The distribution map indicates the locations of breeding colonies.

Habitats and habits

The grey seal is typically a creature of the waters along rocky exposed coasts. They breed on exposed rocky shores, on sand bars or in sea-caves with ready access to deep water. Other haul-out areas are also located on exposed rocky areas or steeply shelving sandbanks.

It is not clear if grey seals are regularly migratory. Young seals may disperse over 100km from their birth area. For example, seals tagged as pups in Scotland and Wales have been found in Irish populations. Adults may also travel long distances. Individuals have been radio-tracked from the east coast of England as far north as the Faroe islands or as far to the west as 450km off the southwest coast of Ireland. Although they are less likely than common seals to be found in estuaries, there are occasional reports of grey seals travelling as far as 30km up rivers.

Large groups may sometimes be seen in haul-out areas and grey seals may have a number of sites that they use depending on tidal and weather conditions. Grey seals usually rest at low tide but it seems that only a small proportion of the population may be on land at the same time. When basking on land they spend considerable time scratching and grooming.

Diet

The diet of the grey seal may be established from the indigestible parts of their prey (ear bones of fish or squid beaks) in their faeces. These may be collected at haul-out sites, but this requires considerable effort, since grey seals usually feed and defecate at sea, so few traces of prey items or droppings are found at the haul-out sites and what can be found is lost at each high tide.

Such studies, when they do take place, reveal that the grey seal is an opportunistic hunter taking whatever species are locally available and catchable. They tend to concentrate on bottom-dwelling fish in waters about 70–80m deep. They may, however, dive deeper than 200m. They also take fast-swimming fish such as mackerel from the surface waters. In all, over 20 different species have been identified in the diet of grey seals in northern European waters. They eat a wide variety of fish including poor cod, whiting, cod, ling, sandeels, flatfish, salmon, mackerel and herring. They also eat squid and a variety of crustaceans as well as seabirds which they capture as they feed on the surface. Off the west of Ireland whitefish (whiting, cod, ling and pollock) and non-commercial species (poor cod, sandeels, wrasse, squid and octopus) were the most important components of the diet. The composition of the diet, however, varies seasonally and in different locations. Estimates of food requirements range from 4–5kg up to 10kg a day, but it is not certain that they feed every day. It is clear, however, that while fasting during the breeding season grey seals lose about 2–3kg per day. The impact of seals on fish populations in Irish waters is far from clear, since we have insufficient information on both the diet and on the size of the seal population.

Reproduction and life-cycle

Grey seals are seasonal breeders, but the breeding season differs in the three main world populations. In the western Atlantic breeding takes place from September to December, with more northerly colonies breeding later in the season.

In Ireland most of the births occur from mid-September to mid-November. Large groups of pregnant females can assemble at the breeding grounds in August and September. These are traditional sites generally used by the same females over several breeding seasons. Adult females are particularly intolerant of others at this time and as soon as a female grey seal finds the spot where she gave birth last year she defends it vigorously against other females. Adult females bear a single pup each year. Birth takes place on land and labour is usually quite brief, less than 30 minutes. The pups weigh about 14kg at birth. They are fed every six hours and grow rapidly during the three-week nursing period. The milk of grey seals is extremely rich and may contain up to 60% fat. Pups increase in weight by about 2kg per day and weigh over 40kg at weaning. About 40% of their body weight at this time is fat. Most pups are weaned by the end of October. It is generally considered that grey pups do not take to the water as early as young common seals, not usually until they are weaned. This may not be the case in all populations and in Mayo and Kerry pups may begin swimming during their second week. Weaning, once started, is completed rapidly. It takes the weaned pups about three weeks to begin feeding for themselves, and they lose weight during this fast. Females do not remain on land for the entire period of lactation but they do not venture far from shore either and apparently do not feed, so in the course of the three weeks of lactation they lose about 25% of their body weight.

As soon as their pups are weaned, females come into breeding condition again and mating takes place. Adult males arrive at the breeding grounds at about the same time as the females come to give birth, and attempt to acquire access to females. They do this by occupying an area of beach which either already contains females or which females must cross to reach their pups. On narrow beaches they may occupy a site in the water. They attempt to exclude other males and fighting is usually severe; peripheral males may attempt to sneak onto territories and mate while the owner is involved in disputes with competitors. A few males may dominate the breeding season depending on the size of the colony. Individual males may gain mating access to up to 10% of the females locally. Males may remain in the breeding site for the whole season and may not feed for up to eight weeks. Females leave the colony soon after mating.

Within the female, the fertilised egg does not implant in the uterus until spring, a delay of about 100–125 days. Development of the foetus then takes a further 214–240 days. Females do not usually breed before they reach four years of age. Males reach adult size at about six years but do not usually breed before they are ten years old. Grey seals are relatively long-lived. Bulls may survive for up to 25 years, females for over 40.

Many grey seal pups die of starvation because their mothers do not bond with them. Others are accidentally killed in the melee of the mating colony. Some drown when washed from the colony by storms. Mortality is increased by exposure, disturbance and high population density. Under these conditions, mortality of pups may range from 20% to 50%, but recent estimates of pup mortality in sheltered and secluded locations in Kerry and Mayo were lower than 5%. Disturbance early in the pupping season may drive females to use less suitable pupping sites and this can contribute to higher losses. Yearlings are also subject to high mortality, sometimes up to 50%.

The major causes of mortality to adult seals appear to be respiratory diseases and infections. In the late 1980s there was an epidemic of the viral disease, phocine distemper, which affected European seals. It appears, in this instance, that grey seals were more resistant than common seals to this virus. It is suspected that reproduction in seals is sensitive to pollutants such as polychlorinated biphenyls (PCBs).

Watching grey seals

Among the best sites for viewing grey seals are the Inishkea islands (Co Mayo), The Blaskets (Co Kerry), Lambay, Skerries, Dalkey (all Co Dublin), Glengarriff (Co Cork) and Wexford Harbour. Special boating equipment is needed for most other sites.

It is important not to disturb seals, particularly during lactation. At worst, pups may be abandoned and will certainly die. At best, the nursing may be interrupted. This can have profound effects on the pups, since they must grow rapidly and lay down a substantial deposit of fat to maintain them after they are weaned. Occasionally orphaned or abandoned grey seal pups are found from October through December. If the pup has dense white fur, then it has not yet been weaned and is less than three weeks old. See page 308 for advice on what to do if you find an apparently abandoned pup.

Conservation and management

Man is probably the only major predator of grey seals. (While killer whales prey on grey seals, the extent of mortality appears to be slight.) Grey seals are occasionally caught in fishing nets. For example one grey seal is caught per 500 towing hours in the herring fishery in the Celtic sea. Grey seals have been protected since 1976 and may only be culled under licence. Prior to that, bounties were paid for grey seals killed. They were also formerly a target for commercial hunting and were taken for oil and meat and on a larger scale for their skins. They were formerly considered a game species and were hunted as such during the 19th century along the west coast of Ireland, and as late as the 1970s grey seal safaris in the west of Ireland were being advertised in continental Europe.

Seals may become pests of fisheries, although the economic effect of their predation is not clear. They steal fish caught in nets or on long-lines. They also damage fish in nets. However, since crabs also scavenge fish in nets, the effect of seals may have been overestimated in the past. Grey seals may also be a nuisance at fish farms or fish cages. They may also raid trawls. It appears that the damage is not directly related to the density of seals and may rather be due to the habits of particular individuals, who have learned to exploit what man is harvesting. A number of deterrent systems are under investigation.

Walrus – *Rosualt*
Odobenus rosmarinus, Linnaeus 1758

The walrus is one of our more exotic occasional visitors. Of late it is being more frequently seen in inshore waters off the west coast.

The names

The original description by Linnaeus in 1758 is based on a specimen that originated in the Arctic ocean. The generic name is derived from the Greek words *odontos* (tooth) and *baino* (to walk), a reference to the belief that its long tusks functioned as auxiliary legs. The specific name derives from the Latin *ros maris* meaning rose of the sea. This is probably a reference to the pinkish skin of the walrus, particularly when it is overheated. The common name is derived from the Scandinavian valross, meaning whale-horse. Male walruses are bulls and females are cows. The Irish name *rosualt* is derived from the Old Norse *hrosshvalr*, which means a sea monster.

Identification and characteristics

The walrus is the third largest of the seals and is the second largest in the northern hemisphere. Bulls are substantially larger than cows, measure about 3–3.5m from nose to tail and weigh about 1100–1200kg. Cows are 2.3–3m long and weigh about 800kg.

The juveniles, sometimes known as calves or pups, are covered with a dense brownish fur that becomes more sparse and paler with age. The skin is generally rough and wrinkled. The thickness of the skin varies in different regions of the body and is particularly thick and warty in appearance over the neck and shoulders. The colour of an adult walrus varies depending on temperature. When a walrus is cold, blood is withdrawn from the skin and the animal appears almost white. When overheated either by exercise or when on land, blood is pumped to the skin to lose heat and the animal appears pink.

The head appears small relative to the body. It is rounded and inset to the trunk with scarcely any neck. The eyes are relatively small and the ears have no external lobes. The upper lip is covered with a dense growth of stiff whiskers and the overall aspect is somewhat mournful and lugubrious. The large upper lips and whiskers are extremely sensitive and mobile and are used to select food by touch.

The most distinctive features of the walrus are the upper canine teeth, which are enlarged to form tusks. These tusks are borne by both sexes. Those of the males may be up to 40cm long and are thicker and less curved than those of females, which may be up to 30cm. The tusks continue to grow during the life of the animal and increase in size with age, but are continually being worn away at the tip. The tusks appear to have multiple functions. They may be used in association with the lips to grub for food on the seabed. They are also used by males for display and as weapons in fights for positions of dominance in the breeding season. A few walruses develop the habit of killing seals; the tusks and teeth of these individuals are often stained by rancid fat from their prey. Walruses sometimes rest by hooking their tusks over the edge of an ice hole and hanging by them in the water. Broken tusks are relatively common. Otherwise walruses have relatively few teeth, 18 in all. They have two incisors in the top only and the lower canines are flat and broad. They have six cheek teeth above and below. The cheek teeth are reduced to flat pads of dentine.

The hind-feet are held under the body, unlike those of seals, and thus all four limbs are used for moving on ice or on land. They swim by lateral movements of the hind-flippers and steer with the fore-legs.

Walruses have two large pouches under the skin behind the shoulders which are attached to the windpipe at the back of the mouth. These can be inflated to the size of footballs and appear to serve two functions. The first use is as a flotation device while the walrus is resting at the surface. The second is as a sound box or resonance chamber that assists in producing a booming bell-like sound. Walruses, particularly the bulls, are extremely vocal and their repertoire includes a range of knocks, taps and bells in addition to snorts and growls. Their hearing is well developed and their eyesight is good.

Distribution

The walrus is mainly found in areas of moving pack ice in shallow coastal waters of the Arctic ocean. Their main range extends along the north coast of Norway, in the Barents Sea, along the Siberian coast as far to the east as

Alaska. They are also found in the waters west of Greenland and extend into Hudson Bay. They are less common around the coasts of Iceland. They are mainly restricted to areas above latitude 65°N but may have formerly extended further southward.

The walrus is an occasional visitor to the coastal waters of Ireland and Britain. The walrus was first reported from Irish waters in 1897, when a single individual was seen in the River Shannon. The first of a recent series of sightings was of an individual seen in the waters off the Donegal coast in 1981. Somewhere between ten and 20 have been seen in the last 20 years, mainly from fishing-boats operating off the northwest coast. Sightings of single individuals, all apparently juveniles, have been reported from Arranmore, Horn Head, Fanad Head and Malin Head in Co Donegal. The carcass of a dead walrus has been found on the shores of Lough Swilly and another was found near Sybil Head (Co Kerry) in 1994. But the most celebrated sighting was that of an individual that came ashore for a nap near Old Head (Co Mayo) in April 1998. The distribution map shows where walruses living and dead were found on Irish coasts (circles) or at sea (shaded area).

Habitats and habits

Walruses are quite gregarious, particularly when on land. They are rarely seen alone, and solitary animals are usually either young or very old males. Walruses are typically associated with moving pack ice, usually within 15km of the coast. They migrate southwards with the ice front in autumn and return northward in spring. They often have traditional rest areas (hauling-out sites) where extremely large herds may congregate. When at sea they may travel up to 50km to feeding grounds. Active dives usually last up to seven minutes, with rests of a minute or two at the surface hanging vertically in the water.

Diet

The walrus feeds on the sea-bottom at depths ranging 10–80m. Their main food items are clams and other bivalve molluscs such as cockles and mussels, which they locate by touch, using their stiff but sensitive whiskers. They can suck out the fleshy contents of shellfish and then spit out the shell. They appear, however, to be opportunistic hunters, taking other species which are locally available, such as sea cucumbers, crabs, starfish and fish. Adults may eat up to 40kg of food a day. Particular individuals sometimes prey on seals.

Reproduction and life-cycle

The breeding system of walruses is an extremely competitive one. Males display in the water, adjacent to ice floes on which the females are resting. The display consists of a complicated song sequence of stereotypical knocks and bells. These sounds are emitted while the animal is submerged. These serenades appear to be directed largely towards the cows. Each song bout lasts for about five minutes and between bouts the male surfaces to breathe for one or two minutes before submerging to sing again. These more-or-less continuous vocal displays may last for over two days.

The mating season is generally in February and March. Mating takes place in the water and a small number of large bulls dominate the rut. The fertilised egg does not implant in the uterus immediately. The usual interval between mating and birth consists of a period of three to five months, during which implantation is delayed, followed by the true gestation of about 12 months. True development of the foetus usually begins in the May after mating and continues for 12 months, so the young are usually born in the following May.

Adult females bear a single pup on the ice. The pups weigh about 60kg at birth and are defended fiercely by the mothers, to whom they cling or on whom they ride. Lactation is relatively prolonged and the young are not weaned for at least two years and may remain with their mother until they are about four. Females produce a pup about every three years.

Females mature earlier than males and breed for the first time at about five years of age. Although males mature at about ten years of age, they probably do not acquire sufficiently high rank to breed until they are about 16. Females may survive to 40 years of age; males probably rarely exceed 30.

The walrus was not apparently affected by the epidemic of a disease related to canine distemper, caused by phocine distemper virus, which affected European seals, particularly common seals, in the late 1980s.

Studying walruses

The walrus does not breed in Ireland and rarely hauls out on land here, but there is probably a steady trickle of walruses visiting the northern coastal waters. To see a walrus in Irish waters requires good fortune indeed. The best sources of information on recent sightings are offshore fishermen and boat crews operating off the west coast, particularly in the northwest. The recent increase in sightings may be due to alterations in the ocean currents in the North Atlantic.

Conservation

The walrus was extensively hunted in former times, particularly from the 17th to the early 20th century. At the height of the hunting effort the principal motivation was ivory, and the tusks were often the only component harvested.

On a worldwide scale the walrus population is currently considered to be vulnerable, but the animal is still an important element in the subsistence hunting economy of some Inuit peoples. It is protected in the Republic of Ireland and Northern Ireland.

CHAPTER 10

Order Artiodactyla – Even-hoofed Mammals

Dord daimh dhithreibhe os aille
Bhios a Siodhmhuinre Glinne,
Nochan fhuil ceol ar talmhain
Im anmain acht a bhinne.

The solitary roaring stag
High on Siodhmhuinre Crag,
Soothes my soul
With music sweeter than earthsong.
(Anon 12th century, trans T. J. Hayden)

The name *Artiodactyla* means even fingers, which refers to the fact that the *Artiodactyla* have an even number of fingers or toes (two or four) on each foot. (The other type of hoofed mammals, the *Perissodactyla*, have an odd number of fingers and toes.)

The Artiodactyla are one of the oldest orders of mammals and arose about 60 million years ago. Incidentally, their immediate ancestors, the condylarthrans, also gave rise to the Cetaceans (whales and dolphins) and the Carnivora (wolves, cats etc).

The early evolutionary history of Artiodactyla is well known. They were extremely common and diverse in the Eocene, although the only survivors of these early types are the pigs, camels and chevrotains (mouse-deer). Most of the modern families evolved between 10 and 20 million years ago.

Characteristics

The two main features of the artiodactyls relate to the structure of the legs and the stomach. They walk on hooves, which are really the modified fingernails of their third and fourth digits (fingers/toes). The second and fifth digits may be present but do not generally carry weight except on soft ground. The first digit is lost.

The legs are relatively long and have become so by extension of the bones in the 'wrist/palm' and 'ankle/sole' region. Thus the part of the fore-leg of, for example, a deer that resembles a knee is in fact the wrist. The legs appear relatively thin because the muscles are concentrated in the upper parts, close to the body. This allows a more economical and rapid movement of the limbs.

The dietary habits of artiodactyls range from omnivorous (pigs) to specialised plant feeders such as reindeer, which depend on lichens in the Arctic tundra in winter, or chevrotains, which specialise in easily digested vegetation and tropical fruits. The most omnivorous artiodactyls have a fairly complete set of unspecialised teeth. The more herbivorous members have lost some teeth, particularly the upper incisors and canines. In the ruminant artiodactyls, a bony pad covered with a thickened gum has replaced the upper incisors. The teeth of artiodactyls are generally designed to grind vegetation that is often tough and fibrous.

Their digestive system is quite the most complex of all the mammals. Mammals, and probably most animals, are unable to digest cellulose, the major structural component of the cell walls of plants. Herbivores have, however, entered into a mutually beneficial arrangement with an array of micro-organisms which can digest cellulose. These include ciliated protozoa and bacteria – the particular species and their abundance depend on the diet of the herbivore. The micro-organisms live in the guts of these herbivores, where they are provided with plant material. This they use to grow and multiply. In the process they convert cellulose to fatty acids, which the mammal can then use. This mutually beneficial process is an example of symbiosis.

The digestion of cellulose, which takes place in an anaerobic atmosphere (one totally lacking in oxygen), is called fermentation. Plant-eating animals have developed specialised chambers in their gut to store and incubate large quantities of food during fermentation and this is why they have rather bulky bodies. There are two locations where the fermentation may take place, either mainly towards the front end of the gut, in the stomach (as in deer and cattle) or towards the hind end in the caecum and colon (as in the pig or the hippopotamus).

Those animals with specially adapted stomachs comprising four chambers are termed ruminants, which means that they 'chew the cud'. Plant material is hard to break down and so it must be chewed thoroughly. In fact, ruminants chew their food more than once: they can pass food that has already been swallowed back up to the mouth for further grinding by the cheek teeth. Initially food is retained in the anterior stomach (rumen) while fermentation proceeds. Fatty acids produced by the micro-organisms are absorbed into the blood here. There is a sorting chamber, the reticulum, connected to the rumen, which sends undigested material back to the mouth and allows completely digested material to pass to the stomach proper. This is where digestible materials released from the plants and indeed the micro-organisms themselves are digested before being absorbed into the blood stream from the intestines. Additional fermentation also takes place in the hind-gut.

While the general anatomy of the gut is similar in all ruminants, there are specialisations. For example, some deer which specialise in highly nutritious and concentrated food items that are low in cellulose have a relatively small rumen. On the other hand, roughage-selectors, such as cattle, which eat mainly grasses, have a relatively large rumen. Most deer are mixed or intermediate feeders and fall between these two extremes.

Diversity

The Artiodactyla is certainly one of the most diverse orders or groups of large mammals and about two hundred living species are recognised. There are ten families within the order, divided into three main groups.

The first group contains the less specialised members of the order, which are included in three families, the pigs (eight species), the peccaries (three species) and the hippopotamuses (two species). The second group consists of one family, the camels (four species). The third contains five families, the chevrotains (four species), the deer (37 species), the giraffes (two species), the pronghorn (one species) and the bovids (cattle and antelopes, 111 species).

Distribution

The Artiodactyla originally evolved in the northern hemisphere. The camels arose in America. The bovids (cattle and antelopes) evolved in Asia and spread to Africa, where they are particularly successful and diverse. Deer remained in the northern hemisphere and spread to the Americas. The pigs, the oldest family, are found throughout Eurasia, the hippos in Africa and the peccaries in central and South America. Artiodactyla are highly adaptable, found from sea level to high mountain tops, and are also present in the northern polar regions. They are naturally absent from remote oceanic islands and Australasia. (They have, however, been widely introduced to areas outside their natural range.) Artiodactyla are quite abundant in temperate climates but are extremely common in the tropics, and in certain areas they outnumber all other orders of large mammals. Cattle, of which there are about 10 million in Ireland, lie at the cultural and economic core of the country.

Of the 190 living species (in nine families), 19 (in three families) are found in Europe. Of these, four species (from two families) are found in the wild in Ireland. These are wild goats descended from domestic stock, together with red, sika and fallow deer. Formerly there were three other species in Ireland, the giant deer and the reindeer, both of which became extinct between about 10,000 and 11,000 years ago, and the roe deer, an introduced species which was exterminated in the early part of the 20th century.

Red deer – *Fia rua*
Cervus elaphus, Linnaeus 1758

The red deer is our largest wild herbivore. It is possibly the only truly native species of deer, although it may have been introduced by our neolithic ancestors.

The names

The red deer was described scientifically from Swedish specimens by Linnaeus in 1758. The generic name is Latin for a stag (*cervus*). The specific name is derived from the Greek for deer (*elaphos*). The Irish name means red (*rua*) deer (*fia*). Adult male red deer are known as stags, the females are hinds and the young are known as calves.

Deer were once common in Ireland and many of our oldest myths and legends feature deer. There are many place names in Ireland which refer to deer such as Keimaneigh (Co Cork), the pass (*céim*) of the deer (*an fhiadh*); Drumanee (Co Derry) and Knockanee in (Co Limerick), both meaning the hill (*drom, cnoc*) of the deer. Knockanoss (*cnoc an os*) and Mullaghanish (*mullach an ois*) (both in Co Cork) mean the hill of the young deer(s) (*os*). There are also many references to deer meadows such as Cloonelt (Co Roscommon) and Clonelty (in Cos Limerick and Fermanagh), which mean meadow (*cluain*) of the hind (*eilit* is a female deer) and *Annahilt* (Co Down), which means the marsh (*eanach*) of the hind. The personal name Oisín, well known from Irish legend and sometimes used for boys in Ireland, means little deer/calf (*os*).

Identification and characteristics

The red deer is the largest of the three deer species currently found wild in Ireland, but the body size and weight is quite variable and depends greatly on habitat quality. Adult stags stand about 120–140cm at the shoulder and weigh about 200kg in late September. Hinds are smaller than stags, 90–100cm tall at the shoulder, and weigh 100–130kg.

The summer coat is usually reddish brown but it ranges from dark brown to beige, with white spots on either side of the line along the back. Faint spots may be seen on the flanks. The belly is grey or yellowish. The birth coat of calves is reddish brown with off-white spots along the flanks. The winter coat ranges from brown to greyish and the stags develop a thick dark shaggy mane for the rut. There is a cream or light-brown rump patch that extends above and in front of the base of the tail. When the deer is alarmed, the hair on this patch is erected and the expanded patch acts as a conspicuous warning signal to other deer. The rump patch does not have a dark line around the top edge as in sika and fallow deer, but the lateral margins are often dark. The tail is relatively short and broad and is about the same length as the ear and reaches about halfway down the rump patch. The tail is beige on top. The metatarsal glands on the outer side of the hocks are small (2–3cm across) and the tufts of hair which overlie them are fawn or beige, never white.

The head of a red deer, particularly the snout, is quite long. The ears are comparatively long and pointed. The margin of the ear is black but the hair on the inside is white. Stags carry branching antlers, which are shed and grown anew each year. When fully developed, in mature stags, they usually have at least three points (tines) each along the main beam of each antler and a fork or cup of points at the top. The first (brow) and second (bez) tines arise relatively close together. The third (trez) tine arises about halfway along the main beam. The main beams of the antlers are curved to form an approximate heart shape when viewed from the front. The

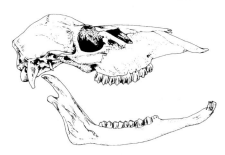

antlers are quite variable and the number of points in mature stags may vary from eight to 40, depending on body size and condition. Antlers generally increase in size, weight and complexity with age, but they are not a reliable method for judging the age of a stag. As stags approach extreme old age, they tend to develop simpler and smaller antlers each year.

Distribution

Red deer have been in Europe and Asia for at least 200,000 years. They were once widespread in the northern hemisphere and there are a number of different races. They ranged from Ireland through most of continental Europe and across central Asia to China, Siberia and North America. A North American form of the red deer, known as the wapiti (or, confusingly, also known as the elk in North America) was once found across the USA and Canada and as far south as Mexico. The wapiti originally evolved in eastern Asia and is very similar to deer from eastern Siberia. A number of subspecies of red deer and wapiti are recognised.

Red deer may be the only deer native to Ireland. It was present in Ireland before the last glacial maximum, during which it went extinct. It reappeared during the Woodgrange interstadial, a period of warmer climate between 12,500 and 11,000 years ago, and presumably went extinct again during the Nahanagan stadial, a cold period which set in from 11,000 to c.10,000 years ago. There are no authenticated red deer remains from any mesolithic or early neolithic faunal samples. This apparent low density of red deer may also explain the relative scarcity of wolves at this time. The earliest dated red deer samples date from 4190 years ago, 3985 years ago and 3760 years ago.

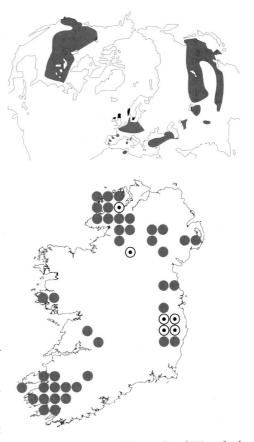

Despite the wide occurrence of remains of red deer in archaeological sites, they are not numerous. Artefacts fashioned from red deer antlers have been found in neolithic contexts, but they are extremely rare. They may not even have originated in Ireland – a cast roe deer antler was recovered in medieval Waterford although roe deer were not present in Ireland then. Red deer therefore may not have reappeared until relatively late and it is possible that humans introduced them as they had to many Mediterranean islands. Red deer had become relatively abundant and widespread by the middle ages.

Red deer evolved as animals of steppes and woodland edges, dependent upon grassy glades and open-canopy woodland. With the loss of forests they have, in certain areas, been forced to adapt to open upland moorlands and mountains. The development of towns, the extension of agriculture and increasing human population caused a serious reduction in numbers in the 18th and 19th centuries, with the near extinction of red deer from much of central and western Europe. In Ireland this was particularly severe just before and during the Great Famine of 1845–7, after which they almost became extinct in the country. For example, the population in Donegal went extinct in the 1860s, but one wild population survived, in the Killarney region of Co Kerry. Since then, red deer from Britain and Europe have been introduced to Irish deer parks on many occasions, particularly in the late 19th and early 20th centuries. Individuals that escaped from these parks founded several of the present wild populations.

Wild red deer are now found in counties Donegal, Fermanagh, Tyrone, Down, Wicklow, Meath and Kerry with a few reported from nine other counties. The herds in the Ulster counties and Wicklow are derived from animals originating from Britain. The Donegal population was re-established in 1891 and the Donegal deer still retain their genetic similarity to Scottish red deer. The deer in the Boyne valley are also escapees from parks. The Kerry population is the only one with claims to be the original native stock. But even this herd was supplemented by stags from abroad and elsewhere in Ireland during the 19th and early 20th centuries. Whether these ever bred is not clear, but the skulls of Killarney red deer are somewhat different from those in Donegal and Scotland, consistent with their long isolation.

There have been no overall censuses of deer in Ireland so an estimate of the total population of red deer is extremely provisional. The population in Kerry is variously estimated to be about one thousand deer. There are about eight hundred in the Glenveagh area of Co Donegal. There are about two hundred red-like deer in Co Wicklow, but these are hybrids and have varying proportions of sika deer in their ancestry. There is a small population of red deer, about a hundred animals, in the Boyne Valley derived from escapees from parks. The map shows the 20km squares in which red deer may be found in Ireland today. The paler symbols show where red-like deer, which are hybrids with sika deer, may be seen. The distribution of red deer is particularly confusing at the moment since escapes or deliberately released animals from deer farms are being reported from several locations.

Habitat and habits

Red deer in western Europe are typically associated with a mosaic of open woodland or woodland edge. Because of habitat changes and disturbance, they now mainly inhabit open upland mountain and moorland and secluded woodland. In Ireland, they will use conifer plantations, particularly open thickets with good food and cover. They may also migrate down from higher altitudes to more sheltered wooded lowlands in winter.

Red deer are opportunistic or intermediate feeders and will take a mixture of plants, depending on their availability. They will eat grasses, leaves such as those of heather, oak, ivy, holly, and fraughans (as bilberries are called in Ireland, from the Irish *fraochán*), as well as herbs and woody shoots, together with acorns and other fruit. The diet of red deer in the Killarney National Park consists of 50–70% grass, depending on season and location. Red deer are active by day and night but tend to feed, in about six bouts, mainly in the early morning and late in the evening.

Stags shed their antlers each spring in March and April and a new set immediately begins to grow. The growing antler is covered with skin called velvet. When antler growth is complete in August, the velvet dies and is cleaned off to reveal the bare bone of the antler. Young male calves begin to grow their first set of antlers at about six to eight months of age.

Social organisation and reproduction

The social organisation of red deer depends on the time of year and the nature of the habitat. Groups of adult males and females occupy separate ranges for most of the year. Group sizes in red deer tend to be small, usually from about ten to 40 animals, but in certain circumstances groups as large as a hundred may be seen. Larger groups tend to form in open habitats or when food is scarce but locally concentrated.

Females are usually organised in matriarchal herds, whose members are related to one another and occupy adjacent, partially overlapping home ranges. These matriarchal herds usually contain adult females, their daughters, calves and yearling males. The size of these female groups varies somewhat, but is usually in the range of five to seven individuals. A group of females may join other groups for short periods before drifting away again. However, there is little exchange of individuals between the groups. On the other hand, groups of stags are usually smaller and less stable. The seasonal home ranges of red deer vary from 200 to 2000ha, depending on the quality of the habitat.

The breeding cycle is controlled by the length of day and the breeding season, known as the rut, is in full swing in late September and early October and may continue until November. In August and September, stags leave their summer range and join the hind groups. During the rut, stags become vocal and emit characteristic deep roars. The roar is a rumbling guttural bellow, delivered about twice a minute, but more frequently when stags are highly excited.

Stags and hinds have special glands that open on the face just below the eyes. These produce an oily scent with which they mark trees and other vegetation during the breeding season. Stags also fray trees and bushes by thrashing with their antlers. They spray urine on their undersides too and develop a strong odour rather like that of a billy goat.

At this time stags are quite aggressive and, despite much ritualised threatening and bluffing, including roaring contests, which would be expected to resolve disputes, fights are quite frequent. (However, they do not fight as frequently as fallow bucks.) Stags fight by locking antlers and attempting to subdue their opponent by wrestling and pushing him backwards, and the sound of the antlers clashing together can clearly be heard on the upland moors or in the woods at this time. Aggressive encounters may persist for up to 30 minutes or more. Competition between males for access to females is intense and males are unlikely to mate successfully before they are five years of age. Successful stags consort with hinds and attempt to gather harems, containing as many hinds as are prepared to remain in their presence or that they can defend from the attentions of rival stags. If hinds do not conceive at their first mating, they may mate again at 20-22 day intervals until pregnancy results. Most conceptions take place in early October. Gestation lasts about 240 days and single calves (very rarely twins), weighing about 6kg, are born from mid-May to mid-June.

Calves do not follow their mothers for about the first week of life. Their survival strategy has evolved to avoid predators, such as wolves, foxes or eagles, by lying motionless, hidden in vegetation. By the second week they become more mobile and begin to follow their mothers. Young calves often associate together in kindergarten groups. They are weaned at about eight months of age. Female red deer calves tend to remain in the vicinity of their birth area; young males disperse when about one year old. Hinds may mate when they are 15 or 16 months of age, particularly in good-quality habitats if population density is low. However, it is more usual for females to conceive for the first time as two-year-olds (that is, in their third year) and bear their first calf on or about their own third birthday. Female red deer may live for twenty years, but this is unusual. Stags are unlikely to survive much longer than 12 years of age.

Hybridisation

Red deer and sika deer hybridise in captivity and in the wild. In fact both phenomena were first reported from Ireland. These hybrids are fertile and are at no apparent competitive disadvantage compared to red or sika deer. The first red x sika hybrids occurred within the confines of Powerscourt deerpark (400ha) within 15 years of their confinement together. The first generation hybrids were capable of interbreeding with one another to produce second generation hybrids and could also interbreed with either the parental red or sika, more likely the latter. It is now clear from recent breeding experiments that the original hybridisation event was the result of a mating between a young red stag (less than 3 years old) and an adult sika female.

First generation hybrids are large and resemble red deer somewhat but there are five certain giveaway clues to their hybrid character. The ears are relatively broader than those of red deer. The hairs on the metatarsal gland on the hocks form a large white patch. The antlers of adult males lack a bez tine and a crown. The prominent rump patch is white, with a brown margin and does not extend much beyond the base of the tail. The spots on the summer coat are more conspicuous than those of red deer. If an animal contains more than 50% red deer genes, as might occur when a first generation hybrid crosses with a red deer, then the most reliable characteristic is that of the rump patch which resembles that of the first generation hybrid. It is impossible to mistake an animal that contains more than 50% sika genes for a red deer. They look like sika.

Red deer have also interbred with wapiti in Ireland. Some red deer in the Boyne valley and in the vicinity of Caledon (Co Tyrone) show traces of wapiti ancestry, particularly in their antlers. Indeed red deer can interbreed with most other species in the genus *Cervus*. Although there are chromosomal differences between some of the species (for example red deer and wapiti have 68 chromosomes, while sika deer have 64), fertile hybrids nevertheless may be produced.

Why should these species which additionally look, sound and behave so differently interbreed? The reason is that they have not evolved mechanisms to prevent it. There are historical reasons for this. The three species, red, sika and wapiti, share a common ancestor that lived about 500,000 to one million years ago somewhere in central Asia. Over 95% of their DNA is identical. As the ancestors spread, different local conditions selected for different features so that descendants in Europe (modern red deer) have come to differ quite substantially from other descendants in North America and continental Eastern Asia (wapiti) and in the Japanese archipelago (sika). Most of the mammalian species in this book do not have the ability to hybridise with others. Over time, mechanisms evolve to make this less likely. The effect of these reproductive barriers is to lock particular genetic adaptations into a particular animal type that we call a species. Of course if two animal types have evolved from a recent common ancestor or they have evolved in different locations, then the barriers may not be complete. This is because in the first case there may not have been sufficient time or in the second any particular pressing need under natural conditions. Both situations probably apply to the red deer. This capacity for red deer to hybridise with other species causes biologists great problems in deciding where one species starts and ends. It also causes problems for the conservation of red deer as a distinct type.

The release of sika deer from Powerscourt to Killarney took place before hybridisation had occurred. Hybridisation has not apparently occurred in Killarney, even where two wild populations of red and sika deer share the same range. Nevertheless, even the possibility of interbreeding poses a threat to red deer. The hybrids thus produced could then interbreed with more red deer and soon the genetic integrity of the red deer would be lost. This has already occurred in Wicklow, which was colonised by sika-like deer from Powerscourt after the initial hybridisation event. The genetic status of individual red-like deer in Wicklow is unclear but most of the deer in Wicklow and surrounding counties are hybrids between red and sika.

Watching red deer

The novice is probably best advised to watch deer in parks or at deer farms. These are sometimes open to the public, but in some cases you may need to make an appointment to visit. It helps to be a member of a deer group. There are two main societies devoted to deer, their conservation, protection and management. These are the Irish Deer Society (c/o Department of Zoology, University College Dublin, Belfield, Dublin 4), and the Northern Ireland Deer Society. The rangers of Dúchas The Heritage Service of the Department of Arts, Heritage, Gaeltacht and The Islands (RoI) or of the Environment Service of the Department of the Environment (NI) or the foresters of Coillte will be able to provide information on the status of deer locally.

Patience is required for watching deer in the wild. Deer are extremely sensitive to scents and it is important to be always aware of the wind direction and to approach from downwind. It is also important to be able to move quietly and slowly, particularly if attempting to see woodland deer. It is preferable to wear clothes which are not only appropriate to the ground and weather conditions but which also tone in with the surroundings and which are not noisy. A good pair of binoculars is essential and a magnification of about 8x40 or 7x50 provides the best compromise between adequate light transmission and ease of use. Provided that a long trek is not involved then a telescope may be used but of course the essential tripod adds to the weight to be carried.

Deer spend their days alternating between periods of feeding in the open and ruminating and resting often in cover. Deer may therefore be seen at any time of the day. In hunted or disturbed populations, however, the best times to see deer are just after dawn and just before dusk when they feed most actively. It is important to be alert to the field signs that indicate that deer are using the locality. A browse line may be evident in the trees where the deer have trimmed off the lower vegetation as high as they can reach. A high browse line about 1.75 or 2m from the ground is usually indicative of red deer. Also, red deer often pull strips of bark from trees. There may be evidence of score marks made by raking the antlers vertically along the bark of trees. There may also be pieces of bark freshly stripped from the trees. Trails may be seen leading out of woods to grassy areas and there may be piles of deer droppings in evidence. Trails used by red deer may be apparent in woodland and their hoof marks (slots), about 8 or 9cm long, may be visible in soft mud. This may indicate a good vantage point from which to observe deer on the next visit. No two male red deer grow identical sets of antlers and individual stags may, with practice, be recognisable by particular features of the antlers.

Red deer stags excavate shallow hollows into which they urinate and in which they wallow, becoming extremely muddy and smelly in the process. Indeed during the rut the mature stags may often be located by their strong musky scent. Cold clear still mornings from mid–September to early October are the best conditions for observing the rut, when the stags are most vocal and active.

It is important not to disturb deer for two reasons. Firstly, deer must spend considerable time feeding, particularly late in spring when food is scarce and of poor quality, and thus any feeding time lost may have serious consequences. Secondly, disturbed deer will rapidly move out of sight and make observation much more difficult. In summer, deer calves may occasionally be found lying motionless in vegetation. Despite appearances these calves have not been abandoned. Their mothers will be somewhere in the vicinity. The calves do not begin to run with their mothers for a week or ten days after birth. Interference, particularly handling or moving calves at this stage, increases the risk of rejection by the mother.

There are enclosed red deer in Doneraile Park (Co Cork), Connemara National Park (Co Galway), Gosford Forest Park (Co Armagh), and Caledon Deer Park (Co Tyrone). Red deer may be seen at relatively close range in a number of open, protected areas such as the lowland areas of Killarney National Park and in Glenveagh National Park. The Old Kenmare Road which runs through the Killarney National Park (Co Kerry), and Glenveagh (Co Donegal) are particularly good sites from which to hear the full vocal range of rutting red stags.

Conservation and management

Because of the threat to the genetic integrity of red deer posed by hybridisation, the red deer, particularly in Killarney, where interbreeding has not taken place, are of high conservation value, since they represent the last population of native red deer. Oddly enough, they owe their survival to the designation, during the 19th century, of the grounds of the Herbert and Kenmare estates in Killarney as a hunting reserve. As part of the conservation strategy for native red deer, subpopulations have been established in a number of locations that are currently secure from sika deer. These are Inishvickillaune in the Blasket islands (Co Kerry), Doneraile Park (Co Cork) and the Connemara National Park (Co Galway). Additionally, two small populations are held on farms in Co Waterford.

The expansion of deer farming has led to the importation of many red deer derived from non-native stocks, including deer of Scottish, English, Hungarian and even Canadian origin. Should such deer escape into the wild in the vicinity of the Killarney herd, then the genetic integrity of the latter would be lost. For this reason farming of red deer of non-native origin is not encouraged within 30km of the edges of the core range of the Killarney population.

Red deer can become a pest of commercial forestry by browsing leader shoots of young trees and by stripping bark with their teeth and scoring bark with their antlers. Given the distribution of red deer, however, damage to woodlands by red deer is likely to be local only.

Red deer are protected under the Wildlife Act 1976 and the Wildlife (Northern Ireland) Order 1985. They are, however, also designated as a quarry species and may be hunted, under licence issued by Dúchas The Heritage Service of the Department of Arts, Heritage, Gaeltacht and the Islands (RoI) and of the Environment Service of the Department of the Environment (NI). The open season usually extends from September to the end of February for stags and from November to the end of January for hinds. Hunting of red deer in Co Kerry is absolutely prohibited, however, and there is a general reluctance to shoot red-like deer in Wicklow. In all, about five hundred wild red deer are legally shot and reported annually, together with three hundred red-like hybrids.

Sika deer – *Fia Seapánach*
Cervus nippon, Temminck 1838

Sika deer were brought to Ireland in the mid-19th century when it was fashionable to 'improve' local European fauna by the introduction of exotic species, in this case from Japan.

The names

The scientific description of the sika deer was written by the Dutch naturalist Temminck in 1838 from specimens sent to the Netherlands from Kyushu in Japan. The generic name is the Latin for a stag (*cervus*). The specific name is a transliteration of the Japanese for Japan (*nippon*). The English name sika is a transliteration of the Japanese word for deer. The Irish name also means the Japanese (*seapánach*) deer (*fia*). Like red deer, sika males are called stags and females, hinds.

Identification and characteristics

Sika deer are the smallest of our wild deer. Adult stags stand about 75–80cm at the shoulder and weigh about 50–60kg in late September. Hinds are smaller than stags, at 65–70cm tall at the shoulder, and weigh from 30 to 35kg.

The summer coat is spotted and ranges from dark brown through chestnut brown to light brown and has a dark stripe along the back. White spots are arranged roughly in lines along the back and flanks. The spots along the back are most distinct. The pattern of spots is unique to each individual and in principle may be used to identify particular deer. The belly is light grey or fawn coloured in front and paler or white between the hind legs. The winter coat

336

ranges from grey to almost black and the stags develop a shaggy mane for the rut. There is a white rump patch that is normally almost concealed by a surrounding fringe of dark hair, which appears as a dark line particularly along the top edge. When these deer are alarmed the hair on this patch is erected and becomes a

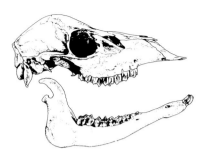

spectacular heart-shaped warning signal or flag to other deer. The tail, which is short (15–20cm) and extends about two-thirds of the depth of the rump patch, is white on top and usually has an incomplete narrow dark line along the upper surface. It is naked underneath and the under surface appears white. There are prominent tufts of white hair coated with a waxy secretion on the outer side of the hocks. These indicate the location of the metatarsal glands. The face has a slightly pale area on the forehead surrounded by a dark band that sweeps upward over each eye. The ears are relatively broad and rounded with a black thumbprint on the lower edge.

The head is relatively short, and the antlers, which are carried only by the stags, are branched and when fully developed have a maximum of four points each. The main beams of the antlers form a V-shape when viewed from the front.

The cycle of antler development is broadly similar to that of red deer. Antlers are shed each spring in March and April and a new set immediately begins to grow. The growing antler is covered with skin called velvet. When antler growth is complete in August the velvet dies and is cleaned off to reveal the bare bone of the antler. Although antler size increases with age, it is not a reliable indicator of age in animals older than two years of age. Very old animals often exhibit poorly developed antlers. In addition, if animals are unwell during the summer, antler growth may be impaired.

Distribution and population density

Sika deer probably originated on the Kuril Islands in northeastern Asia and a number of distinct subspecies are recognised. Sika deer have had a long association (over 4000 years) with humans and have been introduced to many countries where they have established populations in the wild.

Sika deer were introduced to Ireland in 1860 by Lord Powerscourt, who maintained a herd, descended from one stag and three hinds, in his park at Powerscourt near Dublin. This was the first successful introduction to an area outside Asia. In 1864 one stag and two hinds from Powerscourt were released onto the Muckross estate near

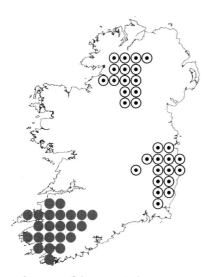

Killarney and these founded the present population in the Killarney National Park. There was another introduction of sika (two stags and five hinds) to the Landsdowne estate at Lauragh (Co Kerry) in the 1890s. These latter deer were apparently transported from Scotland but otherwise their origin is unclear.

Sika were also supplied from Powerscourt to other enclosed parks in Ireland; to Colebrooke (Co Fermanagh) in 1870, to Glenstal (Co Limerick), Castlewellan (Co Down) and Rockcory (Co Monaghan) in 1874. A herd at Baronscourt was established using deer from Colebrooke in 1892. During the early years of the twentieth century, many deer parks fell into disrepair, and deer escaped to found populations in the wider countryside. These populations began to spread during the 1930s and 1940s, and there are now four main centres of wild sika deer in Ireland, central and south Kerry, Wicklow, Tyrone and south Fermanagh. All populations of sika deer are expanding their ranges and they are now found in at least 12 counties: Dublin, Wicklow, Kildare, Carlow, Kilkenny, Wexford, Kerry, Cork, Fermanagh, Tyrone, Donegal and Cavan.

The populations of sika deer in Ireland have low genetic variation, being descended from such a small founder population. However, they are more genetically diverse than our fallow deer.

Current information on the distribution of sika deer comes from hunting records. The map shows the 20km squares in which sika deer have been seen. The solid circles indicate where sika deer may be found. The paler circles show the current distribution of sika-like hybrids. There have not been detailed censuses of deer in Ireland so an estimate of the total population of sika deer in the country is extremely provisional. Sika deer are currently expanding their range and attaining high densities in certain areas. Locally, sika deer attain densities of 15–50 deer per 100ha in coniferous plantations with access to good grazing areas. Deer populations are culled annually by licensed hunters and in the Wicklow area about a thousand sika or sika-like deer are taken legally each year. To this must be added an unknown number which are taken illegally. Since the population is still expanding it seems that the annual cull must represent substantially less than 10% of the standing crop of deer and also less than the annual number added by births to the population each year. Therefore in the Wicklow area there must be between 10,000 and 15,000 sika deer and their hybrids at present. There are probably another two thousand in the remainder of Leinster and about three thousand in Munster, mainly in Kerry. The population in Fermanagh and Tyrone contains at least three thousand deer. Thus the total population on the island may be about 20,000–25,000 but a detailed census is necessary.

Habitat, diet and habits

Sika deer are usually associated with a mosaic of open glades and dense thickets, particularly on acid soils. Whether this is due to the history of their introduction, to a nutritional factor or to the general lower level of cultivation and disturbance is not clear. They quickly colonise the expanding young conifer plantations of the reforestation programme, which are increasingly becoming a feature of the Irish countryside. They do not exhibit major preferences for forest-type and will invade dense woodland irrespective of the dominant tree species. They seem less tolerant of open hillsides far from cover, although, during summer and autumn, bracken may afford sufficient seclusion in areas well away from forests.

Although sika deer readily colonise suitable habitats, once established, their home ranges may be relatively small. For example, females may spend their entire lifespan within an area as small as 50ha. Males tend to travel over greater distances, and during the course of a year they may wander over an area as large as 1000ha.

Sika deer are opportunistic or intermediate feeders and will take a mixture of grass, herb and browse species depending on their availability. They will eat grasses, leaves, herbs, acorns, fruit and woody browse, such as heather and tree shoots. The diet of sika deer in the Killarney National Park consists of 40–60% grass – indeed they show a preference for short-grass swards. Sika deer are active by day and night but tend to feed mainly in the early morning and in the evening.

Social organisation and reproduction

The social organisation of sika deer is not well understood but is generally similar to that of red deer. Groups of sika deer tend to be fewer than ten animals, but in certain circumstances groups as large as a hundred may be seen. These groups usually consist of females of various ages, their dependent offspring and yearling and sub-adult males. Sika stags tend to be dispersed and quite solitary outside the breeding season.

The breeding cycle is controlled by the length of the day. Reproductive activity (the rut) may be observed from late August to early December. Most of the matings take place in late September and early October. The earliest sign of the rut is the tendency of stags to become more vocal. This usually begins in late August and is most marked during September and October.

Rutting stags emit a number of calls, the most characteristic of which is usually termed a whistle. This is a frequency-modulated call. Each whistle begins at a medium pitch progressing smoothly to a higher pitch, changes to a lower frequency again and ends as a low-pitched moan. At this time adult stags are quite aggressive and fights are likely. The sound of the antlers clashing together can often clearly be heard in the woods at this time. These clashes are neither as loud as those between red stags are nor as frequent as those between fallow bucks. Stags fight by locking antlers and attempting to subdue their opponent by wrestling and pushing him backwards. Aggressive encounters are usually brief but may persist for up to 30 minutes or more and injuries and broken antlers are not unusual. During the breeding season, stags mark twigs and other vegetation with an oily scent produced from special glands that open on the face just below the eyes. They also fray trees and bushes by thrashing with their antlers and score and damage the bark of trees with the points of their antlers.

Competition between males for access to females is intense and males are unlikely to rut successfully before they are four years of age. The mating strategy of males is variable. In some locations males are territorial and defend rutting stands that are visited by hinds; in others, stags are more mobile and attempt to gather and defend harems of hinds.

Hinds usually conceive for the first time at one and a half years of age. Exceptionally they may do so as calves, in their first year. If a hind does not conceive at her first mating she may mate again at 22-day intervals until pregnancy results. Most conceptions take place in early October. Gestation lasts 222 days and single fawns (very rarely twins), weighing about 2.8–3kg, are born in May and June. Calves do not follow their mothers for about the first week of life. Their survival strategy has evolved to avoid predators, such as wolves or foxes, by lying hidden in vegetation. By the third week of age they become more mobile and begin to follow their mothers. They are weaned at six to eight months of age. Sika female calves tend to remain in the vicinity of their birth area; young males disperse when about one year old.

Sika deer are closely related to red deer, which are of the same genus, *Cervus*. Most of the deer in this genus have the capacity to interbreed and sika deer are no exception. In spite of the great size-differences between sika and red deer, interbreeding between the two types can occur.

Hybridisation

Just as sika deer pose a threat to the genetic integrity of red deer, they themselves are at risk because they can interbreed. Sika deer and red deer hybridise in captivity and in the wild. In fact observations of these phenomena in Ireland were the first to be reported to the scientific community. It is also occurring in Scotland and England. Red x sika hybrids are fertile and have no apparent competitive disadvantage in Ireland and Britain, compared to the original Japanese sika deer; they readily colonise suitable habitats. The first sika x red hybrids unexpectedly occurred within 15 years of their introduction to the ungulate collection in the Powerscourt deerpark (400ha) in the 1860s. The first generation hybrids are capable of interbreeding with one another to produce second generation hybrids and can also interbreed with either the parental red or sika. Breeding experiments a century later demonstrated that the original hybridisation event was the result of a mating between an adult sika female and a young red stag (less than 3 years old). Such events are likely to occur in the wild when one or other species is extending its range.

First generation hybrids, i.e. deer with 50% sika genes, are large like red deer but have several typical characteristics of sika deer. The hairs on the metatarsal gland form a large white patch. The rump patch is white but more prominent than that of a sika and is never concealed by the surrounding dark hair. The antlers of adult males resemble those of sika but they are larger and the beam is more curved. Nevertheless they are unlikely to be mistaken for a sika. An animal may contain more than 50% sika genes if a first generation hybrid crosses with a sika deer or if two hybrids themselves cross. Depending on the precise pairing involved, a wide range of intermediate types may be produced. In many of these cases it is extremely difficult to identify such an animal as a hybrid. They look superficially extremely like a Japanese sika deer. They tend to be somewhat larger but in the field this may be difficult to judge.

Sika deer, with red and wapiti, form a group that can interbreed with most other species in the Genus *Cervus*. Although there are chromosomal differences between some of the species (for example sika deer have 64 chromosomes while red deer and wapiti have 68) fertile hybrids are produced. Although these species look, sound and behave quite differently they can interbreed because at least 95% of their DNA is identical. There are historical reasons for this. The three species, sika red and wapiti, share a common ancestor which lived about 500,000 to one million years ago somewhere in central Asia. As they spread, different local conditions developed different features, so descendants in the Japanese archipelago (sika) have come to differ quite substantially from other descendants in Europe (modern red deer) and continental east Asia and North America (wapiti). The fact that they evolved largely out of contact with one another probably explains why they have not evolved mechanisms to prevent interbreeding. Of the three, sika deer seem most distinct mainly because they are so small. This is probably because they evolved as they colonised the smaller islands in the Japanese archipelago. It is a general finding that when mammals colonise small islands, large species become smaller and small species become larger. For example, dwarf red deer evolved on Jersey and mice on Ireland's offshore islands tend to be larger than on the mainland.

Most of the mammalian species in this book do not have the ability to hybridise with others. Over time mechanisms evolve to make this less likely. The effect of these reproductive barriers is to lock particular genetic adaptations into a particular animal type that we call a species. Of course if two animal types have evolved from a recent common ancestor or if they have evolved in different locations then the barriers may not be complete. This is because in the first case, there may not have been sufficient time or in the second, any particular pressing need under natural conditions. Both situations probably apply to the sika deer. This capacity for sika deer to hybridise with red deer causes biologists great problems in deciding where one species starts and ends. It also causes problems not only for the conservation of sika deer but for other *Cervus* deer including the red deer as distinct types. Most of the sika-like deer in Wicklow and the north of the island are hybrids between sika and red. The genetic integrity of sika deer is also under threat in Japan. It is unlikely that any true sika exist in their original range in Asia due to man's long history of husbandry, breeding and translocation of deer. For true Japanese sika deer one must turn to the Killarney valley.

Watching sika deer

See page 333 for general advice on watching deer.

Sika deer may be seen at fairly close range in enclosures at Gortin Glen Forest Park (Co Tyrone) and Doneraile Park (Co Cork). There are a few farms of sika throughout the country and these deer may often be visible from public roadways. Otherwise permission may be obtained to visit and view the deer or there may be open days when access is permitted.

In woodland, trails used by sika deer may be evident or their hoof marks (slots), about 5–6cm long, may be visible in soft mud. They are, however, easily confused with the hoof marks of sheep.

Sika deer are typically found in the younger stages of coniferous plantations and are very common in Wicklow and the surrounding counties. They may be also regularly seen by day around Muckross Abbey in the Killarney National Park and in the surrounding countryside and also around Baronscourt (Co Tyrone) and Colebrooke (Co Fermanagh). Rutting sika stags may be heard almost anywhere in Co Wicklow but particularly in the Glendalough valley and the hills around Mullaghcleevaun. Rutting stags may also be heard throughout Killarney National Park but especially in Tomies wood and Muckross.

Conservation and management

Sika deer can become a serious pest of commercial forestry and agriculture. They reduce timber production by browsing leader shoots of young trees, by scoring the bark with antlers and by stripping bark with the teeth. Their major impact is the damage they cause to newly planted trees. They can cause substantial local damage on farms by their fondness for kale, rape and root crops, particularly turnips and carrots. They will eat cereals on the stalk and also hide among the crop causing damage by trampling.

Sika deer are protected under the Wildlife Act 1976 and the Wildlife (Northern Ireland) Order 1985. They are, however, designated as a quarry species and may be hunted, under licences. These are issued by the Dúchas The Heritage Service of the Department of Arts, Heritage, Gaeltacht and the Islands (RoI) and of the Environment Service of the Department of the Environment (NI). The hunting (open) season usually extends from September to the end of February for stags and from November to the end of January for hinds. In all about 4000 wild sika or sika-like deer are legally shot and reported in Ireland each year. Culling by licensed hunters is the main control stategy currently used in Ireland.

Fallow deer – *Fia buí*
Dama dama, Linnaeus 1758

Fallow deer are highly decorative and this is the species most likely to be seen in deer parks. They were first introduced to Ireland after the Norman invasion and are now our most widespread deer.

The names

The scientific description was written by Linnaeus in 1758, based on specimens introduced to Sweden. The scientific name uses the Latin *dama*, which is a general word for deer.

The common name for this species is derived from the Old English *fealu*, which means yellowish brown, and the Irish name means yellow (*buí*) deer (*fia*). Male fallow deer are bucks, females are does and the young are fawns. There is an extensive vocabulary of terms related to fallow deer; for example, male fallow deer in their first six years of life are respectively referred to as fawns, prickets, sorels, soars, bare bucks/bucks of the first head, and great bucks. Some expressions used today had their origins in deer hunting. For example, to 'eat humble pie' has nothing to do with humility; it refers to the liver, kidney and other offal of deer (originally called rumbles, then umbles and finally humbles) which were given to the servants after a hunt.

Many placenames in Ireland are derived from the former presence of fallow deer, or more particularly the parks in which they were confined. There are locations called Deerpark in at least 16 counties.

Identification and characteristics

The fallow deer is intermediate in size between red and sika deer. Adult bucks stand about 100cm at the shoulder and weigh about 100kg in late September. Does are smaller than bucks, 80–85cm tall at the shoulder, and weigh 40–45 kg.

The coat colour is quite variable from almost black to yellowish white. There are five main colour varieties in Ireland. These are black, brown, menil, common and white. All except black and white deer have a white rump patch surrounded by an elongated heart-shaped dark line. Black deer are glossy black with faint brown spots in summer. The winter coat is dull black all over. Brown deer are a rich chocolate in summer but are almost black in winter; there is a black stripe on the back and around the rump patch. Menil deer are pale brown with bright white spots in summer changing to a duller greyish coat with spots slightly less visible in winter; the back and rump stripes are brown. Common deer are chestnut brown with white spots in summer and are greyish-brown in winter; the back and rump markings are blacks. White deer have no dark markings but their eyes have normal pigmentation and their fawns and yearlings are pale brown. In most types the belly is paler than the flanks.

The tail is relatively long and extends below the rump patch. The tail is black on top and white underneath. This is our only deer in which the bucks have broad, flattened (palmate) antlers.

Distribution and population density

Fallow deer probably originated in the eastern Mediterranean region in Turkey and Iran. There are two subspecies, the European fallow deer and the Mesopotamian fallow deer. The larger subspecies, the Mesopotamian fallow deer, is quite rare but is still found in small pockets of its original range in the Middle East, mainly in riverine areas in northern Iran.

European fallow deer were present in Britain in preglacial times but appear to have gone extinct during the ice ages. There is no record of their ever having reached Ireland. They were reintroduced to Britain by the Romans and later by the Normans. The Normans first brought

them to Ireland in the 13th century, probably in about 1244. They have since been introduced to many countries and are now widely distributed throughout the world. They became very popular as park deer and at one time there were over 60 herds in enclosed deer parks in this country. Escapees from parks led to the establishment of herds in the wild as early as the 15th century. Many park herds escaped or were

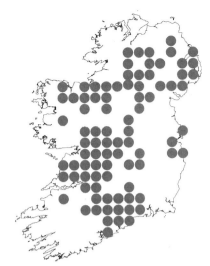

released to the wild about the beginning of the 20th century. These supplemented the existing wild fallow populations to the extent that fallow are now Ireland's most widespread deer and are to be found in virtually all counties.

Habitat, diet and habits

Fallow deer are found in deciduous and mixed woodland. They particularly favour a mosaic of woodland and open pasture. Although they will eat leaves, herbs and acorns and other fruit (browse), they are primarily grazers and will eat grass all year round. For example, the diet of fallow deer in the Phoenix Park (in Dublin) consists of almost 90% grass. Fallow deer tend to feed mainly in the early morning and in the evening and are often difficult to observe during the day. In undisturbed populations, or where the deer have become habituated to humans and are not hunted, they are more active by day. Otherwise they are of a rather nervous disposition.

Antlers are shed each spring from late March to May and a new set immediately begins to grow. The growing antler is covered with skin called velvet. When antler growth is complete in August the velvet dies and is cleaned off to reveal the bare bone of the antler. Antler size increases with age. The area of the palm becomes more triangular and the number of points increases. However, antler size is not a reliable indicator of age, since old animals often exhibit poorly developed antlers and, if animals are unwell during the summer, antler growth may be impaired.

Social organisation and reproduction

Fallow deer are highly social animals and may be seen in large herds. Bucks and does live apart for most of the year and young males join the bachelor herd usually towards the end of their first or during their second year. Group size is to some extent influenced by the amount of cover in the habitat. In some populations bucks are territorial.

The breeding cycle is controlled by the length of day. Males move onto the females' range for the breeding season (rut) which takes place in October. During the rut, bucks can be heard emitting loud, staccato, cough-like belches called groans. At this time they are quite aggressive and fight for access to females. Fallow bucks fight far more frequently than red deer stags. The sound of the antlers clashing together can clearly be heard in the woods at this time. Bucks fight by locking antlers and attempting to subdue their opponent by wrestling and pushing him backwards. Aggressive encounters may persist for up to 30 minutes or more, although most serious fights are decided within a few minutes. Males also scrape out depressions in the ground and mark twigs and other vegetation with an oily scent at this time, produced from special glands that open on the face just below the eyes.

Competition between males for access to females is intense and males are unlikely to rut successfully before they are five years of age. Does may breed at one and a half years of age but often not until they are two. If they do not conceive at their first mating, does may mate again at 21-day intervals until pregnancy results. Gestation lasts about 230 days and single fawns, usually weighing 3.5–4kg, are born in June. Fawns do not follow their mothers for about the first two weeks of life. Their survival strategy, of lying hidden in vegetation, has evolved to avoid predators such as wolves and foxes or large cats such as leopards. By the third week of age they become more mobile and join the herd. They are weaned at nine to 12 months of age.

Watching fallow deer

See page 333 for general advice on watching deer. Fallow deer may be seen at relatively close range in a number of parks and protected areas. The best known herd is in the Phoenix Park in Dublin city. There are also fallow deer in Doneraile Park (Co Cork), in Portumna Forest Park (Co Galway), Shane's Castle and Randalstown Forest (Co Antrim), Lough Fea Estate (Co Monaghan) and Parkanaur Forest (Co Tyrone). There are now many fallow deer farms throughout the country and deer may often be visible from public roadways. Otherwise permission should be obtained to visit and view the deer or there may be open days when access is permitted. Fallow deer are the most widespread of the deer in Ireland and are found in most tracts of woodland in lowland areas. The slots (hoof marks) of fallow deer are about 6–7cm long.

Patience is required for watching fallow deer in the wild. The particular wariness of fallow deer may have evolved as a mechanism to avoid predators, which would originally have been species of large cats that attack their prey by ambush from cover, unlike wolves, which generally hunt by chase.

Rutting fallow deer, in October, are usually relatively easily observed. Bucks are extremely vocal and may continue emitting loud throaty belches for hours on end. They are usually faithful to traditional rutting areas where they excavate shallow scrapes in which they urinate. They also spray themselves with urine and both they and the rutting area have an extremely strong musky smell that is detectable over 100m away.

Conservation and management

Fallow deer may damage woodlands and can become a pest of commercial forestry by browsing leader shoots of young trees and by stripping bark with the teeth. They may also fray saplings by thrashing them with their antlers when cleaning them of velvet in the late summer and early autumn. Ireland will become increasingly suitable for deer as afforestation increases and wild populations will extend their range.

The expansion of deer farming has led to the possibility of further expansion of the range of fallow deer should escapees establish themselves in the wild. There have also been recent imports of the related subspecies, Mesopotamian fallow deer, to improve the stock on farms. If these animals should escape there would be implications for the future of populations of wild

European fallow deer. On the one hand, Mesopotamian fallow deer are probably closer to the ancestral type of fallow deer and might introduce additional genetic variation into populations of what is a highly inbred animal. But on the other hand, since the current appearance of the European fallow deer is a result of intense selective breeding, introduction of Mesopotamian genes might have undesirable side effects, for example, on antler size and shape.

Fallow deer are protected under the Wildlife Act, 1976 and the Wildlife (Northern Ireland) Order 1985. They are, however, designated as a quarry species and may be hunted, under licence issued by Dúchas The Heritage Service of the Department of Arts, Heritage, Gaeltacht and the Islands (RoI) and by the Environment Service of the Department of the Environment (NI). The open season usually extends from September to the end of February for bucks; that for does from November to the end of January. In all about 2000 wild fallow deer are legally shot and reported annually.

Wild (feral) goat – *Gabhar fiáin*
Capra hircus, Linnaeus 1758

Although the feral goats in Ireland are of domestic origin, they have shown a tendency to revert to the wild and there is a long tradition of wild goats in many of our more remote mountainous areas. These goats have now become established as members of our large mammal fauna.

The names
The scientific description based on Swedish specimens was made by Linnaeus in 1758. The scientific name is Latin; *capra* means goat and *hircus* means billy goat. The Irish name means wild (*fiáin*) goat (*gabhar*). Their long history in the wild in Ireland probably accounts for references to goats in some of the placenames of upland and remote localities such as Carnagore (Co Donegal), Carricknagower, *carraig na gabhar*, the goat's rock (Co Westmeath) and Dromgower (Co Kerry). Male goats are known as billies, females are nannies and the young are kids.

Identification and characteristics
The wild goat population in Ireland has been supplemented with individuals of domestic breeds from time to time. The range in size is thus considerable and it is difficult to give an average weight for an adult wild goat. Males are larger and heavier than females and may weigh between 50 and 75kg, while female weights range from about 35 to 60kg.

Domestic goats tend to have a greater variation of coat colour than wild ones, because of selective breeding. But mixing of escaped or released domestic animals with the wild stock in

Ireland has led to a wide variety of coat colour in wild goats also. Coats may be black, brown, white or grey in various patterns and shades. It is difficult to be certain of the original natural colour of the goat, but the traditional Irish goat seems to have been black or dark grey and white. The hair, in winter and spring, is quite long and the males have a pronounced mane. All males and most females also have a beard under the chin. The tail is relatively flat and long but does not have hair on the underside. By contrast that of a sheep is rounded and woolly on all surfaces.

Goats, unlike sheep, have a thickened pad of skin, a callus, on the 'knee' (actually the wrist) of the front legs. The hooves are relatively short. They have a hard margin but a large spongy central pad that allows goats to maintain a foothold on precipitous cliffs and scree slopes.

Both males and females bear horns, those of the males being much larger. The horns of the descendants of earlier introductions of goats to Ireland are set rather close together and sweep backwards like scimitars with a relatively modest spreading of the tips. Horns grow throughout life but growth slows down each year in winter and also as the animal ages. This slower growth produces a thicker band called a growth ring each year during winter. This allows the age of a goat to be readily determined if a clear view of the horns is possible. The horns of goats of more recent domestic origin tend to be set further apart, and curve backwards and outwards.

Distribution and history

Goats belong to the family Bovidae, which includes cattle, antelope and sheep. The latter are their closest relatives. The goat was one of the earliest domestic animals and was probably first domesticated from *Capra aegargus* about 9000 years ago in the Middle East and southwest Asia. They have been introduced into many parts of the world by man. There are now many feral goat populations throughout the world on all continents except Antartica.

Goats probably reached these islands about 3000–4000 years ago. Their bones have been identified from several archaeological sites, although their remains are not numerous. Neolithic, Bronze Age and Iron Age farmers probably maintained only small numbers of goats, mainly for milk, as pigs were a more prolific source of meat. However, in historical times the numbers of goats increased and they were an important domestic animal in this country, particularly in Viking and early Norman towns.

The goat can live and thrive in places unsuitable for sheep and it has been valued for a variety of products in addition to meat and milk. The hair has been used to make items as diverse as wool, ropes, paint brushes and judges' wigs. The fat was used for candles. Horns could be fashioned into musical instruments, handles and bows. The skin was used to make containers for liquids. It was also

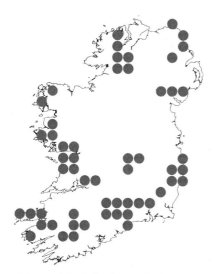

processed to make parchment and bodhráns. In the mid-18th century over 200,000 goats were exported annually to Britain from Ireland. A number of factors were responsible for the subsequent decline in the overall numbers of goats in Ireland. The expansion of sheep farming led to a replacement of goats. The decline in the rural population after the Famine of the mid-19th century meant that there were fewer goat-keepers, and native breeds tended to be replaced by the developing improved dairy breeds.

Goats are engagingly adventurous and independent. They readily revert to a feral state. The original feral populations were probably derived from goats that escaped from neolithic settlers. The earliest account of these wild goats dates from about the 12th century. Escapees have supplemented these herds from time to time ever since, and so it is highly unlikely that there is any ancient feral herd in the country that has not had some recent input from domestic animals.

Wild goats were apparently abundant in Ireland early in the 20th century but were much reduced by hunting during World War II. There were at least 30 wild herds, amounting to a total of about 3000–5000 feral goats, in the early 1970s, spread over 15 counties. The most notable herds today are found in the Burren (Co Clare), Glendalough (Co Wicklow), Bray Head (Co Wicklow), Fair Head (Co Antrim) and Killarney (Co Kerry). Goats are present on many offshore islands such as Rathlin (Co Antrim), Great Blasket and Valencia (Co Kerry), Achill (Co Mayo) and on islands in lakes such as Lough Erne (Co Fermanagh). There have been no recent detailed censuses of feral goats in Ireland, so an estimate of the total population in the country is not possible, but it is probably less than 5000. Feral goats may occasionally attain high densities; the population in the Burren often reaches 14 per square kilometre.

Habitat and habits

Feral goats are mainly found in remote hilly or mountainous areas or on cliffs. They are usually found at altitudes above 200m. They prefer dry well-drained ground and are generally found on steeper slopes where they graze and browse on shrubs. They may also be found in woodland, as they particularly require shelter and will shelter in woodlands, scrub, among boulders on scree slopes or in caves.

Goats may be classified as grazers or browsers depending on what type of food is available. They are selective feeders, taking mainly herbs, sedges and woody plants, but the composition of the diet depends on the habitat. In summer their diet consists mainly of grasses, heather, bilberry, rushes and sedges. In winter they browse on heather, gorse and other shrubs. In coastal areas they will eat seaweeds. They will also strip bark from a range of trees such as willow, holly and mountain ash. Oak, pine and spruce are also attacked, but less frequently.

Social organisation and reproduction

The basic unit of goat society is a group of females, usually consisting of relatives under the leadership of a dominant nanny. These groups tend to occupy a traditional home range and female kids eventually become incorporated into the group to which their mother belongs. Thus they tend to spend their lives on the same range as their mother and grandmother. Group size is quite variable and depends, in part, on population density and time of year; herds of up to 100 goats may be seen. The home ranges of several groups may overlap and there may be some exchange of members. Outside the breeding season the males are generally to be found in small groups, sometimes sharing the general home range of the females, at other times quite separate from them.

The breeding cycle is controlled by the length of the day and the breeding season (rut) begins in late August, is generally at its height in mid-September and October, diminishes through November and ends in December. During this period, billies join the female groups. During the rut, billies develop a powerful odour produced by secretions of glands behind the horns, close to the tail and between the toes. They also urinate over their faces, chests and forelegs to increase the intensity of the odour. At this time billies are quite aggressive and, as well as ritualised threats and bluffing such as staring, beard-shaking and horn lowering, fights are frequent particularly between evenly matched billies. They fight by rearing up and crashing their heads together with considerable force. The sound of skull and horn clashing can clearly be heard from some distance at this time. Aggressive encounters may persist intermittently for hours.

Competition between billies for access to females is intense and males with high dominance rank are most likely to rut successfully. Rutting billies consort for a few days with an oestrous female and attempt to prevent access by younger or lower-ranking males. A female accepts a dominant billy at the peak of her oestrus period after a courtship involving visual, scent and vocal signalling between the pair. She may be courted at other times by subordinate or younger males and may occasionally mate with them.

Nannies may breed at as early as nine months of age and produce their first kid when they are just over one year. Most, however, breed for the first time as yearlings. If they do not conceive at their first mating, nannies may mate again at 20-day intervals until pregnancy results. Most conceptions take place in late September and early October. Gestation lasts about 150 days and most kids are born from mid-February to early April, but some as early as January. Goats are thus born relatively early in the year in comparison with deer, whose births usually occur in May and June. There may be two explanations for the early breeding season of goats. One is that early breeding is not a good strategy but occurs because the goat evolved at lower latitudes and natural selection has not yet altered the breeding season. The second explanation is that although kids born early are more likely to die, the survivors may be able to breed in their first year and in this way maintain the early breeding season.

The usual litter size is one or two, depending on the age and body condition of the nanny, but twins are quite common. Kids weigh 1.6–2.5kg at birth and for the first few days of life lie up in a dry sheltered location in vegetation or in rocks. They tend not to follow their mothers during the first week of life. This survival strategy, hiding by lying motionless for the first week or so, has evolved to avoid predators such as eagles, wolves and foxes. By the end of their first week of age kids become more mobile and begin to follow their mothers. Kids are weaned by about six months of age. Female kids tend to remain in the vicinity of their birth area in their mother's social group; young billies may leave their mother during the rut and generally disperse by joining a group of adults when about one year old.

Highest mortality occurs during the first year of life. Kids are born relatively early in the year and are particularly vulnerable during a cold, wet spring. After the first year, survival is relatively high until about the seventh year of life, though many populations contain goats older than this. Equal numbers of each sex are born but mortality of males is higher so that the sex ratio of adults may often be two females to every male.

Watching feral goats

Feral goats are widely distributed in small herds throughout most of the upland areas, in a number of coastal areas and on some of the offshore islands. Among the best places to watch feral goats are Fair Head (Co Antrim), the Burren (Co Clare), Bray Head and Glendalough (Co Wicklow) and Lahinch Golf Course (Co Clare). Patience is sometimes required when watching goats in the wild. They are extremely sensitive to scents and it is important to be always aware of the wind direction and to approach from downwind. Some herds are, however, partly habituated to humans and allow prolonged observation. A good pair of binoculars (magnification 8x40 or 7x50) is essential and a telescope is useful.

Goats spend their days alternating between periods of feeding, often in the open, and resting to ruminate, often in cover. Goats may, therefore, be seen at any time of the day except in poor weather. They particularly dislike wind and rain and will seek shelter in rock crevices or in woodland or scrub. It is difficult to distinguish between the hoof marks of goats, deer and sheep. The size of the tracks of feral goats depends on body size. They are thus somewhat variable, depending on the age and sex of the animal. The hoof-print of a goat is about 6cm long and about 5cm broad. The individual hoof marks tend to be somewhat splayed, and the inner faces are slightly concave. The individual hooves are curved and rounded at the front. (The tracks of sheep are of similar size but have straight inner edges with more pointed ends and one side of the print is usually larger than the other.)

Trees from which bark is stripped often indicate the presence of goats in woodland. This damage may, however, also be caused by deer or sheep. Favoured refuge and sheltering areas may sometimes be identified by accumulations of goat droppings. The droppings are roughly cylindrical, about 1.5cm long, with flat ends, but they are difficult to distinguish from those of red deer or sometimes sheep. Rutting goats, in late September and October, are more easily observed. Rutting areas may have an extremely strong musky smell that is detectable over a distance of more than 100m.

It is important not to disturb goats for several reasons. Goats must spend considerable time feeding, particularly late in spring when food is scarce and of poor quality, and thus any feeding time lost may have serious consequences. Secondly goats, when disturbed, will rapidly move out of sight and make observation much more difficult.

In February and March newborn kids may occasionally be found lying motionless in cover or in rock crevices. Despite appearances, these kids have not been abandoned. Their mothers will be somewhere in the vicinity. Kids do not begin to run with their mothers for several days after birth. Interference with kids at this stage increases the risk of rejection by the mother.

Conservation and management

Goats are considered to be a part of our wild fauna and are conserved and managed in some of our national parks. The general aim is to maintain a population of animals of the ancestral type. This involves removal of recently released individuals belonging to modern breeds of domestic stock.

The browsing habits of goats have positive and negative implications. Goats browse the leader shoots of young trees and strip bark with their teeth. Because of this, the goat can become a pest in commercial forests. However, it is difficult, except in local areas, to be certain that this damage is not due to one of a number of other large herbivores which may have access to the forests. In areas such as the Burren, the browsing activities of goats contribute to the inhibition of scrubland and the maintenance of species-rich plant communities. Indeed, goats, cattle and horses are, in several countries, translocated to conservation areas and used as active agents in counteracting the development of birch, hazel and willow which would otherwise obliterate species-rich grasslands.

Glossary

Word	explanation
anticoagulant	substance which prevents blood clotting
arboreal	refers to animals that live in trees
artiodactyl	an ungulate mammal with an even number of hooves on each limb, e.g. sheep, cattle, deer
beak	refers to the portion of the face that extends beyond the forehead of some whales and dolphins
beechmast	fruit of the beech tree
blastocyst	stage of mammalian embryonic development at which implantation into the wall of the uterus occurs
blow	the exhalation of whales and dolphins. Usually refers to the cloud of spray produced when a whale releases the air it had held in its lungs and windpipe while it was underwater. The blow is often accompanied by a hissing or snoring sound as the air is released
blowhole	This refers to the nostrils of whales and dolphins which are not at the end of their snouts, but are located as a single or double opening on the top of the head
blubber	layer of fat used for insulation in marine mammals such as seals or whales
bow wave	the wave produced by the bow of a moving ship
breeding season	usually refers to the mating season but for small mammals with short gestations may refer to the period covered by mating and birth
browse	to feed on trees, bushes or herbs as opposed to grasses
browse line	the level up to which the branches of trees are eaten
browser	an animal that feeds predominantly on the foliage of plants, other than grasses
caecum	a blind-ending side chamber of the large intestine
calcar	a bony spine or spur growing from the inner margin of the ankle and which supports the trailing edge of wing membrane of bats
canine	relating to dogs and their relatives, also used to refer to the canine teeth

Word	explanation
canine tooth	the conical and pointed eye-tooth of mammals, particularly conspicuous in dogs
carnivore	an animal whose diet consists mainly of meat
carnivorous	relating to an animal whose diet consists mainly of animal food
caudal	relating to the tail
cellulose	a polymer of plant sugar difficult for animals to digest; they employ microorganisms in the gut to digest it, and then live off the products
cetacean	referring to whales and dolphins
chiroperan	relating to bats
chromosome	one of a set of rodlike structures in each of which a long string of genes is packed, found in the nucleus of cells (see DNA)
coccidiosis	disease caused by a parasitic protozoan of the gut
colon	portion of the large intestine
coprophagy	eating of faeces
copse	dense grove of small trees or shrubs which has been managed
cretaceous	the final period of the age of the dinosaurs (Mesozoic era), which extended from 144 million to 65 million years ago
crustacean	a group of invertebrates which includes crabs, lobsters, prawns, shrimps etc
delayed implantation	a period during which the blastocyst remains dormant in the uterus without further development
dentine	the main constituent of teeth, lies between the surface enamel and the pulp cavity and is similar in composition to bone
digit	a finger or toe
diurnal	refers to activity which takes place during daylight
diversity	the number and relative abundance of species in a taxonomic category or in a geographical location
DNA	deoxyribonucleic acid, a double stranded helical polymer of nucleotides, deoxyribose sugar and phosphate, the chemical component of genes which encode hereditary information

Word	explanation
dominance hierarchy	form of social structure in which a linear or almost linear ranking exists, with each animal dominant to those below it and submissive to those above it in the hierarchy, a 'pecking order'
Doppler effect	refers to the change in frequency of a sound wave being emitted from a moving source or as a result of being reflected off an object moving relative to the wave source
dorsal	located on the back
downwind	in a position such that the prevailing wind is blowing from the animal towards the observer
drift nets	nets usually of fine fibre set floating at or near the surface of water
drive fishery	fishing method in which hunted animals are driven into fixed nets, into shallows or onto the shore
echolocation	method used by animals, e.g. bats and dolphins, to determine the position of objects by the reflection of sound
enamel	hard outer surface layer of teeth
Eocene	a period from about 55 to 40 million years ago
euphausid	a type of oceanic shrimp often called krill, on which baleen whales feed
Family	a taxonomic or classification category into which related genera are grouped
fauna	collective term for animal life of an area or period. The corresponding term for plants is flora
feral	term applied to animals which are descended from domesticated stock but which are now living independently in the wild
fermentation	a method of microbial digestion used when oxygen is not available, for releasing a limited amount of energy
fertile period	the interval during which conception is likely to occur
fertilisation	the union of a sperm and an egg to produce a zygote which will develop through a blastocyst and a foetus to produce a young mammal
foetus	a mammal while in its mother's womb, roughly between the time the blastocyst implants in the uterus and the birth
flukes	the transverse tail fins on whales and dolphins

Word	explanation
fossil record	the evidence of animal and plants of former times as preserved in rocks and other sediments
frequency-modulated	ultrasound produced by bats in which the frequency of the sound (pitch) changes progressively during the call
gait	specific way of moving by using a particular sequence of limb movements e.g. walk, trot, bound etc
gene	a sequence of DNA, found in a chromosome, which encodes information used to construct or regulate some component of the organism
generalist	an animal which has not become specialised for a particular diet, method of locomotion or lifestyle
generic	referring to a genus
genetic variation	the differences in DNA sequences between individuals or populations
genus (genera)	a taxonomic or classification category into which related species are grouped, designated by the first part of the scientific name.
gestation	period between conception and birth (parturition)
gill nets	nets which entrap fish when the meshes slide under the gill covers and prevent the fish from escape by reversing out of the net
glacial maximum	a period or state when ice has extended to its greatest extent before it begins to melt and retreat
glaciation	process by which, during climatic cooling, ice extends to cover land and sea, and the processes by which the ice affects the chemistry of the sea and the form of the land
glade	open space in a forest
gland	an organ which produces components for release to act elsewhere, e.g. sweat glands (watery fluid), sebaceous glands (oils), mammary glands (milk), scent glands (pheromones) etc
grazer	an animal that feeds predominantly on grasses
guard hairs	the long hairs which extend beyond and hide the shorter underfur
habitat	the location where an animal normally lives and which provides the necessities for life
harem	group of two or more females controlled by or consorting with a male during the breeding season

Word	explanation
herbivore	general term for an animal which feeds on plants
hibernation	physiological adaptation of some mammals to survive cold by becoming inactive, lowering their body temperature and conserving energy
hock	the heel of animals that walk on their toes, e.g. deer, fox
home range	the area in which an individual or group lives
hypothermia	unregulated, sometimes fatal, state when an animal's body temperature falls below its normal level
ice age	a time during which large areas of the earth were covered by ice, often for thousands of years at a time
implantation	attachment of the blastocyst of mammals to the wall of the uterus
incisors	chisel-edged teeth at the front of the mouth used for cutting and gnawing
insectivore	an animal whose diet consists mainly of insects
insectivorous	relating to an animal whose diet consists mainly of insects
interstadial	a period of relatively warm climate occurring between two colder periods. The one in which we live today began about 10,000 years ago
invertebrate	animal that lacks a vertebral column or backbone e.g, snails, jellyfish, worms, insects, crabs
kernel	the inner part of a nut or seed
krill	collective term for shrimp-like creatures eaten by baleen whales
lactation	production of milk
lagomorph	an animal which is a member of the order lagomorpha e.g. rabbits, hares
latrine	place where animal regularly defecates
lifespan	period of time between birth and death of an organism
machair	calcareous grasslands found in areas of moist, cool, windy oceanic climate
mammal	vertebrate animal which usually maintains a high body temperature, and whose skin has hair and sweat glands; the females produce milk to feed their young

Word	explanation
mammary gland	milk-producing gland unique to mammals; evolved from sweat gland
maternity drey	nest or drey of squirrel in which young are born
mating season	period during which mating occurs
megachiropteran	referring to fruit bats
melon	fatty deposit in the forehead of some whales and dolphins
metabolic rate	heat energy released by the body per unit time
metatarsal glands	scent-producing glands found on the outer side of the lower hindleg of deer
microchiropteran	referring to insectivorous bats in general
micro-organism	a general term for minute life forms such as bacteria, protists and some fungi
molars	back teeth of mammals used for crushing and chewing
monogamous	mating system in which most individuals have only one sexual partner
moult	the periodic shedding of hair
mustelid	referring to stoats, weasels, otters, martens, badgers and their relatives
natural selection	Darwin's theory that the fittest genotypes survive to breed. It is considered the main force that drives evolution
nocturnal	refers to animals that are mainly active at night
oestrus	sexual receptivity shown by most female mammals around the time of ovulation
oestrous period	the short period of sexual receptivity shown by most female mammals around the time of ovulation
omnivore	an animal with a mixed diet of both animal and plant food
order	a taxonomic or classification category into which related families are grouped, for example rodentia (rodents), cetacea (whales and dolphins)
ovulation	the release of an egg or ovum from the ovary
pinniped	a collective name for seals and walruses referring to their webbed feet
plankton	small, mainly microscopic plants and animals that live in the surface waters of oceans and lakes

Word	explanation
Pleistocene	a relatively recent division of geological time extending from about 2 million to 10,000 years ago
pod	term for a group of whales or dolphins, sometimes called a herd
post-calcaral lobe	a narrow flap or lobe of wing membrane attached to the hind margin of the calcar of bats
predator	an animal which acquires its food by hunting and killing other animals
premolar	cheek teeth used for crushing and chewing; anterior to the molars and posterior to the canines and incisors
pupa	the apparently inactive stage between larva and adult in some insect species
purse seine	type of fishing net shaped like a purse, drawn through deep water and closed with a drawstring in the manner of a pouched purse
radiocarbon dating	method of age determination using the decay of radiocarbon (carbon-14 to carbon-12), also known as carbon-14 dating
reptile	vertebrate animal which does not maintain a high body temperature, whose skin is covered with scales; the females usually lay eggs and do not nurture their young
retina	light sensitive layer in the eye
reticulum	one of the four chambers into which the stomach of ruminants is divided
roost	location where bats rest by day (summer) or hibernate (winter)
rumen	largest of the four chambers into which the stomach of ruminants is divided and where fermentation of sugars takes place
ruminant	a mammal, such as a deer or goat, with an elaborate multichambered stomach specialised for using microorganisms to digest cellulose from plants
rut	period of enhanced sexual activity during the breeding season, usually used in reference to social animals such as deer, goats, seals and some whales
scat	faeces of mink, fox etc
sonar	sound used in navigation and direction finding (SOund NAvigation Ranging)

Word	explanation
species	a particular kind of animal; a taxonomic or classification category in which all members resemble one another and may naturally interbreed to produce fertile offspring. It is designated by the second part of the scientific name
spraint	faeces of otter
stadial	a period of cold climate interposed between two warmer periods. The last one occurred between about 10,500 and 11,000 years ago
subspecies	populations that have been isolated from others of the same species long enough to develop genetic differences, sufficiently distinctive to be considered a separate race
superfamily	a taxonomic or classification category into which Families are grouped
symbiosis	mutually dependent relationship between unrelated organisms
temperate	relating to climate or vegetation found at latitudes between the tropics and the arctic and antarctic circles
territorial	referring to animals that defend a particular area against individuals of their own species
territory	an area defended by an animal or group of animals against others of the same species
torpid	in a regulated physiological state similar to hibernation, in which metabolic rate and temperature are temporarily reduced
tragus	fleshy lobe on the ear of a bat, useful for identification purposes
treeline	the elevation on a mountain or the latitude above which trees do not grow
Triassic	a geological period dating from about 250 to 210 million years ago
tropical	relating to climate or vegetation between the tropics of Cancer and Capricorn
ultrasound	sound which is above about 20kHz, and is inaudible to humans
ungulate	mammals with hooves, e.g. deer, horses
vertebrate	animals whose spines consists of bony elements called vertebrae. Includes fish, amphibians, reptiles, birds and mammals
vibrissae	long hair-like structures e.g. whiskers, which are sensitive to touch and act like antennae

Resource List

The general resources listed here include information on relevant organisations and also general books on mammals. The remainder of the resources are more specific and are grouped according to the types of mammals concerned. The list of books and articles is not comprehensive but emphasises more recent work on Irish mammals carried out mainly in Ireland. For a more complete series of references the reader is referred to the books by Fairley (1972) and Corbet and Harris (1999).

General Resources

There are three scientific journals which regularly publish original research on the mammals which are found in Ireland. These are: *Biology and Environment* published by the Royal Irish Academy, *The Journal of Zoology* published by the Zoological Society of London and *The Irish Naturalist's Journal*.

The Irish Wildlife Trust and the Ulster Wildlife Trust are dedicated to the conservation, welfare and study of mammals and their habitats. Various activities are organised and a newsletter is produced regularly. The Irish Wildlife Trust can be contacted at 107, Lower Baggot Street, Dublin 2, Telephone 01-6768588; Fax 01-6768601; e-mail enquiries@iwt.ie. The Ulster Wildlife Trust is based at 3 New Line, Crossgar, Co. Down and may be contacted at telephone 08-01396-88830282; e-mail: ulsterwt@cix.compulink.co.uk.

There are a number of bat groups that organise activities and publish a newsletter for those interested in bats. Further information may be obtained from Merryfalls Cottage, Harristown Lane, St. Margarets, Co. Dublin (Tel. 01-8347134; http://www.clubi.ie/dbg/irish.htm) or The Northern Ireland Bat Group, Ulster Museum, Belfast.

The Irish Whale and Dolphin Group is dedicated to the study, conservation and dissemination of knowledge of cetaceans in Irish waters. It collects and collates information on Irish cetaceans and regularly publishes an informative newsletter. The contact address is c/o Zoology Department, University College, Cork.

There are two main societies devoted to deer, their conservation, protection and management. These are the Irish Deer Society (c/o Department of Zoology, University College Dublin, Belfield, Dublin 4), and the Northern Ireland Deer Society (Telephone 0849-472626).

An interesting website of general relevance is www.wildireland.ie. The DSPCA (01-4935502) is a useful contact for advice on the care of sick or injured wild animals.

MAMMALS
Books

Benton, M.J. (1991) The Rise of the Mammals. Apple Press. London.

Corbet, G.B. and Harris, S. (1990) The Handbook of British Mammals. Blackwell. Oxford.

Fairley, J.S. (1984) An Irish Beast Book. Blackstaff Press. Belfast.

Fairley, J.S. (1972) Irish Wild Mammals: A Guide to the Literature. Fairley. Galway.

Mitchell, F. and Ryan, M. (1997) Reading the Irish Landscape. Town House and Country House. Dublin

Mitchell-Jones, A.J. et al. (1999) The Atlas of European Mammals. Poyser. London.

McDonald, D.W. (1984) The Encyclopedia of Mammals, Vols 1,2. Allen and Unwin. London.

McDonald, D.W. and Barrett, P. (1993) Mammals of Britain and Europe. Harper Collins. London.

McDonald, D.W. (1995) European Mammals: Evolution and Behaviour. Harper Collins. London.

SHREWS AND HEDGEHOGS
Books

Burton, M. (1973) The Hedgehog. Corgi/Transworld. London.

Churchfield, S. (1986) Shrews. Nelson. Oswestry.

Churchfield, S. (1990) The Natural History of Shrews. Christopher Helm. London.

Fairley, J. (1984) An Irish Beast Book. Blackstaff Press. Belfast.

Morris, P. (1983) Hedgehogs. Whittet. London.

Reeve, N. (1994) Hedgehogs. Poyser. London.

Articles

Doncaster, C.P. (1994) Factors regulating local variations in abundance: field tests on hedgehogs, *Erinaceus europaeus*. Oikos 69: 182-192.

Grainger, J.P. and Fairley, J.S. (1978) Studies on the biology of the pygmy shrew *Sorex minutus* in the West of Ireland. Journal of Zoology 186: 109-141.

Ellenbroek, F.J.M. (1980) Interspecific competition in the shrews *Sorex araneus* and *Sorex minutus* (Soricidae, Insectivora): a population study of the Irish pygmy shrew. Journal of Zoology 192: 119-136.

Meharg, M.J. , Montgomery W.I. and Dunwoody, T. (1990) Trophic relations of common frog *Rana temporaria* and pygmy shrew *Sorex minutus* in upland Antrim, Northern Ireland. Journal of Zoology 222: 1-17.

O'Keefe, D.A. and Fairley, J.S. (1981) Two population studies of Irish pygmy shrews. Irish Naturalists' Journal 20: 269-275.

Searle J. (1989) Genetic studies of small mammals from Ireland and the Isle of Man. Irish Naturalists' Journal 23: 112-113.

Yalden, D.W. (1981) The occurrence of the pygmy shrew *Sorex minutus* on moorland and the implications for its presence in Ireland. Journal of Zoology 195: 147-155.

Videotapes

The Complete Hedgehog. Les Stocker. Watchword Video.

The Truth about Mrs. Tiggywinkle. Junior Survival. Stylus Video.

Wild Britain Vol 2. Survival. Warner Home Video.

BATS

Books

McAney, C., Shiel, C., Sullivan, C. and Fairley, J. (1991) The analysis of bat droppings. The Mammal Society. London.

O'Sullivan, P. (1994) Bats in Ireland. Special Supplement to The Irish Naturalists' Journal.

Russ, J. (1999) The Bats of Britain and Ireland: echolocation calls, sound analysis and species identification. Alana Books. Powys.

Stebbings, R.E. (1986) Which Bat is it? A guide to bat identification in Great Britain and Ireland. The Mammal Society. London.

Stebbings, R. (1992) Bats. The Mammal Society. London.

Stebbings, R. and Walsh, S. (1988) Bat Boxes. Flora and Fauna Preservation Society. London.

Swift, S. (1998) Long-eared Bats. Poysers. London.

Articles

McAney, C. (1989) Observations at summer roosts of the lesser horseshoe bat in Co.Clare. Irish Naturalists' Journal 23: 1-6.

McAney, C. M. and Fairley, J.S. (1988) Activity patterns of the lesser horseshoebat *Rhinolophus hipposideros* at summer roosts. Journal of Zoology 216: 325-338.

McAney, C. (1993) Horseshoes in souterrains–regular archaeological finds! Archaeology Ireland 7(3): 18-19.

McGuire, C. (1998) Survey of lesser horseshoe bats *Rhinolophus hipposideros* (Bechstein) and other bat species in northern Co. Clare, Ireland. Irish Naturalists' Journal 26: 43-50.

Russ, J.M. (1996) First record of bimodality in the echolocation calls of the common pipistrelle *Pipistrellus pipistrellus* in Ireland. Irish Naturalists' Journal 25: 225-226.

Russ, J. M., O'Neill, J.K. and Montgomery, W.I. (1998) Nathusius' pipistrelle bats *Pipistrellus nathusii* (Keyersling & Blasius 1839) breeding in Ireland. Journal of Zoology 245: 345-349.

Shiel, C.B., Fairley, J.S. (1998) Activity of Leisler's bat *Nyctalus leisleri* in the field in Ireland. Journal of Zoology 247: 439-447.

Shiel, C.B., Fairley, J.S. (1999) Evening emergence of two nursery colonies of Leisler's bat *Nyctalus leisleri* (Kuhl) in the field in south-east county Wexford, as revealed by a bat detector. Biology and Environment 98B: 105-112.

Shiel, C.B., Duvergé, P.L., Smiddy, P. and Fairley, J.S. (1998) Analysis of the diet of Leisler's bat *Nyctalus leisleri* in Ireland with some comparative analyses from England and Germany. Journal of Zoology 246: 417-425.

Sullivan, C.M., Shiel, C.B., McAney, C.M. and Fairley, J.S. (1993) Analysis of the diets of Leisler's *Nyctalus leisleri*, Daubenton's *Myotis daubentoni* and pipistrelle, *Pipistrellus pipistrellus* bats in Ireland. Journal of Zoology 231: 656-663

Audiotapes

King, D. (1992) British Bats. Stag Electronics, 1 Rosemundy, St. Agnes, Cornwall, UK.

Richardson, P. (1985) The Bat Tape - identification of bats using a bat detector. Northants Bat Group, 10 Bedford Cottages, Great Brington, Northampton NN7 4JE, UK.

HARES AND RABBITS

Books

Evans, G.W. and Thomson, D. 1972 The Leaping Hare. Faber. London.

Fairley, J. (1984) An Irish Beast Book. Blackstaff Press. Belfast.

Hughes, D. (1993) Mammal Survey of 5 Species. Ulster Wildlife Trust. Crossgar.

Mc Bride, A. (1988) Rabbits and Hares. Whittet Books. London.

Sheail, J. 1971 Rabbits and their History. Country Book Club. Newton Abbot.

Smal, C.M. (1995) The Badger and Habitat Survey of Ireland. The Stationery Office. Dublin.

Webb, D. (1955) A Hare about the House. Hutchinson. Dublin.

Articles

Barret-Hamilton, G.E.H. (1898) Notes on the introduction of the brown hare into Ireland. Irish Naturalists' Journal 7: 69-76.

Duffy, S.G., Fairley, J.S. and O'Donnell, G. (1995) Food of rabbits *Oryctolagus cuniculus* on upland grassland in Connemara. Biology and Environment 96B: 69-75.

Fairley, J.S. (1974) Notes on the winter breeding condition of hares in the West of Ireland. Irish Naturalists' Journal 18: 17-19.

Fairley, J.S. (1981) Species of hares in the north-west. Irish Naturalists' Journal 20: 351.

Hewson, R. (1990) Interactions between mountain hares *Lepus timidus* and other mammals. Journal of Zoology 221: 302–305.

Riley, D.H. (1984) Grazing and changes in a dune grassland in Co. Londonderry, 1969-1980. Irish Naturalists' Journal 21: 288–296.

Tangney, D., Fairley, J. and O'Donnell, G. (1995) Food of Irish hares *Lepus timidus hibernicus* in western Connemera, Ireland. Acta Theriologica 40: 403–413.

Trout, R.C., Chasey, D. and Sharp, G. (1997) Seroepidemiology of rabbit haemorrhagic disease (RHD) in wild rabbits *Oryctolagus cuniculus* in the United Kingdom. Journal of Zoology 248: 846–853.

Whelan, J. (1985) The population and distribution of the mountain hare *Lepus timidus* on farmland. Irish Naturalists' Journal 21: 532–534.

Wolfe, A., Whelan, J. and Hayden, T.J. (1996) The diet of the mountain hare *Lepus timidus hibernicus* on coastal grassland Journal of Zoology 240: 804–810.

Wolfe, A., Whelan, J. and Hayden, T.J. (1996) Dietary overlap between the Irish mountain hare *Lepus timidus hibernicus* (Bell) and the rabbit *Oryctolagus cuniculus Linnaeus* on coastal grassland. Biology and Environment 96B: 89–95.

Videotapes

The Tale of the Big Bad Fox. David Attenborough's World of Wildlife. BBC Natural History.

Wild Britain Vol 2. Survival. Warner Home Video.

RODENTS

Books

Berry, R.J. (1981) Biology of the House Mouse. Academic Press. London.

Gurnell, J. (1987) The Natural History of Squirrels. Christopher Helm. London.

Gurnell, J. and Flowerdew, J.R. (1982) Live Trapping Small Mammals – a practical guide. The Mammal Society. London.

Holm, J. (1987) Squirrels. Whittet. London.

Hughes, D. (1993) Mammal Survey of 5 Species. Ulster Wildlife Trust. Crossgar.

Meehan, A.P. (1984) Rats and Mice: their biology and control. Rentokill. West Sussex.

Smal, C. (1991) Feral American Mink in Ireland. Office of Public Works. Dublin.

Twigg, G. (1975) The Brown Rat. David and Charles. Newton Abbot.

Yalden, D.W. (1977) The Identification of Remains in Owl Pellets. The Mammal Society. London.

Articles

Bentley, E.W. (1959) The distribution and status of *Rattus rattus* L. in the United Kingdom in 1951 and 1956. Journal of Animal Ecology 28: 299-308.

Berry, R.J. (1969) History in the evolution of *Apodemus sylvaticus* (Mammalia) at one edge of its range. Journal of Zoology 159: 311-23.

Berry, R.J. (1978) Town mouse, country mouse: adaptation and adaptability in *Mus domesticus* (*M. musculus domesticus*). Mammal Review 11: 91-136.

Butler, F.T. and Whelan, J. (1994) Population structure and reproduction in brown rats *Rattus norvegicus* from pig farms, Co. Kildare, Ireland. Journal of Zoology 233: 277-291.

Byrne, J.M., Duke, E.J. and Fairley, J.S. (1990) Some mitochondrial DNA polymorphisms in Irish wood mice *Apodemus sylvaticus* and bank voles *Clethrionomys glareolus*. Journal of Zoology 221: 299-302.

Claassens, A.J.M. and O'Gorman, F. (1965) The bank vole, *Clethrionomys glareolus* Schreber: a mammal new to Ireland. Nature 205: 923-924.

Fairley, J.S (1972) The fieldmouse in Ireland. Irish Naturalists' Journal 17: 152-159.

Fairley, J.S. (1983) Exports of wild mammal skins from Ireland in the eighteenth century. Irish Naturalists' Journal 21: 75-79.

Fairley, J.S. and Smal, C.M. (1987) Feral house mice in Ireland. Irish Naturalists' Journal 22: 284-290.

Hillis, P., Fairley, J.S., Smal, C.M. and Archer, P. (1988) The diet of the long-eared owl in Ireland. Irish Birds 3: 581-588.

Matheson, C. (1939) A survey of the status of *Rattus rattus* and its subspecies in the seaports of Great Britain and Ireland. Journal of Animal Ecology 8: 76-93.

Montgomery, W.I. and Dowie, M. (1993) The distribution of the wood mouse *Apodemus sylvaticus* and the house mouse *Mus domesticus* on farmland in north-east Ireland. Irish Naturalists' Journal 24: 199-203.

Montgomery, W.I. and Dowie, M. (1993) The distribution and population regulation of the woodmouse *Apodemus sylvaticus* on field boundaries of pastoral farmland. Journal of Applied Ecology 30: 783-791.

Moffat, C.B. (1928) The black rat. Irish Naturalists' Journal 2: 47-49.

Nelson, E.C. (1977) Summer feeding of red squirrels, *Sciurus vulgaris* L., in County Derry. Irish Naturalists' Journal 19: 46-47.

Preece, R.C., Coxon, P. and Robinson, J.E. (1986) New biostratigraphic evidence of the post-glacial colonization of Ireland and for Mesolithic forest disturbance. Journal of Biogeography 13: 487-509.

Ryan, A.W., Duke, E.J. and Fairley, J.S. (1993) Polymorphism, localization and geographical transfer of mitochondrial DNA in *Mus musculus domesticus* Irish house mice. Heredity 70: 75-81.

Ryan, A., Duke, E. and Fairley, J.S. (1996) Mitochondrial DNA in bank voles *Clethrionomys glareolus* in Ireland: evidence for a small founder population and localized founder effects. Acta Theriologica 41: 45-50.

Smal, C.M. (1990) The diet of the barn owl *Tyto alba* in southern Ireland with reference to a recently introduced prey species-the bank vole *Clethrionomys glareolus*. Bird Study 34: 113-125.

Smal, C.M. and Fairley, J.S. (1980) Food of wood mice *Apodemus sylvaticus* and bank voles *Clethrionomys glareolus* in oak and yew woods in Killarney, Ireland. Journal of Zoology 191: 413-418.

Smal, C.M. and Fairley, J.S. (1982) The dynamics and population regulation of small rodent populations in the woodland ecosystems of Killarney, Ireland. Journal of Zoology 196: 1-30.

Smal, C.M. and Fairley, J.S. (1984) The spread of the bank vole *Clethrionomys glareolus* in Ireland. Mammal Review 14: 71-78.

Montgomery, S.S.J. and Montgomery, W.I. (1990) Intrapopulation variation in the diet of the wood mouse. Journal of Zoology 222: 641-651.

Walsh, P.M. (1988) Black rats *Rattus rattus* L. as prey of short-eared owls *Asio flammeus* (Pontopiddan) on Lambay Island. Irish Naturalists' Journal 22:536.

Videotapes

Bright-eyed and Bushy-tailed. Junior Survival. Stylus Video.

Daylight Robbery. BBC Enterprises.

The Mouse's Tail. BBC Wildlife Specials. BBC Enterprises.

WHALES AND DOLPHINS

Books

Carwardine, M. (1995) Whales, Dolphins and Porpoises. Dorling Kindersley. London.

Evans, P.G.H. (1987) Whales and Dolphins. Helm. London.

Fairley, J. (1981) Irish Whales and Whaling. Blackstaff Press. Belfast.

Watson, L. (1981) Whales of the World. Hutchinson. London.

Articles

Amos, B., Barrett, J. and Dover, G.A. (1991) Breeding behaviour of pilot whales revealed by DNA fingerprinting. Heredity 67: 49-55.

Berrow, S. (1993) Constant effort cetacean sighting survey of Ireland. Irish Naturalists' Journal 24: 344.

Berrow, S., Hilliard, W. and Hilliard, N. (1990) Risso's Dolphin *Grampus griseus* (Cuvier). Irish Naturalists' Journal 23: 332-333.

Berrow, S. D. and Rogan, E. (1997) Review of cetaceans stranded on the Irish coast, 1901-1995. Mammal Review 27: 51-76.

Berrow, S. D. and Rogan, E. (1998) Incidental capture of cetaceans in Irish waters. Irish Naturalists' Journal 26: 22-31

Berrow, S.D., Evans, P.G.H. and Sheldrick, M.L. (1993) An analysis of sperm whale *Physeter macrocephalus* stranding and sighting records, from Britain and Ireland. Journal of Zoology 230: 333-337.

Berrow, S.D., Holmes, B. and Kiely, O.R. (1996) Distribution and abundance of bottle-nosed dolphins *Tursiops truncatus* (Montagu) in the Shannon estuary. Biology and Environment 96B: 1-9.

Booth, W. (1988) The social life of dolphins. Science 240: 1273-1274.

Bruton, T., Cotton, D. and Enright, M. (1989) Gulf stream beaked whale *Mesoplodon europaeus* (Gervais). Irish Naturalists' Journal 23: 156.

Carmody, M. (1988) White whale *Delphinapterus leucas* (Pallas). Irish Naturalists' Journal 22: 540.

Clapham, P.J. (1993) Social organisation of humpback whales on a North Atlantic feeding ground. Symposia of the Zoological Society of London 66: 131-145.

Cummings, W.C. (1985) Right Whales, *Eubalaena glacialis* (Muller, 1776) and *Eubalaena australis* (Desmoulins, 1882). In S.H. Ridgeway and R. Harrison (eds) Handbook of Marine Mammals 3: 275-304. Academic Press. London.

Danielsdottir, A.K., Duke, E.J. and Arnason, A. (1992) Genetic variation at enzyme loci in North Atlantic Minke whales, *Balaenoptera acutorostrata*. Biochemical Genetics 30: 189-202.

Fairley, J. (1981) Possible mass strandings of pilot whales near Killala, Co. Mayo. Irish Naturalists' Journal 20: 351.

Fraser, F.C. (1940) Three anomalous dolphins from Blacksod Bay, Ireland. Proceedings of the Royal Irish Academy, 45B: 413-455.

Gambell, R. (1985) Fin whale, *Balaenoptera physalus* (Linnaeus, 1758). In S.H. Ridgeway and R. Harrison (eds) Handbook of Marine Mammals 3: 171-192. Academic Press. London.

Gambell, R. (1985) Sei whale, *Balaenoptera borealis* (Lesson, 1828). In S.H. Ridgeway and R. Harrison (eds) Handbook of Marine Mammals 3: 155-170. Academic Press. London.

Gresson, R.A.R. (1966) Pilot whales, *Globiocephala melaena* (Traill) stranded at Cloghane, Co. Kerry. Irish Naturalists' Journal 15: 163-166.

Haug, T., Gjosaeter, H., Lindstrom, U. and Nilssen, K.J. (1995) Diet and food availability for north-east Atlantic minke whales *Balaenoptera acutorostrata*, during the summer of 1992. ICES Journal of Marine Science 52: 77-86.

Leopold, M.F., Wolf, P.A. and Vandermeer, J. (1992) The elusive harbour porpoise exposed - strip transect counts off southwestern Ireland. Netherlands Journal of Sea Research 29: 395-402.

Lockyer, C. (1986) Body fat condition in Northeast Atlantic fin whales, *Balaenoptera physalus*, and its relationship with food and resource. Canadian Journal of Fisheries and Aquatic Sciences 43: 142-147.

Mead, J.G. (1989) Bottlenose whales, *Hyperoodon ampullatus* (Forster, 1770) and *Hyperoodon planifrons* (Flower, 1882). In S.H. Ridgeway and R. Harrison (eds) Handbook of Marine Mammals 4: 321-348. Academic Press. London.

Mead, J.G. (1989) Beaked Whales of the Genus Mesoplodon. in S.H. Ridgeway and R. Harrison (eds) Handbook of Marine Mammals 4: 349-430. Academic Press. London.

O'Corry-Crowe, G.M., Suydam, R.S., Rosenberg, A.,Frost, K.J. and Dizon (1997) Phylogeography, population structure and dispersal patterns of the beluga whale *Delphinapterus leucas* in the western Neartic revealed by mitochondrial DNA. Molecular Ecology 6: 955-970.

Preston, K. (1995) Mammals at Cape Clear Island in 1993 and 1994. Cape Clear Bird Observatory Reports 23: 34-35.

Rice, D.W. (1989) Sperm whale, *Physeter macrocephalus* (Linnaeus, 1758). In S.H. Ridgeway and R. Harrison (eds) Handbook of Marine Mammals 4: 177-233. Academic Press. London.

Rogan E. and Berrow, S.D. (1996) A review of harbour porpoises, *Phocoena phocoena,* in Irish waters. Reports of the International Whaling Commission 46: 595-605.

Schaeff, C.M., Kraus,S.D., Brown, M.W. and White, B.N. (1993) Assessment of the population structure of western North Atlantic right whales *Eubalaena glacialis* based on sightings and mtDNA data. Canadian Journal of Zoology 71: 339-345.

Simila, T. and Ugarte, F. (1993) Surface and underwater observations of cooperatively feeding killer whales in northern Norway. Canadian Journal of Zoology 71: 1494-1499.

Stewart, B.S. and Leatherwood, S. (1985) Minke whale, *Balaenoptera acutorostrata* (Lacepede, 1804). In S.H. Ridgeway and R. Harrison (eds) Handbook of Marine Mammals 3: 91-136. Academic Press. London.

Whitehead, H. (1993) The behaviour of mature sperm whales on the Galapagos Islands breeding grounds. Canadian Journal of Zoology 71: 689-699.

Wilson, J.P.F. and Pitcher, T.J. (1979) Feeding and behaviour of a killer whale *Orcinus orca* L. in the Foyle estuary. Irish Naturalists' Journal 19: 352-355.

Winn, H.E. and Reichley, N.E. (1985) Humpback whale, *Megaptera novaeangliae* (Borowski, 1781). In S.H. Ridgeway and R. Harrison (eds) Handbook of Marine Mammals 3: 241-273. Academic Press. London.

Yochem, P.K. and Leatherwood, S. (1985) Blue Whale, *Balaenoptera musculus* (Linnaeus, 1758). In S.H. Ridgeway and R. Harrison (eds) Handbook of Marine Mammals 3: 193-240. Academic Press. London.

Videotapes

In the Company of Whales. Pickwick.

The Dolphin of Dingle Bay. Creation Entertainments.

Killer Whales: wolves of the sea. National Geographic Video.

Audiotapes

Songs from the Deep. Sitelle/Wildsounds, Holt, Norfolk.

CARNIVORES

Books

Chanin, P. (1985) The Natural History of Otters. Croom Helm. Beckenham.

Conroy, J.W.H., Watt, J., Webb, J.B. and Jones, A. (1993) A Guide to the Identification of Prey Remains in otter Spraint. The Mammal Society. Reading.

Fairley, J. (1984) An Irish Beast Book. Blackstaff Press. Belfast.

Harris, S. (1986) Urban Foxes. Whittet Books. London.

Harris, S. and White, P. (1994) The Red Fox. The Mammal Society. London.

Hayden, T.J. (ed) (1993) The Badger. Royal Irish Academy. Dublin.

King, C. (1989) The Natural History of Weasels and Stoats Christopher Helm. London.

Kruuk, H. (1989) The Social Badger. Oxford University Press. Oxford.

Kruuk, H. (1995) Wild Otters: predation and population. Oxford University Press. Oxford.

Lloyd, H.G. (1980) The Red Fox. Batsford Press. London.

MacDonald, D.W. (1987) Running with the Fox. Unwin Hyman. London.

MacDonald, D.W. (1992) The Velvet Claw: a natural history of carnivores. BBC Books. London.

Mason, C.F. and Macdonald, S.M. (1986) Otters: ecology and conservation. Cambridge University Press. Cambridge.

Neal, E. (1986) The Natural History of Badgers. Croom Helm. London.

Neal, E. and Cheeseman C. (1996) Badgers. Poyser. London.

Sleeman, P. (1989) Stoats and Weasels, Polecats and Ferrets. Whittet. London.

Smal, C. (1991) Feral American Mink in Ireland. Office of Public Works. Dublin.

Smal. C.M. (1995) The Badger and Habitat Survey of Ireland. The Stationery Office. Dublin.

Webb, J.B. (1976) Otter Spraint Analysis. The Mammal Society. Reading.

Articles

Boyle, K. and Whelan, J. (1990) Changes in the diet of the badger *Meles meles* L. from autumn to winter. Irish Naturalists' Journal 23: 199-202.

Fairley, J.S. (1970) The food, reproduction,form, growth and development of the fox *Vulpes vulpes* L. in north-east Ireland. Proceedings of the Royal Irish Academy 69B: 103-137.

Fairley, J.S. (1971) New data on the Irish stoat. Irish Naturalists' Journal 23: 49-57.

Fairley, J.S. (1982) A north-south cline in the size of the Irish stoat. Proceedings of the Royal Irish Academy 81B: 5-10.

Fairley, J.S. (1983) Exports of wild mammal skins from Ireland in the eighteenth century. Irish Naturalists' Journal 21: 75-79.

Feore, S. and Montgomery, W.I. (1999) Habitat effects on the spatial ecology of the European badger *Meles meles*. Journal of Zoology 247: 537-549.

Forbes, T.O.A. and Lance, A.N. (1976) The contents of fox scats from western Irish blanket bog. Journal of Zoology 179: 224-226.

Kyne, M.J., Smal, C.M. and Fairley, J.S. (1989) The food of otters *Lutra lutra* in the Irish midlands and a comparison with that of mink *Mustela vison* in the same region. Proceedings of The Royal Irish Academy 89B: 33-46.

Lunnon, R.M. and Reynolds J. D. (1991) Distribution of the otter *Lutra lutra* in Ireland, and its value as an indicator of habitat quality. In D.W. Jeffrey and B. Madden (eds) Bioindicators and Environmental Management 435-443. Academic Press. London.

Lynch, J.M. (1996) Postglacial colonisation of Ireland by mustelids with particular reference to the badger *Meles meles* L. Journal of Biogeography 23: 179-85.

Lynch, J.M. and Hayden, T.J. (1993) Multivariate morphometrics and the biogeography of Irish mustelids. In M.J. Costello and K.S. Kelly, Biogeography of Ireland: past, present and future. Occasional Publications of the Irish Biogeographical Society 2: 25-34.

Lynch, J.M. and Hayden, T.J. (1995) Genetic influences on cranial form: variation among ranch and feral American mink *Mustela vison* (Mammalia: Mustelidae). Biological Journal of the Linnean Society 55: 293-307.

Lynch, J.M., Conroy, J.W.H., Kitchener, A.C., Jefferies, D.J. and Hayden, T.J. (1996) Variation in cranial form and sexual dimorphism among five European populations of the otter *Lutra lutra*. Journal of Zoology 238: 81-96.

Lynch, J. M., Whelan, R., Fituri, A. and Hayden, T.J. (1997) Craniometric variation in the Eurasian badger, *Meles meles*. Journal of Zoology 242: 31-34.

O'Corry-Crowe, G., Hammond, R., Eves, J. and Hayden, T.J. (1996) The effect of reduction in badger density on the spatial organisation and activity of badgers *Meles meles* L. in relation to farms in central Ireland. Biology and Environment 96B: 147-158.

O'Sullivan, P.J. (1983) The distribution of the pine marten *Martes martes* in the Republic of Ireland. Mammal Review 13: 39-44.

O'Sullivan, W.M. (1991) The distribution of otters *Lutra lutra* within the Munster Blackwater catchment, a major Irish river system. Irish Naturalists' Journal 23: 442-446.

O'Sullivan, W.M. (1993) The nature and distribution of otter resting sites on part of the river Blackwater catchment, southern Ireland. Biology and Environment 93B: 159-162.

Robertson, P.A. and Whelan, J. (1987) The food of the red fox *Vulpes vulpes* in Co. Kildare, Ireland. Journal of Zoology 213: 740-743.

Sleeman, P. (1984) Ireland's carnivorous mammals. Problems with their arrival and survival. In P. Sleeman, R.J.N. Devoy, and P.C. Woodman (eds) The Proceedings of the Postglacial Colonisation Conference. Occasional Publications of the Irish Biogeographical Society 1: 42-8.

Sleeman, D.P. (1991) Home ranges of Irish stoats. Irish Naturalists' Journal 23: 486-488.

Sleeman, D.P. (1993) Habitats of the Irish stoat. Irish Naturalists' Journal 24: 318-321.

Sleeman, D.P. (1992) Diet of Irish stoats. Irish Naturalists' Journal 24: 151-153.

Smal, C.M. (1990) Den excavation by feral American mink *Mustela vison* (Schreber) in the Irish midlands. Irish Naturalists' Journal 23: 204-205.

Videotapes

Brockside. BBC Enterprises.

On the Tracks of the Wild Otter. BBC Enterprises.

Shak the Fox. Start Records.

The Tale of the Big Bad Fox. David Attenborough's World of Wildlife. BBC Natural History.

Audiotapes

British Wildlife Habitats, No.3, The Fox. Richard Margoschis.

SEALS AND WALRUSES
Books

Anderson, S. (1988) The Grey Seal. Shire Publications. Aylesbury.

King, J.E. (1983) Seals of the World. Oxford University Press. Oxford.

Articles

Berrow, S.D., O'Neill, M. and Brogan, D. (1998) Discarding practices and marine mammal by-catch in the Celtic Sea herring fishery. Biology and Environment 98B:1-8.

Bord Iascaigh Mhara (1997) The physical interaction between Grey seals and fishing gear. Report to the European Commission DG XIV. Reference PEM/93/06.

Kennedy, S., Smyth, J.A., Cush, P.F., Duigan, P., Platten, M., McCullough, S.J. and Allan, G.M. (1988) Confirmation of cause of recent seal deaths. Nature 335: 404.

Kiely, O. and Myers, A.A. (1998) Grey seal *Halichoerus grypus* pup production at the Inishkea island group, Co. Mayo and Blasket islands, Co. Kerry. Biology and Environment 98B: 113-122.

Lockley, R.M. (1966) The distribution of grey and common seals on the coasts of Ireland. Irish Naturalists' Journal 15: 136-143.

Nairn, R.G.W. (1979) The status and conservation of the common seal *Phoca vitulina* L. in Northern Ireland. Irish Naturalists' Journal 19: 360-363.

Summers, C.F., Warner, P.J., Nairn, R.G.W., Curry, M.G. and Flynn, J. (1980) An assessment of the status of the common seal *Phoca vitulina vitulina* in Ireland. Biological Conservation 17: 115-123.

Viney, M. and Berrow, S. (1995) Walrus *Odobenus rosmarus* L. in Co. Kerry. Irish Naturalists' Journal 25:150.

Warner, P. (1983) An assessment of the breeding populations of common seals *Phoca vitulina vitulina* L. in the Republic of Ireland. Irish Naturalists' Journal 21: 24-26.

Wilson, S.C. (1974) Mother-young interactions in the common seal, *Phoca vitulina vitulina*. Behaviour: 23-36.

Videotapes

Seals: people of the sea. The World Of Survival. Stylus Video.

DEER AND GOATS
Books

Chapman, N. (1991) Deer. Whittet Books. London.

Chapman, D.I. and Chapman N. (1975) Fallow Deer. Terence Dalton. Lavenham.

Clutton-Brock, J. (1987) A Natural History of Domesticated Animals. Cambridge University Press. Cambridge.

Clutton-Brock, T.H., Guinness, F. and Albon, S.D. (1982) Red Deer: behaviour and ecology of two sexes. University Press. Chicago.

Clutton-Brock, T.H. and Albon, S.D. (1989) Red Deer in the Highlands. BSP Professional Books. Oxford.

Mowlem, A. (1992) Goat Farming. Farming Press. Ipswich.

Prior, R. (1987) Deer Watch. David and Charles. Newton Abbot.

Whitehead, G.K. (1972) The Wild Goats of Great Britain and Ireland. David and Charles. Newton Abbot.

Articles

Bonham, F.R.H. and Fairley, J.S. (1984) Observations on a herd of feral goats Capra (domestic) in the Burren. Irish Naturalists' Journal 21: 208-212.

Bullock, D. (1995) The feral goat-conservation and management. British Wildlife 6: 152-159.

Harrington, R. (1979) Hybridisation among deer and its implications for conservation. Irish Forestry Journal 30: 64-78.

Harrington, R. (1982) The hybridisation of red deer *Cervus elaphus* L. (1758) and Japanese sika deer *C. nippon* (Temminck, 1838). Proceedings of the International Game Congress 14: 559-571.

Hayden, T.J., Lynch, J.M. and O'Corry-Crowe, G. (1994) Antler growth and morphology in a feral sika deer *Cervus nippon* population in Killarney, Ireland. Journal of Zoology 232: 21-35.

Larner, J.B. (1977) Sika deer damage to mature woodlands of southwestern Ireland. Transactions of the International Congress of Game Biologists 13: 192-202.

Linnell, J.C.D. and Cross, T.F. (1991) The biochemical systematics of red and sika deer genus Cervus in Ireland. Hereditas 115: 267-273.

Long, A.M., Moore, N.P. and Hayden, T.J. (1998) Vocalisations in red deer *Cervus elaphus*, sika deer *Cervus nippon*, and red x sika hybrids. Journal of Zoology 244: 123-134.

McElligott, A.G., Mattiangeli, V., Mattiello, S., Verga, M., Reynolds, C. A..M. and Hayden, T.J. (1998) Fighting tactics and choice of opponent in fallow bucks *Dama dama*, Cervidae: reducing the risk of serious conflict. Ethology 104: 789-803.

McElligott, A.G., O'Neill, K. and Hayden, T.J. (1998) Cumulative long-term investment in vocalization and mating success of fallow bucks, *Dama dama*. Animal Behaviour 57: 1159-1167.

McElligott, A.G. and Hayden, T.J. (1999) Context-related vocalization rates of fallow bucks, *Dama dama*. Animal Behaviour 58: 1095-1104.

McElligott, A.G. and Hayden, T.J. (2000) Lifetime mating success, sexual selection and life history of fallow bucks *Dama dama*. Behavioural Ecology and Sociobiology 48: 203-210.

Moore, N.P., Kelly, P.F., Cahill J.P. and Hayden, T.J. (1995) Mating strategies and mating success of fallow *Dama dama* bucks in a non-lekking population. Behavioural Ecology and Sociobiology 36: 91–100.

Moore, N.P., Cahill, J.P., Kelly, P.F., and Hayden T.J. (1995) An assessment of five methods of age determination in an enclosed population of fallow deer *Dama dama*. Biology and Environment 95B: 27–34.

Powerscourt, Viscount (1884) On the acclimatization of the Japanese deer at Powerscourt. Proceedings of the Zoological Society of London 1884: 207–209.

Sherlock, M.G. and Fairley, J.S. (1993) Seasonal changes in the diet of red deer *Cervus elaphus* in the Connemara National Park. Biology and Environment 93B: 85–90.

Whelan, J. (1991) Practical considerations in the management of a population of red deer *Cervus elaphus*. Transactions of the International Congress of Game Biologists 20: 522–526.

Videotapes

Rush the Fallow Deer. Start Records.